Data and Knowledge in a Changing World

Springer

Berlin
Heidelberg
New York
Barcelona
Budapest
Hong Kong
London
Milan
Paris
Santa Clara
Singapore
Tokyo

J.-E. Dubois · N. Gershon (Eds.)

The Information Revolution: Impact on Science and Technology

With 50 Figures and 17 Tables

 Springer

CODATA Secretariat
Phyllis Glaeser, Exec. Director
51, Boulevard de Montmorency
F - 75016 Paris

Editors:

Professor Dr. Jacques-Emile Dubois
Université Denis Diderot Paris VII
Institut de Topologie et de
Dynamique des Systèmes
(ITODYS)
1 rue Guy de la Brosse
F - 75005 Paris

Dr. Nahum Gershon
The MITRE Corporation
7525 Colshire Drive
McLean, VA 22102
USA

The image on the front cover comes from an animation which shows worldwide Internet traffic. The color and height of the arcs between the countries encode the data-packet counts and destinations, while the "skyscraper" glyphs (or icons) encode total traffic volume at any site. This image was generated by Stephen G. Eick at the AT&T Bell Laboratories.

ISBN 3-540-60855-9 Springer-Verlag Berlin Heidelberg New York

Cataloging-in-publication Data applied for

Die Deutsche Bibliothek – CIP-Einheitsaufnahme
The information revolution : impact on science and technology ; with 17 tables / J. E. Dubois ;
N. Gershon (ed.) - Berlin ; Heidelberg ; New York ; Barcelona ; Budapest ; Hong Kong ;
London ; Milan ; Paris ; Santa Clara ; Singapore ; Tokyo : Springer, 1996
(Data and knowledge in a changing world)
ISBN 3-540-60855-9
NE: Dubois, Jacques-Emile [Hrsg.]

© Springer-Verlag Berlin Heidelberg 1996
Printed in Germany

The use of general descriptive names, registered names, trademarks, etc. in this publication does not imply, even in the absence of a specific statement, that such names are exempt from the relevant protective laws and regulations and therefore free for general use.

Product liability: The publisher cannot guarantee the accuracy of any information about dosage and application contained in this book. In every individual case the user must check such information by consulting the relevant literature.

Typesetting: Camera-ready by editors
SPIN:10526032   51/3020-5 4 3 2 1 0 - Printed on acid-free paper

INTRODUCTION TO THE SERIES

E. Fluck
Chairman of the Publication Advisory Board

CODATA's primary purpose in launching the Series "Data and Knowledge in a Changing World" is to collect from widely differing fields the wealth of information pertaining to the intelligent exploitation of data in the conduct of science and technology and to make that information available to a multidisciplinary community. This series, in support of that goal, will provide a forum for many types of submission, both theoretical and applied. Directories and Glossaries of compiled scientific and technical data or of Space and Time Observation data could be included in a separate **CODATA** Reference Data Series.

The present series will be wide in scope as it encompasses a broad range of data and knowledge contributions, including computer-related handling and visualization of data, to the major scientific, technical and medical fields.

To this end, the series on Data and Knowledge is open to contributions of various kinds, namely those:

- Fostering the improvement, not only of the quality and accessibility of quantitative and qualitative data, but of the classical and ground-breaking methods by which numeric and symbolic data are acquired, analyzed and managed;

- presenting new data and knowledge interfaces designed to optimize interoperability and thereby increase the potential of sharing data among databases and networks;

- intensifying international cooperation in communication and data sharing-this implies works dealing with standardization, data quality agreements and conceptual data descriptions (metadata, syntactic and semantic approaches) along with papers dealing with the evolution of Internet-based facilities, other forms of worldwide communications and electronic publishing;

- providing new insights into, or interpretations of, processes leading to creative design in the field of concurrent and/or cooperative engineering, including cognitive aspects critical to data-based decision making.

In view of the emergence of the cyclic nature of information needs in the study of complex systems, **CODATA**'s scope now includes data activities and modeling of an interdisciplinary nature such as that encountered in far-reaching projects (e.g. Global Change, various Genome projects, environmental and biodiversity issues, etc.) or in certain medical information systems. Most of the above will therefore be highlighted in this Series.

Attempting, however, to predict the contents of such series is itself paradoxical, reflecting the particular challenge in the field of data and information management whose essence is to proceed at such pace as to outstrip the very information highways it is building.

In an evolving information world in which our traditional ways of transferring information as an essential resource are being altered, this Series should capture emerging and innovative concepts thereby leading ultimately to new information paradigms. Its ambition is to be concurrently a catalyst of change and a thought-provoking forum.

ACKNOWLEDGEMENT

At the invitation of the French National Committee of **CODATA**, the Fourteenth International **CODATA** Conference took place in Chambéry from 18-22 September, 1994.

The Scientific program of this Conference was planned in three Symposia. For one of them on **"Computer Aided Systems and Communication"**, our then CODATA President, David Abir and the International Scientific Program Committee decided to organize constructive debates by panels of experts to discuss the many issues highlighted by the Information Revolution and to investigate the impact of the new communication concepts on the various phases of data production and management.

International Scientific Program Committee
Prof. J.-E. Dubois, France (Chairman)
Dr. F. Bisby, U.K.
Dr. M. Chinnery, U.S.A.
Prof. S. Iwata, Japan
Prof. E. Fluck, Germany
Academician F.A. Kuznestov, Russia
Dr. J.R. Rodgers, Canada
Dr. J. Thieman, U.S.A.
Prof. A. Tsugita, Japan
Prof. Z. Xu, China

Most of the contributions to this book, produced at this Symposium or sollicited thereafter, result from the challenging exchanges that took place in the following sessions (S) or Forum (F), chaired by eminent scientists.

- **Obstacles to Open Exchange of Scientific Data (F)**

  Michael A. Chinnery
- **Distributed Data and Computer Networks: New Information Retrieval (F)**

  Fionn Murtagh
- **Databases : Policies and Innovative Features (S)**

  Jean-Loup Delcroix
- **Bioinformatics : Infrastructure in the World Today (S)**

  Harrie Lalieu and Akira Tsugita
- **Bioinformatics Worldwide : The Role of CODATA (F)**

  Harrie Lalieu, Akira Tsuguta and Louis Rechaussat

In cooperation with UNESCO a special Forum on "**Information Requirements in Developing Countries : Local Needs and Solutions**", chaired by Abdoulay Gaye and Belhadri Messabih, led to investigation of the need for data sharing and information transfer with developing countries in light of the new communication highways like Internet and the Web facilities.

CODATA's President is happy to express his warm gratitude to all those who contributed with talent and interest to preparing and conducting all these fruitful meetings.

Nowadays **CODATA** provides this wealth of information in its new series: "**Data and Knowledge in a Changing World**".and is grateful to those who help stress the importance of good data in the new paradigm and simulation models presented as printed information to the scientific community.

*The organizing committee of the 14th International **CODATA** conference is privileged to acknowledge the sponsorship of the French Academy of Sciences for the 1994 Lavoisier Celebration Year, of the International Council of Scientific Unions, the European Centre of Reflection and Studies in Thermodynamics, the University of Savoie and several organizations : ADME, SML, IRPL, AFNOR.*

Sincere thanks are expressed for the patronage of the French Ministry of the Environment, the Ministry of Higher Education and Reseach, the Ministry of Defense and the Ministry of Industry.

***CODATA** is especially grateful for the generous and constant support of the Regional Council of Rhône Alpes, the Departmental Council of the Savoie and the city of Chambéry, its Mayor and Deputy Mayor.*

CONTENTS

CHAPTER 2 : OBSTACLES TO A FREE OR FAIR CIRCULATION OF SCIENTIFIC DATA

CHAPTER 3 : DISTRIBUTED DATA AND INFORMATION NETWORKS

PART TWO : WORLDWIDE AND REGIONAL INFORMATION SYSTEMS, POLICIES AND PROGRAMS

CHAPTER 4 : UNESCO POLICY, WORLDWIDE NETWORKS, REGIONAL EXCHANGE EQUITY

CHAPTER 5 : NUMERICAL, TEXTUAL AND IMAGE DATABASES

CHAPTER 6 : CASE STUDY : WORLDWIDE BIOINFORMATICS DISTRIBUTED DATABASES

AUTHORS

Lamine ABDAT
Laboratoire MASI - Université PARIS VI - 4, place Jussieu 75252 Paris Cedex 05,
France, E-mail : abdat@masi.ibp.fr

Alberto ACCOMAZZI
Harvard-Smithsonian Center for Astrophysics, 60 Garden Street, Cambridge, MA 02138,
U.S.A.

Shelton ALEXANDER
Dept. of Geosciences, The Pennsylvania State University, 537 Deike Bldg., Burrows
Road, University Park, PA 16802, U.S.A.

Marcella ATTIMONELLI
Dipartimento di Biochimica e Biologia Molecolare and CSMME CNR, Via Amendola
168/5, 70126 Bari, Italy

Adnan BADRAN
UNESCO, 7 place de Fontenoy, 75700 Paris, France

Lois D. BLAINE
Bioinformatics Dept., American Type Culture Collection, 12301Parklawn Drive,
Rockville, MD 20852-1776, U.S.A.

D. CALO
Dipartimento di Biochimica e Biologia Molecolare and CSMME CNR, Via Amendola
168/5, 70126 Bari, Italy

Michael A. CHINNERY
National Geophysical Data Center, 325 Broadway, Boulder, CO 80303, U.S.A.

Jacob CURDES
Department of Physics, Carl von Ossietzky University, 26111 Oldenburg, Germany

Phillipe DARCHE
Laboratoire MASI, Institut Blaise Pascal, Université Pierre et Marie Curie, 4 Place Jussieu, 75252 Paris Cedex 05, France, E-mail: darche@masi.ibp.fr

A. DEPASCALI
Dipartimento di Biochimica e Biologia Molecolare and CSMME CNR, Via Amendola 168/5, 70126 Bari, Italy

Brian DICKENS
The MITRE Corporation, 7525 Colshire Drive, McLean, VA 22102, U.S.A.

Bernd DIEKMANN
Department of Physics, Carl von Ossietzky University; 26111 Oldenburg, Germany

Jacques-Emile DUBOIS
Institut de Topologie et de Dynamique des Systèmes, Université de Paris VII 1, rue Guy de la Brosse, 75005 Paris, France, E-mail: dubois@paris7.jussieu.fr

Jacques DUCLOY
CNRS/CRIN - Centre de Recherche en Informatique de Nancy, Campus Scientifque, Bât.Loria, BP 239, 54501 Vandoeuvre lès Nancy Cedex, France

Andy EDWARDS
Bioline Publications, Stainfield House, Stainfield, Bourne, Lincs, PE10 0RS, UK, E-mail: bio@biostrat.demon.co.uk

Guenther EICHHORN
Harvard-Smithsonian Center for Astrophysics, 60 Garden Street, Cambridge, MA 02138, U.S.A.

Ekkehard FLUCK
Gmelin Institute for Inorganic Chemistry of the Max-Planck-Society, Varrentrappstraße 40/42, D-60486 Frankfurt, Germany

Bertil FOLLIOT
Laboratoire MASI, Institut Blaise Pascal, Université Pierre et Marie Curie, 4 Place Jussieu, 75252 Paris Cedex 05, France, E-mail: folliot@masi.ibp.fr

Charles. T. GARTEN,Jr
Environmental Sciences Division Oak Ridge National Laboratory, Oak Ridge, Tennessee 37831 U.S.A.

Abdoulaye GAYE
République du Senegal, Secrétariat Commission Nationale pour L'Unesco, 67, rue Cornot Boyeux, Dakar, Senegal

Nahum GERSHON
The MITRE Corporation, 7525 Colshire Drive, McLean, VA 22102, U.S.A.
E-mail: gershon@mitre.org

André HECK
Strasbourg Astronomical Observatory, 11, rue de l'Université, F-67000 Strasbourg, France. E-mail: heck@astro.u.-strasbg.fr, URL: http://cdsweb.u-strasbg.fr/~heck

Eberhard R. HILF
Department of Physics, Carl von Ossietzky University; 26111 Oldenburg, Germany, E-mail : hilf@merlin.physik.uni-oldenburg.de

Katsuhisa HORIMOTO
Department of Electronics and Computer Science, Science University of Tokyo in Yamaguchi, Noda 278, Japan

Arild JANSEN
Dept. of Information Technology, Finnmark College, Follums vei 1, N-9500 Alta; Norway; E-mail: arild@hifm.no

Frank KAPPE
Institute for Information Processing and Computer Supported New Media (IICM), Graz University of Technology, A-8010 Graz, Austria, E-mail : fkappe@iicm.tu-graz.ac.at

Henry V. KEHIAIAN
ITODYS, Université Paris VII, 1 rue Guy de la Brosse, 75005 Paris, France

Barbara E. KIRSOP
Bioline Publications, Stainfield House, Stainfield, Bourne, Lincs, PE10 0RS, UK, E-mail: bio@biostrat.demon.co.uk

Ashok S. KOLASKAR
Bioinformatics Centre, University of Pune, Ganeshhind, PUNE 411 007, India

Michael J. KURTZ
Harvard-Smithsonian Center for Astrophysics, 60 Garden Street, Cambridge, MA 02138, U.S.A.

M.L.Harrie LALIEU
Library KNAW, P.O. Box 41950, Amsterdam, The Netherlands

Jean-Charles LAMIREL
CNRS/CRIN - Centre de Recherche en Informatique de Nancy, Campus Scientifque, Bât.Loria, BP 239, 54501 Vandoeuvre lès Nancy Cedex, France

Joshua LEVASSEUR
The MITRE Corporation, 7525 Colshire Drive, McLean, VA 22102, U.S.A.

Lunjiang LING
Research Institute for Biosciences, Science University of Tokyo, 2641 Yamazaki, Noda, Chiba 278, Japan

Belhadri MESSABIH
Institut de Topologie et de Dynamique des Systèmes, Université de Paris VII 1, rue Guy de la Brosse, 75005 Paris, France, E-mail : messabih@jussieu.fr

Stephen S. MURRAY
Harvard-Smithsonian Center for Astrophysics, 60 Garden Street, Cambridge, MA 02138, U.S.A.

Fionn MURTAGH
Space Telescope-European Coordinating Facility European Southern Observatory, Karl-Schwarzschild-Str. 2 D-85748 Garching, Germany, E-mail : fmurtagh@eso.org

Prashant.S. NAIK
Bioinformatics Centre, University of Pune, Ganeshhind, PUNE 411 007, India
Emmanuel NAUER
CNRS/CRIN - Centre de Recherche en Informatique de Nancy, Campus Scientifque, Bât.Loria, BP 239, 54501 Vandoeuvre lès Nancy Cedex, France

Valdiodio NDIAYE
Département de Sciences Naturelles, École Normale Supérieure, B.P. 5036, Université Cheikh Anta Diop ,Dakar-Fann, Senegal

Richard. J. OLSON
Environmental Sciences Division, Oak Ridge National Laboratory, Oak Ridge, Tennessee 37831 U.S.A.

Bartolomé ORFILA
European Climate Support Network INM, Apdo. 285, Madrid 28040, Spain

Kunio OSHIMA
Department of Electronics and Computer Science, Science University of Tokyo in Yamaguchi, Noda 278, Japan

Jinya OTSUKA
Department of Applied Biological Science, Science University of Tokyo in Yamaguchi, Noda 278, Japan
George PAPAPAVLOU
European Commission, Direction General XIII, Bât. Jean Monnet, 2920 Luxembourg, Luxembourg

M. PORZIO
Dipartimento di Biochimica e Biologia Molecolare and CSMME CNR, Via Amendola 168/5, 70126 Bari, Italy

Jean-Charles PROFIZI
University of Savoie - L.G.I.S, 73340 Le Bourget du Lac, France

Pierre-Guillaume RAVERDY
Laboratoire MASI, Institut Blaise Pascal, Université Pierre et Marie Curie, 4 Place Jussieu, 75252 Paris Cedex 05, France, E-mail: raverdy@masi.ibp.fr

Steve F. ROSSOUW
School of Business Informatics, Cape Technikon, P.O.Box 652, 8000 Cape Town, South Africa

William RUH
The MITRE Corporation, 7525 Colshire Drive, McLean, VA 22102, U.S.A.

C. SACCONE
Dipartimento di Biochimica e Biologia Molecolare and CSMME CNR, Via Amendola 168/5, 70126 Bari, Italy

Junko SHIMURA
The Institute of Physical and Chemical Research (RIKEN), 2-1 Hirosawa, Wako, Saitama 351-01, Japan

Pål SORGAARD
Department of Informatics, University of Oslo, PO Box 1080 Blindern, N-0316 Oslo, Norway; E-mail: paalso@ifi.uio.no

Sidnei SOUZA
Base de Dados Tropical, Campinas, SP. Brazil, E-mail: sidnei@ftpt.br

Heinrich STAMERJOHANNS
Department of Physics, Carl von Ossietzky University, 26111 Oldenburg, Germany

Carolyn STERN-GRANT
Harvard-Smithsonian Center for Astrophysics, 60 Garden Street, Cambridge, MA 02138, U.S.A.

Hideaki SUGAWARA
The Institute of Physical and Chemical Research (RIKEN), 2-1 Hirosawa, Wako, Saitama 351-01, Japan

F. TANZARIELLO
Dipartimento di Biochimica e Biologia Molecolare and CSMME CNR, Via Amendola 168/5, 70126 Bari, Italy

Akira TSUGITA
Research Institute for Biosciences, Science University of Tokyo, 2669 Yamazaki, Noda 278, Japan

Robert. S. TURNER
Environmental Sciences Division Oak Ridge National Laboratory, Oak Ridge,
Tennessee 37831 U.S.A.

Paul F. UHLIR
National Research Council, 2101 Constitution Avenue, Washington, DC 20418, U.S.A.

M. VITALE
Dipartimento di Biochimica e Biologia Molecolare and CSMME CNR, Via Amendola
168/5, 70126 Bari, Italy

Joel WINSTEAD
The MITRE Corporation, 7525 Colshire Drive, McLean, VA 22102, U.S.A.
E-mail: winstead@lash.mitre.org

Zhihong XU
Laboratory of Computer Chemistry, Chinese CODATA Committee, Chinese Academy
of Sciences, P.O.Box 353 , Beijing, 100080, China

PREFACE

J.-E. Dubois and N. Gershon

This book was inspired by the Symposium on "Communications and Computer Aided Systems" held at the 14th International CODATA Conference in September 1994 in Chambéry, France. It was conceived and influenced by the discussions at the symposium and most of the contributions were written following the Conference. This is the first comprehensive book, published in one volume, of issues concerning the challenges and the vital impact of the information revolution (including the Internet and the World Wide Web) on science and technology.

Topics concerning the impact of the information revolution on science and technology include:

- Dramatic improvement in sharing of data and information among scientists and engineers around the world

- Collaborations (on-line and off-line) of scientists and engineers separated by distance

- Availability of visual tools and methods to view, understand, search, and share information contained in data

- Improvements in data and information browsing, search and access and

- New ways of publishing scientific and technological data and information.

These changes have dramatically modified the way research and development in science and technology are being carried out. However, to facilitate this information flow nationally and internationally, the science and technology communities need to develop and put in place new standards and policies and resolve some legal issues.

The central theme of the book is the combination of a survey of several fundamental aspects of this information revolution with an evaluation of issues involved in circulating science and technology data. Besides policy and standards, the important issues and challenges include the maintenance of certain cultural disparities in the era of world-wide information systems, encouraging everybody to provide as well as to use information, and the changing face of collaboration in science and technology.

The papers in this book address the topics associated here with the information revolution both at the conceptual and application levels. Concrete problems in the fields of textual, numerical and image databases are presented, while the complex variety of concepts and standards needed for efficient worldwide networks and intelligent access tools are demonstrated in the bioinformatics case study.

Many of the challenges and difficulties facing the information revolution and its successful implementation in science and technology will have to be dealt with and resolved in the years to come; they are essential elements of the emerging Knowledge and Information Society of the Future.

Acknowledgments: We would like to thank all the authors of this book for their contributions and hard work. We would also like to acknowledge the hard work and dedication of Bernice Dubois in helping to bring this book to the world and the efforts of Belhadri Messabih in assembling the pieces literally coming from all the four corners of the world.

PART ONE

EMERGENCE OF AN
INFORMATION SOCIETY

FACTS AND CHALLENGES

2

Information Space Visualization with NCSA Mosaic

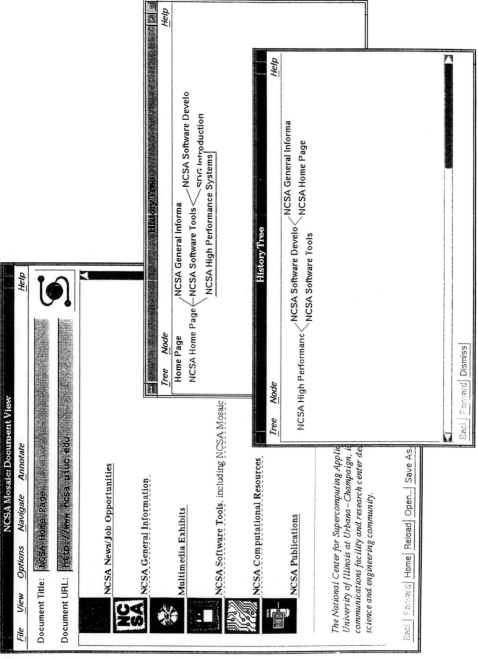

See page 22

Chapter 1

INFORMATION HIGHWAYS INTERNET AND WEB SERVICES

Dealing with the Data Deluge. Visualization and Data Management

Nahum GERSHON*, William RUH*, Brian DICKENS, Joshua LEVASSEUR and Joel WINSTEAD

The MITRE Corporation McLean, VA 22102, U.S.A.

ABSTRACT

This paper describes solutions to some difficulties with handling, querying, browsing, accessing, and retrieving data and information from large distributed repositories of complex data and information. In one prototype, we integrated the capabilities of a geographic information system, statistical analysis, visualization, graphic user interface, a storage system, and a data base management system. In another system, relevant information in n dimensions could be aggregated and visualized enabling a more rapid understanding of the informational content when the representation is adapted to the particular problem or application. In an enhancement to NCSA Mosaic, the user can modify interactively the otherwise rigid structure of linking pieces of information (hyperlinks) and view the information space and its relationships visually.

* Requests for further information should be sent to N. Gershon and W. Ruh. Mailing Address: {Nahum Gershon, William Ruh} The MITRE Corporation, 7525 Colshire Drive, McLean, VA 22102, U.S.A. Electronic mail: {gershon,war}@mitre.org.

RESUME

Dans cet article, on expose des solutions pour lever certaines difficultés relatives aux opérations de manipulation, interrogation, parcours et recherche de données et d'information à partir de dépôts importants de données et d'informations complexes et réparties. Dans un prototype, nous intégrons diverses possibilités d'un système d'informations géographiques, telles que l'analyse statistique, la visualisation, l'interface graphique et un système d'exploitation de base de données. Dans un autre, les informations acquises en n dimensions peuvent être agrégées et visualisées permettant ainsi une compréhension plus rapide pour un problème ou une application particulière pour lesquels on adapte la représentation d'étude. Dans une amélioration de Mosaïque, l'utilisateur peut modifier de façon interactive les liens associatifs dans les structures d'information et visualiser l'espace de l'information et des liens internes.

1   INTRODUCTION

Two centuries of industrial-age pollution has begun altering the Earth's climate and environment. The result is that the future quality of life on Earth is at stake. Together with other national and international agencies, the U.S. National Aeronautics and Space Administration (NASA) is planning to embark on an international effort to monitor the state of our planet, the Earth Observing System. This program will provide orbiting and terrestrial infrastructure for monitoring and modeling the global climate and environment. It will include space-based, airborne, and surface instruments that will monitor the state of planet Earth.

By the year 2,000, satellites employed by NASA will transmit 1 terabyte of data to Earth every day. If stored on magnetic tape, this data deluge would require a stack of reels as high as the 169-meter Washington monument in the U.S. capital every day. This record torrent of remotely sensed data and information has to be made readily accessible to :

- The global change community
- Medical and other researchers
- Policy makers
- Students (Kindergarten to 12th grade, college, or lifetime learning)
- The general public.

2   SOME DIFFICULTIES

Besides being voluminous, environmental data and information are complex and diverse. The data and information are of many types, e.g. :

- Original data

- Processed data
- Metadata (information about the data), e.g. :
  - Information about how the experiments were conducted
  - Information about the units of the measurements
  - Visualization protocols
- Appended data (e.g., researchers' notes)

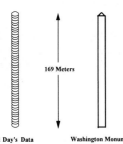

1 Day's Data   Washington Monument, DC

Figure 1. Earth Observing Systems <u>daily</u> data & information. If stored on magnetic tape, this data deluge would require a stack of reels as high as the 169-meter Washington monument in the U.S. capital every day.

Data could come in various formats, e.g. : Tabular, Non tabular, Various numerical formats. It is not simple to deal with this array of data and information. Traditional methods for collecting and managing the data are insufficient to handle these complex data. In addition, visualization and presentation of these data and information could be quite complicated.

3   LOOKING FOR RELEVANT DATA AND INFORMATION

To find required information, users need to browse through data and conduct searches. The search and browsing processes could be structured or unstructured. Unstructured search and browsing are important since they could potentially enhance creativity and thinking which are important to the scientific and to problem solving processes. Some of the remote sources are massive and once the user has obtained the requested information, he or she needs to browse through large amounts of text, data tables, and images. How should the user know where the sources of the relevant information reside, how to get them, and, once the sources are retrieved, how to get the relevant information from them? Present data and information systems cannot cope effectively with these browsing and navigation problems. The queries scientists generate might be quite complex. Consequently, the retrieval processes might be complicated too. To ensure effective and efficient query and retrieval, the data and information systems need to be properly organized. Different applications or problems, however, might require different organizations of the data and information. Currently, traditional data base management systems (DBMSs) support of complex queries is quite limited. One of the big stumbling blocks of the use of data and information is user interface. To find required information or to browse through data information, users usually need nowadays to confront frustrating searches through arrays of sometimes user-debilitating menus and belligerent computer systems. The organization of data and information on distributed systems over the Internet, especially on the World Wide Web (WWW), has increased the possibilities. The captivating and crisp NCSA Mosaic, a WWW browser, has revolutionized information retrieval over the Internet [Schatz and Hardin, 1994].

When the user knows what he or she is after and where the information is, this browser could be a life saver. However, at the present time, it is still difficult to conduct searches and browsing even with keywords using these browsers. Alternatively, Hyper-G, an Internet distributed information system, and its X-Windows browser, Harmony, allow searches using keywords. NCSA Mosaic can be interfaced with relational data bases and could initiate searches over such DBMSs. But, these searches and interfaces could not be better that what the DBMS search engine could provide.

One of the major problems of current information systems distributed over the Internet is that the information is rigidly put in place. Pieces of information are linked together in a rigid structure with hyper links-- no changes are allowed. However, these pieces of information could be related to each other in various ways depending on the application, problem, personal way of thinking and perception, or culture. For distributed information systems to be effective and enhance problem solving, they should allow each user to construct his or her own information space with links and associations (among pieces of information and whole documents and images) that fit the problem, application, or ways of thinking and perception. Another major problem facing systems of today is that while surfing over the Internet, users often do not know where they are in information space and do not remember how they got there. In short, users are lost. One solution is to provide users with both a local and a global view of the information space. These views should be represented visually to promote quick perception and understanding. The user can "jump" from one document to another by pointing and clicking the mouse button without the necessity to go back resource by resource. This eliminates the necessity to go back "page by page".

Enabling the user to modify interactively the links among the documents and images using a visual display and to (visually) view the information space globally and locally have been implemented over the World Wide Web in a MITRE enhancement to NCSA Mosaic[1] .

The system response time has to be considered. To conduct intuitive and thinking enhancing searches and browsing, the system response time needs to be fast and

---

[1] The work, done by Joshua LeVasseur, Joel Winstead, and Nahum Gershon, is briefly described in [Gershon and Ruh, 1995].

perceived to be responsive. At present, in many cases it is quite slow for the process to be really interactive.

4   LOOKING AT A PIECE OF THE PUZZLE

The solutions to these enormous problems are not easy. Because of this practical reason, we have decided to address a piece of the puzzle: the issues of loading, digesting, and querying the data and information. The objective of building this prototypic system was to demonstrate that traditional relational DBMSs could be enhanced to have the features that science and other users require for their work. This includes the integration of a :

- Geographic query capability (e.g., show me the data over Sicily)
- Statistical calculations
- Advanced visualization of reduced-resolution browsing versions of the data and the full-resolution data (once the data is retrieved)
- Integration of a file system with a DBMS
- Graphic (visual) user interface

The MITRE system includes a UNIX workstation and a Teradata Data Base Computer. It uses Application Visualization System (AVS) for visualizing and integrating the following pieces of software :

- ARC/INFO, a geographic information system (GIS)
- SAS, a statistical package
- A fast data loader (takes a data set, transforming it, and puts it under control of the data base
- Visualization software

The characteristics of this system (figure 2) can be described as follows :

Distributed storage. Data is stored in a 2-level system. Large data sets are stored as properly organized files on a high-capacity-slow-access medium (array of magnetic tapes), while the metadata and other information are stored on a low-capacity-fast-access medium (hard disk).

Parallel architecture. The Teradata machine allows the process of loading and retrieval of data to be parallel.

Data formats and data loading. Many data formats (e.g., all formats accessible in AVS) are accepted, including uniform and non-uniform spatial data and text data description (that could be made searchable). The data is automatically parsed into small pieces called tiles. Each tile is stored in a separate SQL (Standard Query Language) record and is directly queryable. The data could be loaded onto the Teradata computer or on a file system. It could be extended to a multi-server environment. The architecture is flexible allowing extensions to distributed systems.

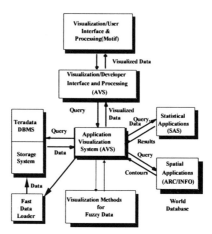

Figure 2. MITRE system for looking at a piece of the puzzle.

User interface. No exposure to query language, e.g., to SQL is required and minimal amount of special coding is required when importing a data set with a non-supported format. The interface to the system is graphic and is done using Motif.

Extended query capability. Many types of queries could be generated without the knowledge or the use of SQL. This also includes geographic queries, such as asking for particular data contained in a region defined by a given Latitude-Longitude range, names of geographic physical or political entities, and by point-and-click on a selection of a geographic entity over a displayed map.

5   VISUALIZATION

One way of dealing with the data deluge is to maximize the use of visual interfaces for information and data. This allows a faster "scanning" of data by the user (images talk faster than words-- after all, "A picture is worth a thousand words") and also some information could be seen by viewing the information and not by reading the individual numbers).

Visualization is more than a method of computing. Visualization is the process of transforming information into a visual form, enabling users to *observe* the information.

The resulting visual display enables the scientist or engineer to perceive visually features which are hidden in the data but nevertheless are needed for data analysis and exploration. This process uses interactive graphics and imaging and relies on the visual system to perceive the information. If one knew well the way the brain and the visual system perceive information, one would be able to improve the visualization process and results.

Figure 3. The visualization process

6   DATA VISUALIZATION

Data visualization deals with data generated by different sources:

- Sampled data (e.g., NASA or medical instruments, such as Magnetic Resonance Imaging-- MRI)
- Simulations (e.g., weather prediction)
- Models (e.g., molecular interaction)

Visualization methods based on advances in computer graphics and image processing have achieved a remarkable degree of success in areas such as fluid dynamics, medical imaging, simulations, and Earth science. Visualization provides researchers and practitioners with means of displaying and visually manipulating two- and three-dimensional (3-D) data. In cases where 3-D data come in a form of a series of 2-D slices, it needs to be converted to a data volume using 3-D reconstruction. The 3-D data volume is then visualized as a collection of surfaces (using surface rendering) or directly as a volume containing volume elements (voxels[2]) using volume rendering methods.

7   INFORMATION VISUALIZATION

Most recent advances in visualization have occurred in the area of visualization of scientific data. Information spaces are abstract and different from physical data spaces. For example, the correlation among words in a document could not be easily described in visual terms. Thus, information visualization might require modified or

---

[2] A voxel is a small cubic element analogous to the pixel (in 2-D images) containing information about the value of the data and associated information such as color, opacity, and density.

different approaches   However, since we live and perceive in a physical world it is advantageous to represent information spaces using physical analogs.

To visualize information, it is necessary to define an appropriate information space. Generally speaking, this is not a trivial problem. A particular information could be represented by more than one information space. However, the representation of the information within this space could be more flexible than that of physical data. The choice of which information space and which representation should be chosen depends on the kind of information and also on the specific task or goal.

An example is a representation of incidence of diseases related to pollution in different parts of Washington, DC metropolitan area (the numbers are not real and should serve as an example only). The data could be represented by the following table:

	Falls Church, VA	Greenbelt, MD	Arlington, VA
Head Aches	10	3	11
Stomach Ailments	2	4	4
Nausea	15	5	33

Table 1. Incidence of pollution diseases in different areas of Washington DC (not real data).

The analyst wishing to find where are the high hits of incidence needs to "fish" the high hits from the various table cells. This is a slow process which could require the user to be very meticulous when the tables are large.

Since the order of the entities in the columns and rows is arbitrary, one could permute it to yield the following representation depicted in Table 2.

	Falls Church, VA	Arlington, VA	Greenbelt, MD
Head Aches	10	11	3
Nausea	15	33	5
Stomach Ailments	2	4	4

Table 2. Incidence of pollution diseases in different areas of Washington DC (not real data) after aggregation (the high incidences are aggregated in the upper left corner).

In this representation, the high hits are aggregated and it is easy to see that they occur in the neighboring areas of Falls Church and Arlington, VA. The analyst can then ask why they occurred there and if there is any correlation of these ailments with recent outbreaks of polluting air contaminants. The same finding could be reached by yet another visual representation: viewing the incidence plotted on a map.

We have implemented a fast algorithm that can aggregate information in n dimensions and the results are visualized on the computer display for visual inspection and analysis (humans still tend to perform pattern recognition faster and better than any existing computer).

Since information is abstract, the process of mapping it to a physical space used in visualization might not be straightforward. Another difficulty is that information spaces could be multi-dimensional and 3-D graphics might not be sufficient for all purposes. Dealing with all of these problems makes the field of information visualization more difficult than scientific visualization. However, these problems and the vast number of important potential applications make the field of information visualization both exciting and challenging.

8   SEEING IS NOT ALWAYS BELIEVING

Visualization of data and information is a powerful technique and could benefit both users and applications. However glittery, it is sometimes difficult to produce visualizations that portray the data and information realistically or ones that point out clearly the required features in the data and information.

Why is visualization difficult? As art, visualization creates illusions. A representation of a 3-D object on a 2-D screen is an illusion. The trick though is to choose those depth cues that will create a realistically looking illusion. This requires the knowledge of how the object would look in real life. Contrary to art, we do not always know what is the information embedded in the data and so how do we a priori know how it should look like in real life. This is one of the reasons why it is so difficult to portray data and information realistically without distortions.

In addition, the choice of color or other parameters might inappropriately over emphasize or de-emphasize some features. Color is in particular a tough subject since its perception might be different from person to person and might change over time (in one person's view). Also, different cultures and even professions attach different meanings to colors. To be able to create more faithful visualizations, we need to understand human visual perception and to take it into account. We could also use the knowledge of perception to improve the visibility of details in the image and to make the process of observing the information faster and less tedious.

Dealing with unknown information embedded in the data could prevent us from orienting the image properly when looking for familiar shapes or for symmetry of objects. As I. Rock noted [I. Rock, 1988] "Ambiguous figures can be perceived in different ways depending on the orientation assigned to them." and "Impression of symmetry is spontaneous only when a figure is symmetrical around a vertical axis." More examples on the role of perception in visualization can be found in [Gershon, 1994].

CONCLUSION

To deal with the data deluge, we need to provide the users with appropriate

- Data base management systems
- Heterogeneous storage management systems

- Browsing, search, and retrieval methods
- Visualization and user interface methods

in addition to hardware supporting these systems. The challenge is not easy, but it is the only way to make the collections of environmental data and information useful to our communities.

KEYWORDS

Data and information systems, data base management systems, Internet, World Wide Web, WWW, Mosaic, geographic information systems, visualization, user interface.

REFERENCES

[1]   Andrews K., Kappe F., Soaring through Hyper Space: A Snapshot of Hyper-G and its Harmony Client, in Proc. of Eurographics Symposium of multimedia/Hypermedia in Open Distributed Environments, Graz, Austria,. Hezner W. , Kappe F. (eds) 181-191, Springer Verlag, June (1994).

[2]   Gershon N.D., From Perception to Visualization, in Scientific Visualization: Advances and Challenges, L. Rosenblum et al (eds) 129-139 (1994).

[3]   Gershon N.D., Ruh W.A., The Information Highway: Putting the User in the Driver's Seat (If we do not balance user needs with technical innovation, we will create useless information systems), IEEE Spectrum, to be published (1995).

[4]   Rock I., The Perception of Disoriented Figures, Scientific American, 230, 78-85 (1988)

[5]   Schatz B.R, Hardin J.B., NCSA Mosaic and the World-Wide Web: Global Hypermedia Protocols for the Internet, Science, 265, 895-901 (1994).

Content-Based Information Retrieval: New Tools for Textual Data, New Problems for Image Data

Fionn MURTAGH

Space Telescope—European Coordinating Facility European Southern Observatory, Karl-Schwarzschild-Str. 2 D-85748 Garching, Germany, E-mail : fmurtagh@eso.org

ABSTRACT

Retrieval of data and information is something which every scientist and technologist does many times over in each working day. However there are still problems to be overcome before heterogeneous data can be integrated for the user in a seamless way. We discuss three case-studies. The first deals with textual information retrieval in a modern science environment, using a particular set of text segments— astronomical observing proposal abstracts. Secondly, we discuss viable approaches to content-based image retrieval, using accompanying textual information. Finally we examine the role that multiresolution vision models can play in facilitating content-based image retrieval. The immediate focus of this third case-study is the retrieval of information about objects, characterized by their morphological shapes, from large image databases.

RESUME

La recherche de données et d'informations est une opération répétée de nombreuses fois dans la journée de travail d'un chercheur ou d'un ingénieur. Il reste cependant des problèmes à résoudre avant que des données hétérogènes puissent être intégrées pour l'utilisateur d'une manière fluide. Nous discutons trois cas type. Le premier se réfère à la recherche d'information textuelle dans un environnement scientifique moderne, en utilisant un jeu particulier de segments textuels, celui des résumés relatifs aux propositions d'observation astronomique. Dans le second cas, nous discutons d'approches viables de la restitution du contenu à base d'image qui accompagne l'information textuelle. Enfin, nous examinons le rôle que les modèles de vision à multirésolution peuvent jouer en facilitant la recherche du contenu d'une base d'images. L'objectif immédiat de ce troisième cas type est la recherche d'informations relatives à des objets, caractérisés par leurs formes morphologiques, dans une large base de données d'images.

1   INTRODUCTION

The automation of text and image retrieval is not sufficiently standardized at present. Yet many if not most of those involved in science and technology face the need to interrogate large data collections, using content and context. A number of facets of this problem will be discussed. The application areas will be noted. Some current solution techniques will be described.

2   FREE-TEXT INFORMATION RETRIEVAL

Astronomical observation proposals are submitted for peer review at regular time-intervals. In the case of Hubble Space Telescope observations, the abstracts are available for successful proposals. These abstracts provide convenient raw-material for description of the images which are taken later. Associating the abstracts and images will be described in section 3, below. Firstly we address the following issue: just as in the case of text segments in other fields (company reports, for financial appraisal purposes; legal reports; etc.), can the text segments be used for other purposes also? If so, what types of useful operations can be performed on them?

Three objectives of free text querying of observation proposal abstracts are envisaged:

- As an aid to observation proposal assessors, and scheduling planners, it is helpful to look for closely related proposals.
- As an aid to the user who is preparing a proposal, it is useful to check on what has been already achieved, and by whom, using general phrases which express his or her envisaged research.
- As a general approach to image retrieval from the HST image archive, we may search through the proposal abstracts, which we hope express in a few natural language sentences what the associated images (observed later) are meant to contain.

An HST observing proposal abstract is shown in the following.

Prop. Type: GO

GALAXIES & CLUSTERS -- (GAS & DUST) --

3840- CT - "THE ABUNDANCES AND TIME EVOLUTION OF CARBON, NITROGEN AND OXYGEN IN

STAR-FORMING GALAXIES"

Continuation of Program Number 3840

Keywords :

Proposers: Evan D. Skillman (PI; University Of Minnesota), R.Dufour (Rice University), D.Garnett (Space Telescope Science Institute), M.Peimbert (Unam; Mexico), G.Shields (University Of Texas), E.Terlevich (Royal Greenwich Observatory; United Kingdom), R.Terlevich (Royal Greenwich Observatory; United Kingdom), S.Torres-Peimbert (Unam; Mexico)

We propose to observe UV emission lines of carbon, nitrogen, and oxygen from high-surface brightness extragalactic H II regions drawn from a sample of irregular and spiral galaxies having a large spread of known oxygen abundance (2% solar to nearly solar). From the emission-line data we will derive C/O and N/O abundance ratios for which systematic uncertainties - due to reddening corrections, temperature and density effects, and mismatched aperture sizes (typical in IUE+optical studies) - are greatly reduced. We will use the derived abundances to study the time evolution of C/O and N/O in nearby galaxies, and compare the results with those obtained from observations of stars in our own Galaxy. We will be able to test the suggestion (from far-infrared observations of H II regions) that nitrogen abundances derived from optical spectra are systematically in error by factors of two or more. We will also be able to measure the gas phase abundance of silicon, allowing us to study Si depletion as a function of metallicity. Our target sample size of 28 is sufficiently large to study both trends in relative abundance and search for anomalous regions (for example, those affected by the presence of WR stellar winds). The order of magnitude increase in s/n over IUE will allow the measurement of C/O and C/N with the requisite accuracy for the first time.

As an experiment in constructing an astronomically knowledgeable search engine, we took the IAU Thesaurus (Shobbrook and Shobbrook, 1993) to generate a list of astronomical phrases. No particular attention was paid to object names (e.g. globular cluster 47 Tuc); or to additional semantics related especially to data in numeric form ("wavelengths less than 7000 Å"; "distant"; etc.).

We took the accepted observing proposals, for Hubble Space Telescope, for the first four observing cycles (1989--1993), and experimented with publicly available information retrieval software tools which support free text querying. About 1500 proposal abstracts were used. Due to the control allowed the user in supporting querying by phrase ("IRAS galax*", "spectral energy distribution", "elliptical galax*", "spectral type", "absorption line"), its ignoring dashes, and its case insensitivity, a publicly available Unix tool, *lq-text*, was used. This software is available by anonymous ftp from ftp.cs.toronto.edu. Problems which remained included the limited capabilities to handle such astronomical terms as "A star", "B star", etc.

A set of 286 phrases was ultimately retained, each of which is present in one or more proposal abstracts. To assess the potential for such phrases to describe the interrelationships between the proposal abstracts, a clustering was carried out on the 1434 proposals, crossed (presence/absence) by the 286 phrases. The Kohonen "self-organizing feature map" (Murtagh and Hernández-Pajares, 1994) offers a simultaneous clustering and dimensionality reduction. Characterizing the clusters found on a 8 x 8 regular grid was quite successful. Major categories of observations were obtained: "stars", "planetary nebulae", "solar system", etc. See Murtagh (1994) for further details of this particular study.

3   CONTENT BASED IMAGE RETRIEVAL

It is not an easy matter to characterize meaningfully, and for general purposes, the subject matter of images. One possible solution is to use textual information accompanying an image.

We constructed such a prototype for the HST archive, which around the time of the CODATA'94 meeting contained about 50,000 2-dimensional and 1-dimensional (spectral) images. The set of available observing proposals had grown to 2006, and these provided a convenient body of text to characterize the images. A proposal was an advance statement of what the image was to contain, so a working hypothesis was that the image actually was related to the description in the observing proposal.

More than one image could be related to a proposal. For instance, a snapshot survey of protoplanetary nebulae requested, and subsequently obtained, 100 different images.

In an initial prototyping phase we concentrated on Wide Field/Planetary Camera (WF/PC) images, taken before HST's refurbishment in December 1993. Each such image is of dimensions 1600 x 1600, and is 10.5 MB in size. However many images have a preview version. This is a binned, and compressed version (using a wavelet H-transform), and leads to images of dimensions approximately 800 x 800, of size 40 kB, which can be stored on-line. When using such images, we further reduced their size and converted them to GIF format (in order to allow them to be viewed inline, when using a World-Wide Web browser such as Mosaic).

About 4340 unique images (different coordinates of the sky were observed; but we allowed for exclusion of images of the same location on the sky with different exposure times, or using different filters, simply to cut down on the processing involved in this prototype) were finally sought, and 2362 preview images were found to be available. Generally, non-existence of a preview image means that the proprietary period of one year is still running.

We used WAIS (Wide-Area Information Server) to index the observing proposal text, having first created an HTML file from the proposal with a link to any accompanying images. Then, accessing WAIS via Mosaic provided a list of "hits" resulting from a free-text query. Each item in this ranked list corresponded to a proposal. Clicking on any such item provided the text of the proposal, and associated images which were displayed in an inline manner.

This approach is quite a feasible one for the quick and easy delivery of information. It is flexible, in that the user's request is expressed in free-text. Figure 1 shows the result in the case of a particular proposal. The query term used was "extragalactic distance scale". The prototype version set up is at this time accessible at URL `http://ecf.hq.eso.org/~fmurtagh/hst-navigate.html`.

4   IMAGE RETRIEVAL THROUGH IMAGE INVENTORY

A more difficult way to carry out content-based image retrieval is through first analyzing the image, using appropriate pattern recognition methods, and building up an inventory of the image's contents. Traditional approaches to object inventory have used thresholding. An enhanced approach to adaptive thresholding is used here which incorporates a vision model relating to the type of object which is sought as a priority. This vision model is based on multiresolution analysis, and mathematical morphological operations.

Proposal: 4658 Target: NGC5457-FLD2

```
Prop. Type: GO
TAC Panel:  GALAXIES AND CLUSTERS
ID:         4658
Title:      DETERMINATION OF THE EXTRAGALACTIC DISTANCE SCALE. III. M101
Keywords:
PI:         JEREMY MOULD (California Institute of Technology)
```

Many fundamental problems in cosmology and astrophysics remain unsettled because the value of the expansion rate is uncertain to a factor of two. HST will provide the opportunity to break this impasse. We propose a program which in combination with other GTO and GO work should lead to a measurement of Ho to 10 % accuracy. Our main goal is the observation of Cepheids in two dozen fields in 20 nearby galaxies, for the purpose of calibrating the infrared Tully -Fisher relation as well as other secondary distance indicators, including the Planetary Nebula Luminosity Function, the Globular Cluster Luminosity Function, the Luminosity Variance method, supernovae, and the Faber-Jackson relation. Much of this work must wait for the availability of WFPC2; so our limited goals for Cycles 2 and 3 are: (a) to learn how to find Cepheids and measure their periods and amplitudes from WFC images, (b) to complete the determination of a reliable distance to M81 (and thus to furnish an important calibrator for four of the secondary distance indicators listed above), (c) to discover Cepheids in two radially different (and chemically distinct) fields in the giant spiral galaxy M101. The primary purpose here is to perform an end-to-end test of our method of determining reddening and metallicity independent distances.

 Image W1AG0101T

Figure 1. Text (proposal abstract) and inlined image(s) found when using a free-text search. This illustrates one approach to content-based image retrieval.

Multiresolution analysis (Starck et al., 1995) is motivated by the fact that the human visual system deals with visual scenes at differing resolution scales. It handles these resolution scales simultaneously. Using wavelet transforms, or other approaches (Starck et al.,1995), the first phase is to arrive at a set of 4 or 5 resolution scales related to the original image. Next we use the fact that astronomical images are always noisy. Hence we seek to find what is real and what is noise-related in the set of multiresolution images. We represent the images at each scale by boolean versions, -- a one represents a pixel associated with a real object, and a zero represents a noise pixel. Contiguous sets of 1-valued pixels demarcate astronomical images of interest. This allows a range of quantitative properties of the objects, i.e. the pixels in a given contiguous "island", to be determined.

A report is built up on the objects found. Figures 2 and 3 show the first stages of this.

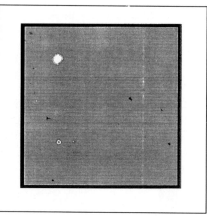

Figure 2. An image (WF/PC, from Hubble Space Telescope). We seek to demarcate and then characterize the astronomical objects which are present.

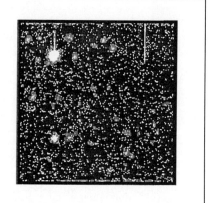

Figure 3. From the image shown in Figure 2, boolean images are created which serve to specify -on varying resolution levels- the object present.

These results relate to the searching in a large number of images, for faint edge-on galaxies. Figure 2 shows the original image, where some objects are very faint indeed. It is a WF/PC image from HST. This image was filtered to remove the spoiling effect of cosmic-ray hits --a common problem for such CCD detectors when the Earth's atmosphere provides little protection. Figure 3 depicts the multiresolution-related boolean images. Further processing involves performing mathematical morphology opening operations on Figure 3, to remove detector artifacts (long linear features) and the many left-over effects of cosmic ray hits. Then the remaining objects are labeled, and quantitative characterizations made (peak-to-background intensity, roundness, moments, ellipticity, etc.).

The problem of finding effective approaches which span varying image exposure levels is not an easy one, and is being tackled empirically. The multiresolution approach, in producing boolean images, allows Minkowski (mathematical morphology) operators such as openings and closings to be used on these boolean images, such that the user's a priori knowledge of objects of interest is availed of. For example, objects which are too small to be of practical use can be suppressed by a sequence of openings (erosion followed by dilation), and this often includes the left-over effects of cosmic ray hits.

The kernel or structuring element used in the multiresolution transform, and later in the use of Minkowski operators, are related to the types of objects wanted, e.g., point-symmetric shapes of limited extent. Convolving with appropriate kernels yields clearer peaks, better definition of regions and greater ease of implementation of subsequent image analysis operations.

CONCLUSION

Section 1 reviewed objectives, and one implementation approach, for the handling of relatively homogeneous "chunks" of text. Software tools such as WAIS have progressed significantly in recent years. Such tools are distributed, i.e. the user and the server can be geographically distant. Recent versions support fields (e.g. author name, or date), and the association of files of different types (e.g. text and image). We believe that there is some way to go, still, before such tools are as often used as, say, a news reader or an image display utility on the user's machine. Such tools provide access to text or image information; but text analysis provides not only secondary analyses, but also a different type of access --not based on novelty, but rather on directed subject-driven search.

Section 2 described a prototype image retrieval system, based on natural language query specification. The aim was to express the image's contents using associated text fragments which are conveniently available. A challenging task which lies ahead is to bring about more linkages with online abstract servers, which comprehensively represent the published astronomical literature.

Section 3 described on-going research in using idealized astronomical objects in order to catalog, or perform an inventory of, all objects in an image. The image databases of the future will be interrogated in natural language, and will reveal their secrets in a way which is more natural than today's cumbersome access mechanisms.

ACKNOWLEDGEMENTS

The work described in section 3 is in collaboration with E.J.A.M. Meurs, Dublin Institute of Advanced Studies. A similar study, involving globular cluster systems in the neighborhood of elliptical galaxies, is ongoing with W. Zeilinger, University of Vienna. Section 3 is based on work with J.-L. Starck, CEA Paris, and A. Bijaoui, Observatoire de la Côte d'Azur, Nice.

KEYWORDS

Pictorial database retrieval, image processing, pattern recognition, astronomical archives and databases, semantic information, information systems.

REFERENCES

[1]   Murtagh F., Free text information retrieval: an assessment of publicly available Unix-based systems, report (unpublished), Feb. (1994).
[2]   Murtagh F., Hernández-Pajares M., The Kohonen self-organizing map method: an assessment, Journal of Classification (1994).
[3]   Shobbrook R.M., Shobbrook R.R. , The Astronomy Thesaurus, Version 1.1, IAU, (1993).
[4]   Starck J.-L., Bijaoui A., Murtagh F., Multiresolution and astronomical image processing, in Payne H., Shaw D., Hayes J. (eds) ADASS'94 Astronomical Data Analysis Software and Systems IV,ASP, San Francisco, 279-288 (1995).

THE WORLD-WIDE WEB: A GLOBAL SOURCE OF DATA AND INFORMATION

Joel WINSTEAD and Nahum GERSHON

The MITRE Corporation, 7525 Colshire Drive, McLean, VA 22102
E-mail: winstead@lash.mitre.org , gershon@mitre.org

ABSTRACT

The World-Wide Web (WWW, or the Web) is a distributed information system on the Internet. This distributed information system could contain data, text, images, and other type of data and information. Documents are stored in hypertext form with links to other relevant documents that could be kept on various machines around the network. Users can retrieve these pieces of data and information (from wherever they reside on the Web) by pointing and clicking with a mouse and interact with services such as databases by using forms and menus. There are several programs available that allow a user to view, write, and publish documents on the Web. Information can be located on the WWW by using subject indexes, Web crawlers, and on-line databases.

New capabilities and information resources are continuously created on the Web making it a very dynamic system. However, there are some limitations due to the rigid structure of the hypertext model and the chaotic distribution and management of Web resources. These difficulties pose some challenges for future developments of the WWW.

RESUME

Le World Wide Web (WWW ou le Web) est un système d'information distribué sur Internet. Il peut contenir des données, du texte, des images et d'autres types de données. Les documents sont stockés sous forme d'hypertextes avec des liens à d'autres documents pertinents sur diverses machines réparties dans le réseau. Les utilisateurs peuvent extraire ces éléments d'information (quels que soient leurs lieux de stockage) en interagissant par le biais de menus et d'icones avec des serveurs de données. Divers programmes permettent la visualisation et la publication de documents du Web. Les informations peuvent être localisées à l'aide d'indexes et de "Web crawlers" dans des bases de données en ligne.

Le Web est en évolution très rapide. Cependant des contraintés sevères sont liées à la rigidité structurale du modèle hypertexte ainsi qu'à la répartition et la gestion chaotique des ressources du Web. Elles constituent de serieux défis à relever au cours des développements futurs du Web.

1   INTRODUCTION

The World-Wide Web (WWW) is a distributed information system in which documents, data, and images are located on different computers dispersed around the Internet. The main advantage of the WWW is that it provides an easy and uniform way to access information from around the world by unifying the various methods of obtaining information from the Internet into a single, simple interface.

A variety of information is available on the Web. People have created documents that contain information on current events, academic research, commercial advertising, information on recreational activities and hobbies, up-to-the-minute weather images, and computer software. New documents, search, retrieval, and computational capabilities are continuously being placed on the Web. To interact with and to access this information, the user can employ a variety of browsers to download and view Web documents (see Figure 1).

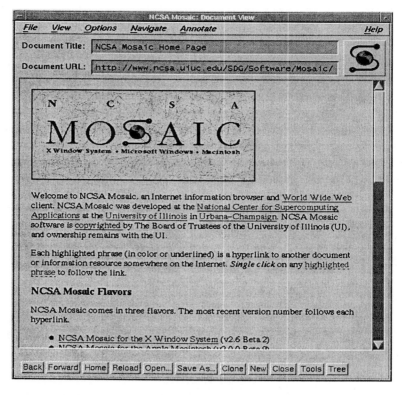

Figure 1. A typical WWW page on *NCSA Mosaic* Browser

2 STRUCTURE OF THE WEB

Documents on the World-Wide Web, stored on a variety of computers around the world, are retrieved via the client-server model. When a user wishes to view a particular document, client software on his desktop computer sends a request to server software on the computer that stores the document. The server then sends a copy of the document back to the client, where it can be viewed. This document transfer is done over the Internet using the HyperText Transfer Protocol, or HTTP. This system allows users to access documents that are stored anywhere in the world, without placing the burden of maintaining the large collection of documents on a single computer. The distributed nature of the system makes it easy for anybody to put his own material on the Web, and access material placed on the Web by others. Because the Web is not centrally controlled, this ever growing collection of documents could be incomplete on particular subjects, and is not always well-organized.

2.1 Hypertext

Most documents stored on the Web are in a hypertext format known as the HyperText Markup Language, or HTML. HTML allows documents to include tables, pictures, sounds, and animations as well as text, and even allows multimedia documents that have more than one type of data (e.g. text, still and animated images, and sound). In hypertext, an author can link together related documents through hyperlinks. A hyperlink in a document is a word, phrase or picture that represents a connection to another document. By using a mouse to point and click on a hyperlink, a user can access the other document referenced by the hyperlink. Thus, links in hypertext documents are used to provide cross-references to related information, organize large quantities of information into hierarchies, and to hide information that might not be of interest of the user until later. A user who is not interested in a document can simply skip over the link to it and go on to other information that is more useful, without wasting time reading irrelevant information. An author can create structure between his documents and existing documents by inserting appropriate hyperlinks. A example of hyperlinked Web documents is given in Figure 2.

HTML documents are stored as machine-independent ASCII text files with additional formatting tags that describe how the text is to be displayed, what titles and headings to use, and where to insert images and other media. The Web client is responsible for interpreting and displaying the text, while making the most appropriate use of the machine's display capabilities. This system allows documents stored on the Web to be displayed by nearly any platform connected to the Internet, regardless of the differences between the displays of different kinds of computers.

2.2 Uniform Resource Locators

A document on the World-Wide Web is uniquely referred to by a Uniform Resource Locator, or URL. The URL provides a simple, consistent way of describing the means of accessing nearly any resource on the Internet. It contains fields describing how the document is to be retrieved, on what server it is located, and its filename and directory within that server [2]. For example, 'http://lcweb.loc.gov/homepage/lchp.html' is a typical URL, which points to the home page of the Library of Congress. Broken into parts, 'http:' refers to the method that should be used to retrieve the document, 'lcweb.loc.gov' is the Internet address of the server that stores the document, 'homepage' is the directory in which the document is stored, and 'lchp.html' is the filename of the document.

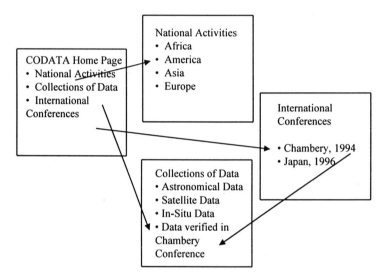

Figure 2. Example of hyperlinked Web documents

3   WEB SOFTWARE

A large number of software packages are available on the Internet (in many cases for free) to facilitate use of the World-Wide Web. In the following paragraphs, we describe a number of these software systems. This is not meant to be a comprehensive list, but merely to give an idea of what sort of software capabilities are available.

3.1   Browsers

Users can retrieve and display documents from the Web interactively using a family of client programs known as Web browsers. These programs provide a simple way for users to access and display documents, follow hyperlinks, save them to disk, and print hard copies. Browsers have been written and ported to a variety of platforms and operating environments, and many are distributed freely on the Internet.

Mosaic is a graphical Web browser developed by the National Center for Supercomputing Applications (NCSA), and has been ported to Unix/Motif, Microsoft Windows, and the Macintosh. It provides a simple, point-and-click interface which is easy to learn and use. Hyperlinks in a document are displayed as underlined words or phrases, and a simple mouse click on a hyperlink will retrieve and display the referenced document. Mosaic was one of the first Web browsers to gain popularity, and remains widely available. A more powerful commercial version of *NCSA Mosaic* was developed and distributed by SpyGlass [6].

Netscape is a commercially developed graphical Web browser that is similar to *Mosaic*. It includes an efficient retrieval of documents and an improved user interface. Several extensions to standard HTML are supported, including forms, tables, and additional text formatting tags. *Netscape* is available for a number of platforms and operating systems, and is one of the most commonly used browsers on the Web today [11].

Lynx is a text-based browser developed by the University of Kansas which allows users who do not have access to graphical environments to browse the Web. Users can select URLs and follow hyperlinks using keyboard commands. *Lynx* provides text-based equivalents of most features that hypertext documents have. Although it cannot display images like *Mosaic* and *Netscape*, it is a popular choice among those who must access the Internet via modem or text terminal and cannot display graphics [4].

3.2   Servers

Web servers are the programs that manage documents and send them to clients on request. They understand HyperText Transfer Protocol and are responsible for distributing requested documents on their computers, processing Web forms, and providing the interface between Web clients and on-line databases. *NCSA httpd* is a freely distributed program available for Unix and Windows NT which serves documents to client programs over the Internet. It is capable of distributing simple documents and running programs which process forms and generate documents upon request [12]. It does not include database support, although there are other programs such as *GSQL* which can work with *httpd* to access databases [13].

3.3   HTML Editors

Although HTML files can be created using a simple text editor, the formatting tags are often difficult to read in their raw form. A number of HTML editors are available that can make hypertext documents much easier to write. *TkHTML* is an HTML editor available for Unix/X [1]. *HTML Author* is an extension to Microsoft Word for Windows that allows editing and creation of HTML documents [5]. *HTML Editor* for the Macintosh also provides a WYSIWYG interface for editing HTML documents [8]. These programs make it easier to write HTML documents without requiring the user to know the special formatting tags.

4   LOCATING AND INTERACTING WITH INFORMATION

Often we do not have the URL for a document which we need. Because there are so many documents on the Web distributed over such a wide space, locating a document on a given topic can appear overwhelming. Several sites have attempted to organize information on the Web so that documents are easier to find. These sites make it possible to find a document on a given topic even when the URL is not known.

4.1   Subject Indexes

Subject indexes are hypertext documents that contain hierarchical menus of links to other documents. The hierarchy is designed to organize information by subject, so that users can quickly find a link to a document that contains the needed information. The user can follow links down the hierarchy, narrowing the search, until he or she finds a document that contains useful information. These indexes are very common types of documents on the Web. They are often set up by universities that wish to provide a means of finding relevant information, or by individuals who wish to share a list of their favorite Internet sites. Often a subject index will contain links to other indexes, so that one can navigate the Web by jumping from index to index until a link to the information sought is found. The WWW Virtual Library at http://www.w3.org/hypertext/DataSources/bySubject/Overview.html is a good example.

4.2   Forms

One common extension to HTML is the ability to interact with Web services via forms. Some Web documents have special tags that allow the user to enter information through type-in fields, check boxes, and radio buttons. The client program gets the information from the user, and then sends the requested information back to the server which processes the data and sends a response to the user's input. Forms are often used as an interface to databases, Web search engines, opinion polling, and commercial services. Form support makes two-way interaction possible on the Web, instead of simple retrieval of documents.

4.3   Web Crawlers and Search Engines

Web crawlers are programs that automatically follow hyperlinks and traverse the Web, indexing as they go. Several Web crawlers have been making indexes of the Web for some time. Often the data collected from a Web crawler will be placed in an on-line search engine that can be accessed through a form, such as has been done with the WWW Worm [10] and Yahoo [7]. With a few keywords, the user can retrieve a list of documents which were found by the crawler that match that description.

4.4   Database Interfaces

There are several on-line databases on the Web. Query information can be passed to the database through HTML forms, and query results are passed back to the user as an HTML document. The user need not know how to use a database query language, and can simply enter the query information into a simple form. An example of a Web interface to a database can be found at `http://atsdr1.atsdr.cdc.gov:8080/hazdat.html`, which is a database of information related to hazardous substances. The end user does not need to know how the database is implemented, and only sees the hypertext interface. This simple yet powerful concept allows users to access large quantities of information from the Web.

4.5   Hot Java

Hot Java is an interpreted programming language which is used to write small applications, or applets, which are embedded within hypertext documents. A user can download a Web document containing an applet written in Java, and then execute the applet on his own computer. Since Java is an interpreted language, it is machine-independent and can run on any computer that has a Java interpreter installed. This system makes it possible for Web authors to have better control over the interface presented to the user. Applets can be used to provide more sophisticated user interfaces than are possible with forms, and can be used to make animations and map queries [14].

5   FUTURE OF THE WEB

Although the World-Wide Web's lack of a rigid structure allows for tremendous flexibility and expandability, this design often makes it difficult to find specific information. The structures that authors write into their documents are not always useful to the end user, and make it difficult for the user to find what he or she wants. Navigating through the often tangled hierarchy of hyperlinks can be confusing as well. The numerous subject indexes and Web crawlers form a partial solution to the problem of finding the right document on the Web. Another proposed solution is a system of servers that archive the titles of Web documents and their links, similar to the Archie system that indexes ftp sites [9]. Neither are complete solutions because Web documents are not always appropriately named and often contain information about more than one subject. Improved Web browsers may form a part of the solution. Navigational aids that help the user find his or her way through the Web without getting lost in the myriads of hyperlinks will improve upon the situation. A new system similar to the Web called Hyper-G [see Kappe, this volume], which is used primarily in Europe, offers a more organized hierarchy of hypertext documents that is easier to search. Hyper-G allows documents to be clustered together and treated as a single collection. Hyperlinks can be created between documents and collections as well as to the existing documents in the World-Wide Web. The hyperlinks are bidirectional, unlike those on the Web, and are stored along with metadata about the documents on machines other than those that manage the documents themselves. This system has better search capabilities and is much more structured.

The Web of the future may have two types of information: unstructured and uncontrolled as it is today, and structured and controlled like in Hyper-G. Authors and organizations publishing information on the Web will be able to decide how they would like the information to be handled. The Web continues to grow as new solutions are found. Its ease of use and existing store of information contributes to its growth, and new documents and sites are created every day. It is a vast source of information in many forms, and will likely continue to serve the Internet and the information communities for a long time.

KEYWORDS

Link,Web-crawlers, prospective.

REFERENCES

[1]   Bahneman, TML - tcl HTML Editor Information
        http://www.ssc.com/~roland/tkHTML/tkHTML.html
[2]   Berners-Lee T., Uniform Resource Locators: A Syntax for the Expression of Access
        Information of Objects on the Network, March (1994)
        http://www.w3.org/hypertext/WWW/Addressing/URL/url-spec.txt
[3]   Berners-Lee T., Cailliau R., Luotonen A., Nielsen H. F., Secret A., The World-Wide Web,
        communications of the ACM, 37(8), August (1994).
[4]   Blythe G., Montulli L., Grobe M., Ware S., Lynx Users Guide 2.3
        http://www.cc.ukans.edu/lynx/lynx_help/Lynx_users_guide.html
[5]   Cooper G.S., HTML Author Summary, May (1995)
        http://www.salford.ac.uk/docs/depts/iti/staff/gsc/htmlauth/summary.html
[6]   Dougherty D., Korman R., Ferguson P., The Mosaic Handbook for the Macintosh.
        O'Reilly & Associates, Oct. (1994).
[7]   Filo D., Yang. J., Yahoo Frequently Asked Questions,(1995)
        http://www.yahoo.com/faq.html
[8]   Giles R. TML Editor for the Macintosh, (1994)
        http://dragon.acadiau.cs/~giles/HTML_Editor/Documentation.html
[9]   Krol, E. The Whole Internet. O'Reilly & Associates, April (1994).
[10]   McBryan, Oliver A., GENVL and WWWW: Tools for Taming the Web, (1994)
        http://www.cs.colorado.edu/home/mcbryan/mypapers/www94.ps
[11]   Netscape Communications Corporation. About Netscape, (1995)
        http://home.mcom.com/comprod/about_netscape.html
[12]   NCSA Development Team. NCSA httpd Overview
        http://hoohoo.ncsa.uiuc.edu/docs/overview.html
[13]   Ng J., GSQL - a Mosaic-SQL gateway, Dec.(1993).
        http://www.ncsa.uiuc.edu/SDG/People/jason/pub/gsql/starthere.html
[14]   Sun Microsystems, The Java Language: A White Paper
        http://java.sun.com/1.0alpha3/doc/overview/java/index.html
[15]   Torkington N., World Wide Web Primer, Dec.(1994).
        http://www.vuw.ac.nz/who/Nathan.Torkington/ideas/www-primer

STRUCTURING AND VISUALIZING HYPERSPACE WITH HYPER-G

Frank KAPPE

Institute for Information Processing and Computer Supported New Media (IICM), Graz University of Technology, A-8010 Graz, Austria, E-mail : fkappe@iicm.tu-graz.ac.at

ABSTRACT

Users of large, distributed, hypermedia information systems (like the World-Wide Web) often find it difficult to get the information they are looking for. They get "lost in hyperspace". The Hyper-G hypermedia system developed at the Graz University of Technology is a large-scale, distributed, hypermedia information system designed to alleviate this problem. This is accomplished by a combination of two approaches : a-priori and a-posteriori structuring of the hyperspace. For a-priori structuring, the author can make use of Hyper-G's collection and cluster concepts to model the information as seen by the user according to its inherent structure. For a-posteriori structuring, Hyper-G clients offer the user powerful tools for visualization of a navigation through the information structure. The chapter analyzes the problems associated with navigation in large hypertexts, and describes how they are solved or at least reduced in Hyper-G by structuring and visualization techniques.

RESUME

Les utilisateurs d'informations dans de larges systèmes distribués du type hypermédia (voir World Wide Web) rencontre des difficultés pour trouver les informations souhaitées. Ils se perdent dans "l'hyper espace". Le système hypermédia "Hyper-G" développé à l'Université de Technologie de Gratz est un système conçu pour simplifier ce problème. Ceci est obtenu par la combinaison de deux approches : la structuration à-priori et à-postériori de l'hyper espace. Dans la structuration à-priori l'auteur peut utiliser les concepts de collection des Hyper-G et de treillis pour modéliser l'information conformément à la perception de l'utilisateur et en fonction de la structure propre. Avec la structuration à-postériori les clients de Hyper-G offrent aux utilisateurs des outils puissants de visualisation pour assister la navigation dans la structure informationnelle. Dans cet article on analyse les problèmes liés à la navigation dans de larges fichiers hypertextes et on décrit comment ils sont résolus ou en partie réduits en Hyper-G par des techniques de structuration et de visualisation.

1   GETTING LOST IN HYPERSPACE

A problem associated with using a large-scale hypermedia system is that one can get lost quite easily [5]. This phenomenon is usually described as the "Lost in Hyperspace" syndrome [14]. Looking at it more closely, we may distinguish a number of symptoms, which we will discuss below, together with possible treatments:

How to get an overview?

In most popular hypermedia systems (e.g. the World-Wide Web [6]), users see only one document at a time (the so-called "current document"). Outgoing links are visualized and may be activated. However, it is unclear how the current document is related to other documents (e.g. what links of other documents lead to the current document). The user is like a stranger in an unknown city who can only look forward until the next crossing. Looking backwards or even a map is not available.

How can visualization techniques be used to overcome or at least alleviate this problem?

Of course, a map would help. Unfortunately, in a large hyperspace, a complete (global) map of all the documents and links is too complex to be useful. A hand-crafted map drawn by the author of the information content is more organized than an automatically created map, but because of the manual labour involved this seems only feasible for relatively small and static material.

Therefore, it seems feasible to use *local maps* instead of global ones. A local map shows only the vicinity of the current document. Local maps were first implemented in the Intermedia System [16,22] and are now being used in Hyper-G as well as shown in section 3. In our city analogy a local map is like a radar screen with limited range.

A variant of local maps are the so-called *fish-eye views*, which behave like extreme wide-angle lenses that enlarge everything in the vicinity and reduce the size of things far away. In analogy, fish-eye views emphasize more important documents by enlarging their visual appearance [20,21] and distorting the graph accordingly. Automatic *clustering* algorithms can be used to identify closely related documents. Such *clusters* can then be visualized as one object, thus reducing the number of cross-references and the complexity of the resulting map [12,7].

A different method tries to group together related material in advance ("a priori") in so-called *collections*, which behave like directories in file systems. By recursion, a *collection hierarchy* is defined. This structural information may be contained in links of a special type ("is-a-member-of"), sometimes called *structure=representing* or *organizational* hyperlinks, as opposed to the usual *referential* hyperlinks. This concept was already used in Engelbart's Augment system [10] and KMS [4]. The NoteCards system [15] did have the concept of "file boxes" which could contain files or other file boxes, but did not use a separate link type for them, which led to significant confusion. It is possible --with restrictions -- to separate organizational and referential hyperlinks subsequently ("a posteriori") [8], but classification by the author is of course more exact. The distinction may reduce the number of referential links significantly, since the local map may be configured to show only links of a particular type, which in turn reduces the complexity of the local map. Alternatively, the collection hierarchy may be browsed by a different mechanism, as we will see in section 3. An important means of reducing the "lost in hyperspace" effect is *location feedback*, i.e. showing the current position in the (global) collection hierarchy.

In our city analogy the collection hierarchy is equivalent to a hierarchy of overview maps of different scale (e.g. world, continent, country, region, city, city district), with the current position highlighted on all maps (e.g. using a satellite navigation system). In conjunction with a *local map* we now have pretty good means of navigation.

How do I avoid seeing the same information again and again?

To reduce the possibility of wandering around in circles, most hypermedia systems offer a *footprint* feature (sometimes also called *bread crumbs*). Links that point to documents already visited are marked in a special way (e.g. with a check mark or in a different color). This requires that the system remember what documents have already been visited, either within the current session or in all sessions. However, this is not sufficient: If a document that I have visited is subsequently modified (e.g. new information is added), it should not be marked as seen any more. This means that the system needs to take version numbers or modification time stamps of documents into account.

How much information exists (on a certain topic)?

Let us assume I would like to go on a trip to New Zealand, and would like to get some information about New Zealand before I physically go there. Let us further assume that I find some references to hypermedia information on New Zealand (e.g. in some World-Wide Web servers). How do I find out (fast, of course; before following the reference rather than after), if the reference will lead me to substantial information on New Zealand (say, with 500 documents) or not (say, only 3 documents).

Again, the collection hierarchy can help a little bit, if it can tell the user how much information (e.g. how many documents, how many megabytes) exist within a certain collection (recursively down the tree).

How much of it has been seen already?

A principal advantage of linear text (e.g. a book) over hypertext is the following: When I start reading on page one and continue to the end, I can always tell how much I have already read and how much I still have to do. In particular, when I am at the end, I can be sure that I have seen everything.

In a hypertext, this is not at all trivial. Let us assume that I start to read the hypertext shown in Figure 1 at document A, and continue by following the link to document C, and then documents D, E, F, G, and H. Should I meanwhile have forgotten that I still need to follow the link from A to B, I will never see documents B and I. Please observe also that document J cannot be reached from A at all! A lot depends on your entry point.

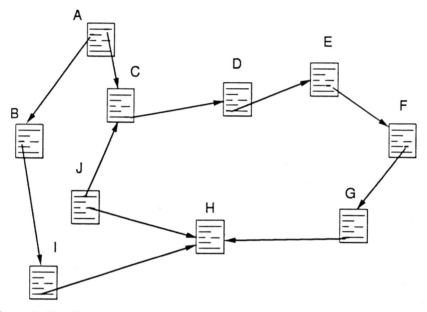

Figure 1. Non-linear text

Of course, the more complex the hypertext gets, the more difficult to see everything. We discovered this problem when we assigned students to read hypertext lessons as part of preparation for an exam. They found it very difficult to make sure that they had seen and learned everything contained in the lesson.

A hierarchical structure of the material (e.g. by organizing it into a collection hierarchy) in conjunction with the "already seen" marks can solve this problem: The hierarchy implicitly defines a linear sequence of documents (e.g. by depth-first traversal), so that it becomes possible to read it in linear order. Even if one does not want to navigate in the hierachical fashion but would rather follow the (referential) links in the documents, it is possible to verify at the end whether everything has been seen, and to access documents that are nor reachable from the entry point just by following referential hyperlinks.

How do I find specific information?

If instead of browsing in random ways ("surfing the web") we need to perform more serious, goal-directed work, we need a special search function. A full-text search is nice, but sometimes not sufficient. In addition, we would like to have searchable attributes (*meta-information*) attached to each document, such as title, author, keywords, type, modification time, etc.

In a large system, it is imperative that the search scope can be reduced to part of the information space. Otherwise, we would always have to search globally, and almost certainly find too much. Again, the collection hierarchy can be used nicely to restrict the search scope to a set of collections.

How do I find information which I have already seen?

Sometimes I remember a certain document that I looked at some time ago and want to look at it again but cannot remember where it was and how I got there, i.e. which entry point I used and which links I followed from there.

So-called *bookmarks* allow one to save a list of documents and to access them directly later on. In fact, these bookmark documents become new entry points. The obvious disadvantage is that I have to know in advance that I will want to find a specific document again later. Also, if I save too many bookmarks, I will get lost in the bookmarks.

Conversely, the *history* is a trace of my way through the hyperspace and allows me to find and access documents again based on the first time I accessed them. Some systems keep the history only within a session, some support saving and loading the history of previous sessions. Most systems offer only a linear list of previously accessed documents which can be navigated by functions like "`back`'" and "`forward`'". A more general approach is to visualize the history as a tree, showing also documents that were accessed after stepping back in the history [13].

What's new?

Let us assume I have already found some interesting sources of information for my particular interests in a distributed hypermedia information system like the World-Wide Web. It would be a tedious exercise to keep monitoring these resources (e.g. servers) every day to find out if something has changed or something new has been added. "Monitoring" essentialy means re-traversing everything. Of course, the information providers could be kind enough to maintain a "what's new" document with links to updated or new documents, but because of the human effort involved this solution is not very satisfying.

If the system would support searches by modification or creation date, I could simply search for new things. Even more elegant would be an information system that performed these searches itself (e.g. once per day) by launching a set of predefined queries and mailed me the results. Such a system could be called an *active information system* [18].

A similar idea involves so-called *intelligent agents*: programs, that constantly seek useful information on behalf of the user [9,19]. Efficient agents require use of artificial intelligence, and are sometimes also called *knowbots* ("knowledge robots") and *softbots* ("software robots") [11].

How do I recognize outdated information?

In a way, this is the inverse problem of finding new information but much more difficult. The information system is usually not able to discover old information by itself, unless the author has attached an expiration date when it was inserted (which can only be done for some kinds of information).

A special problem with hypertexts is version control. From the user's perspective, it should be possible to recognize that the user is currently looking at an old version of a document, and directly get to the new version of it. This can be implemented using a special "new-version-of" link type. A more advanced system would also highlight the parts changed in the new version.

2   STRUCTURED HYPERMEDIA IN HYPER-G

This section describes the Hyper-G data model and its implementation, as far as the a-priori structuring of information is concerned, and without digging into implementation aspects (the interested reader is referred to [2]). The most fundamental design decision was to provide support for orthogonal yet closely coupled structuring, linking, and search facilities at the database level (as shown in Figure 2):

Structuring: Documents may be grouped into aggregate collections, which may themselves belong to other collections. Every document must belong to at least one collection. Navigation may be performed down through the collection hierarchy (the collection "hierarchy" is, strictly speaking, a directed acyclic graph), access rights assigned on a collection-by-collection basis, and the scope of searches restricted to particular sets of collections. Collections may span multiple HyperG servers, providing a unified view of distributed resources.

Linking: Hyperlinks connect a *source anchor* within one document to either a *destination anchor* within another document, an entire document, or a collection. Links are not stored within documents (as in W3) but in a separate link database (as pioneered by Intermedia [16]). This has a number of important advantages:

Source and destination anchors are not limited to text documents, but can be attached to any kind of media (image, audio, film, 3D scene, formatted PostScript document, etc.).

Links can be attached to otherwise read-only documents (for example documents on CD-ROM or with read-only access rights).

Links can be followed backwards.

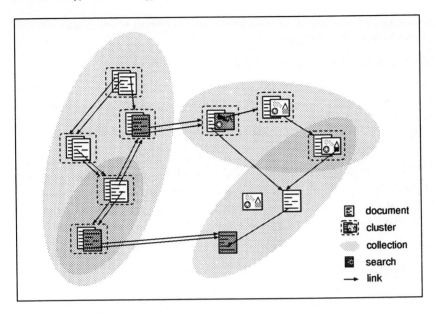

Figure 2: The Hyper-G Data Model

– Source and destination anchors are not limited to text documents, but can be attached to any kind of media (image, audio, film, 3D scene, formatted PostScript document, etc.).

– Links can be attached to otherwise read-only dcoments (for example documents on CD-ROM or with read-only access rights).

– Links can be followed backwards.

– A local map (fish-eye view) can be readily computed and visualised using the link database.

– Consistency constraints can be met more easily (for example when moving or deleting a document, it is important to know which other documents contain links to it).

• *Attribute and Content Search:* Documents and collections have an associated set of attributes (author, title, keywords, etc.) which may be searched for, including boolean combinations and term truncation. Full text (content) search facilities include vector and fuzzy boolean queries. Every document and collection is automatically indexed upon insertion into the database - no extra indexing steps are requiered. The scope of a structure diagram, or any combination of these). Other design features supported by HyperG and not found in comparable systems include:

Anonymous and identified user identification modes.

A scheme of user groups and subgroups maintained by the server.

Access rights for users and user groups on a document or collection basis.

"Home collections", personal information spaces for identified users (kept on the server) used to organise personal documents and pointers to resources.

Language preferences, applied both to document retrieval and to the user interface.

An underlying object-oriented database, which guarantees the consistency and integrity of data (for example the updating of links when a document is moved or deleted).

3   VISUALIZING AND NAVIGATING DEEP HYPERSPACE

I will now give an overview on the features of Harmony, the UNIX/X11 client for Hyper-G, concentrating on navigation and visualization aspects. More details on Harmony can be found in [1]. The Harmony Collection Browser (see Figure 3, top left) allows navigation through the collection hierarchy. Collections may be opened and closed and clusters or individual documents activated within the graphical collection display by double-clicking. Central to the design of Harmony is the concept of *location feedback*. When a document or collection is visited, its location within the collection structure is automatically displayed in the Collection Browser (by opening up the path to it), regardless of whether the object was reached as the result of a search, by following a hyperlink, or via the local map.

This unique feature of Harmony is a powerful instrument in the fight against becoming "lost in hyperspace" -- users can orient themselves with reference to a fixed structural framework.

In the example of Figure 3, the user first "activated" two collections with bibliographies (shown in the "Active Collections" window on the left bottom) by navigating to them in the Collection Browser and then adding them to the "Active Collections" window. In the search dialog, the user restricted the search to the active collections (top line of search dialog), and then entered the word "Maurer" for a search in document titles and attached keywords (not the document's content). The search matched 17 documents. Clicking on the last one once gives immediate location feedback in the collection browser, and we see that it was found in the HCI Bibliography; more precisely, in volume 4 of the journal "Hypermedia". Double-clicking would - in addition to the location feedback - actually open the document.

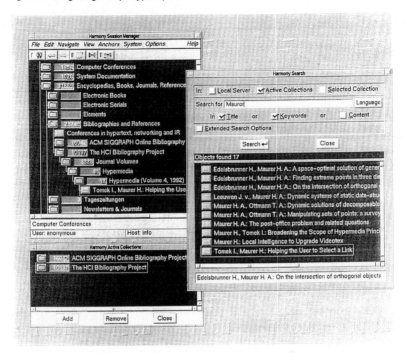

Figure 3. Collection Browser and Search Dialog.

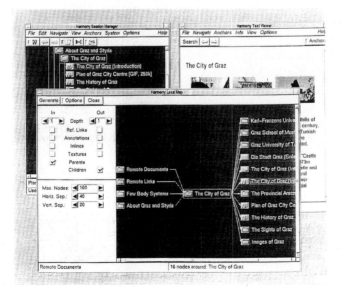

Figure 4. The Harmony Local Map

The Harmony Local Map facility provides a kind of short-range radar, generating on request (dynamically) a map of the hyperlink and/or collection membership relationships of a chosen document, similar to the local map of Intermedia [16], as shown in Figure 4. An options panel allows one to configure the recursion depth for both incoming and outgoing links, as well as restrict the display to certain link types (referential links, annotations, inline images and textures, as well as parent/child relationships, i.e. the collection hierarchy). The local map is active, i.e. users can navigate within the local map by selecting (single-clicking) an object and generating a new display; any object can be activated by double-clicking. In this figure, you can also see little checkmarks on some of the icons that show the document's type. This means that the corresponding document has already been visited. Of course, the local map is always in sync with the collection hierarchy.

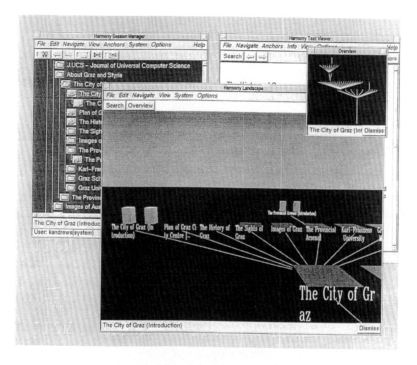

Figure 5. The Harmony Information Landscape.

Harmony's Information Landscape, shown in Figure 5, is an interactive, three-dimensional visualisation of the collection structure, tightly coupled to the Session Manager's two-dimensional collection browser display (changes in one are reflected in the other). The collection hierarchy is mapped out onto a plane, documents within a collection are arranged on top of the corresponding block; colour and height are used to encode document type and size respectively. Users can "fly" over the landscape looking for salient features. A flat overview window (top right) provides a further aid to orientation. Through their ability to compactly display many thousands of objects, 3D visualisations are perhaps the only effective means of browsing in and judging the extent of large, dynamic information spaces.

Work on the Information Landscape is still at an early stage. We are currently experimenting with the use of textured landscapes, and will introduce simple 3D icons to replace the basic blocks currently used. A default set of 3D icons will represent document type, with colouring used to represent document age and hence giving a rapid visual impression of where new information is located.

A further innovation will be the superimposition of arced cables upon the landscape to represent the link relationships of a specific document. All the visualizations so far are dynamically generated on demand. Of course, HyperG also supports navigation in hand-crafted 3D scenes, encoded in VRML. For example, Figure 6 shows a model of the campus of the University of Auckland.

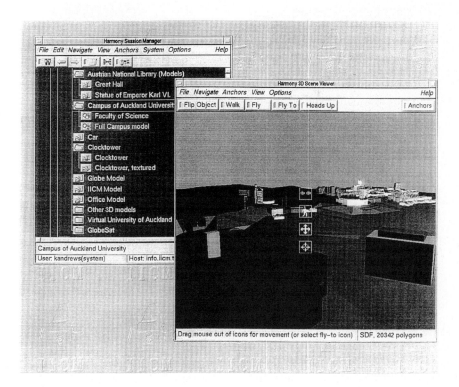

Figure 6. The Harmony 3D Scene Viewer.

Users typically explore a model of a scene by moving themselves (walk, fly, fly to, heads-up) and view a model of an object by moving the model (translate, rotate, zoom). 3D models are fully-fledged hypermedia documents: hyperlinks may be attached to individual objects within a model or to groups of polygons within an object.

CONCLUSION

Information on a Hyper-G server can and most often is accessed using World-Wide Web clients such as Mosaic or Netscape [3]. Most of the navigation features described are not available using this interface. However, we plan to enhance the World-Wide Web gateway so that JAVA-compatible World-Wide Web clients will be able to utilize the powerful structuring and visualization features of Hyper-G.

In order to visualize information from ordinary Web servers, the following features are missing:

- the standard WWW data model (the node-link model) needs to be enhanced with additional structuring mechanisms, very much like the traditional GOTO statament of programming languages has been replaced by structured programming.

- meta-Information (attributes) need to be attached to documents (e.g. title, author, creation time, size, type, access permissions), so that they can be visualized without visualizing their content.

- links need to be stored in a separate link database. This enables to visualize the link structure in local maps, and adds additional metadata information to documents (e.g., the number of incoming links). Links themselves should have metadata attached (e.g., link type, title, access rights) so that they can be visualized more meaningfully.

- the information itself should be separated from the user interface, i.e. content should be separated from presentation. This allows to change the user interface without problems (e.g. to navigation in 3D-space instead of clicking on 2D-pages). It also eases migration to future information systems without rewriting of the documents.

These features affect the server more than the client side, and are available already now in Hyper-G.

More information about Hyper-G and Harmony may be found on the Hyper-G servers of IICM (http://hyperg.iicm.tu-graz.ac.at) and the Hyper-G Consortium (http://hyperg.hgc.org). The reference book on Hyper-G ("*Hyper-G: The Second Generation Web Solution*"; Addison-Wesley) will appear in

January 1996. The software itself may be retrieved by anonymous ftp from ftp://ftp.iicm.tu-graz.ac.at/pub/Hyper-G, or one of its mirrors.

KEYWORDS

Hyper-G, hypermedia, a-priori structuring, a-posteriori structuring, cluster, navigation, visualization.

REFERENCES

[1]   Andrews K., Kappe F., Soaring Through Hyperspace : A Snapshot of Hyper-G and its Harmony Client , In Herzner W. and Kappe F. (eds) Proc. of Eurographics Symposium on Multimedia/ Hypermedia in Open Distributed Enviroments, 181-191, Graz, Austria, Springer, June (1994).

[2]   Andrews K., Kappe F., Maurer H., The Hyper-G Network Information System , Journal of Universal Computer Science, 1(4), 206-220, April (1995), available at URL http://info.iicm.tu-graz.ac.at/Cthe_hyper_g_network_information_system

[3]   Andrews K., Kappe F. , Maurer H., Serving Information to the Web with Hyper-G , Computer Networks and ISDN Systems, 27(6), 919-926, April (1995), Proc. 3rd International World-Wide Web Conference, available at URL http://www.elsevier.nl/www3/welcome.html

[4]   Akscyn R., McCraken D., Yoder E., KMS: A Distributed Hypermedia System for Managing Knowledge in Organizations , In Proc. ACM Hypertext '87, 1-20, (1987).

[5]   Bernstein M., The Navigation Problem Reconsidered, In Berk E., Devlin J. (eds), Hypertext/Hypermedia Handbook, Software Engineering Series, 285-297. McGraw-Hill, New York (1991).

[6]   Berners-Lee T., Cailliau R., Luotonen A., Nielsen H.F., Secret A., The World-Wide Web, Communications of the ACM, 37(8), 76-82, Aug. (1994).

[7]   Botafogo R.A., Cluster Analysis for Hypertext Systems, In Proc. SIGIR '93, 116-125, ACM Press, Pittsburgh, PA, June (1993).

[8]   Botafogo RA., Rivilin E., Shneiderman B., Structural Analysis of Hypertexts: Identifying Hierachies and Useful Metrics, ACM Trabsactions on Information Systems, 10(2), 267-272 Dec.(1988).

[9]   Crowston K., Malone T.W., Intelligent Software Agents -Using AI Techniques in groupware has the potential to dramatically alter the way we organize our work, Byte, 13(13), 267/272 Dec.(1988).

[10]   Engelbart D.C., A Conceptual Framework for the Augmentation of Man's Intellect , In Howerton P.D., Weeks D.C. (eds), Vistas in Information Handling Vol. 1, 1-29, Spartan Books, Washington D.C. (1963).

[11]   Etzioni O., Weld D., A Softbot-Based Interface to the Internet, Communications of the ACM, 37(7), 72-76 , July (1994).

[12]   Feiner S., Seeing the Forest for the Trees: Hierarchical Display of Hypertext Structure, In Proc. OIS'88, 205-212, Palo Alto, CA, ACM Press, March (1988).

[13]   Foss C., Effective Browsing in Hypertext Systems, In Proc. RIAO'88, 82-89, Cambridge, MA, MIT, March (1988).

[14]   Gay G., Mazur J., Navigating in Hypermedia, In Berk E., Davlin J. (eds), Hypertext/Hypermedia Handboook, Software Engineering Series, McGraw-Hill, New York (1991).

[15]   Halasz F.G., Reflections on Note Cards: Seven Issues for the Next Generation of Hypermedia Systems, Communications of the ACM, 31(7), 836-852, July (1988).

[16]   Haan B.J., Kahn P., Riley V.A., Coombs J.H. and Meyrowitz N.K., IRIS Hypermedia Systems, Communications of the ACM, 35(1), 36-51, Jan.(1988).

[17]   Kappe F., A Scalable Architecture for Maintaining Referential Integrity in Distributed Information Systems, Journal of Universal Computer Science, 1(2), 84-104, Feb.(1995). Available at URL
http://info.iicm.tu-graz.ac.at/Ca_scalable_architecture_for_maintaining

[18]   Kappe F. , Maurer H., From Hypertext to Active Communication/Information Systems, Journal of Microcomputer Apllications, 17(4), 333-344 , Oct.(1994).

[19]   Maes P., Agents that Reduce Work and Information Overload, Communications of the ACM, 37(7), 31-40, 146, July (1994).

[20]   Noik E.G., Exploring Large Hyperdocuments: Fisheye Views of Nested Networks, In Proc. Hypertext'93, 107-121, Seattle, WA, ACM Press, Nov.(1994).

[21]   Sarkar M. and Brown M.H., Graphical Fisheye Views, Communications of the ACM, 37(12): 73-84, Dec.(1994).

[22]   Utting K. , Yankelovich N., Context and Orientation in Hypermedia Networks, ACM Transactions on Information Systems, 7(1), 58-84, Jan.(1994).

Internet-Web and ST Data Management: Harmonization and New Horizons

Jacques-Emile DUBOIS and Belhadri MESSABIH

Institut de Topologie et de Dynamique des Systèmes de l'Université de Paris VII, associé au CNRS, 1, rue Guy de la Brosse, 75005 Paris, France

ABSTRACT

Internet and the World Wide Web, a multimedia space, have become a popular success surprising for this kind of documentation. This success is due to the choice of simple indexing tools and to an organization based on hypermedia links and methods of visual navigation.We present here on the one hand a critical analysis of the advantages and disadvantages of these multimedia methods, while on the other hand we look for their possible synergy with less delocalized Specialized Information Systems (SIS) available for handling scientific and technical data.

RESUME

Internet et le système d'information hypermédia Web ont suscité un enthousiasme populaire étonnant pour une certaine forme de documentation. Leur succès repose sur le choix d'outils d'indexation simples d'une organisation centrée sur des liens hypertextes et de moyens de navigation visuelle. On analyse ici de façon critique d'une part les aspects positifs et les inconvénients de ces moyens multimédia et d'autre part on recherche leur synergie possible avec les Systèmes d'Information Spécialisée moins délocalisés (SIS) utilisés pour le traitement des données scientifiques et techniques.

1 INTRODUCTION

Computers are present in all fields of technical, scientific, intellectual and social activity. Some long familiar human activities, such as information transmission chains, went from the typewriter to the computer, incorporating along the way many stages concerning editing, correcting and structuring of texts. In their present and latest progress, they begin to interfere with our communication processes and will thus induce greater changes in our traditional methods. The success of Internet in creating an easily accessible worldwide network, consulted by a very broad-based audience, is explained by the ease of its communication tools. It allows fast, free or cheap, access to information that is "a priori unstructured". This easy access to information contained in the Web is largely due to the sacrifice of rigour and of data reliability. In fact, information used as a resource is usually managed by complex systems of data and knowledge that are "a priori structured". We call them Specialized Information Systems (SIS). The reliability of their information is an essential objective.

One can ponder whether the mutations arising from the Internet/Web systems may supplant the present SIS systems. More likely, through a normal evolution affecting many of our modes of access to information (press, primary and secondary information, passive or interactive access), systems currently opposed to one another will lead to complementary methods of complex organization.

This article studies the adjustments required for current SIS systems (where data circulates among experts) and systems deriving from the Internet/Web network to compare them to those of the Specialized Information Systems (e.g. LAN, WAN).
The final part is devoted to adapting these systems, not on a general level, but specifically where management of data, metadata and specialized knowledge is concerned.

2. DATA : A RESOURCE FOR CAD SYSTEMS AND INTERNET [10]

2.1. System Science

In the past half century, many activities progressed thanks to the Science of Systems that formalized the sets of stages involved in such progress, from the starting step to the final one. This system engineering, where the word system gives birth to two adjectives: systemic and systematic, enables one to approach a system holistically (static or dynamic global situation) and to solve problems therein in local elements by step by step procedures. This last systematic approach is important in problem management.

In science complex reasoning can be tackled in this way by using a double approach, both systemic and systematic. In practice, such problems are dealt with through models and simulation tools. Informatics supplied the calculation tools for these methods and made it possible to use models based on many data. Indeed computers are the king pins of such working modes in nearly all sectors. Their power and their flexibility have often transformed research, process simulation in the Corporate Information Flow, the general organization of some institutions and their functioning processes. Among the important contributions of computing assistance, three should be stressed particularly. The first enables us to now tackle and solve problems which were previously beyond our grasp. The second is the visual communication between man and computer and between computers; computational three dimensional graphics and graphic synthesis are often powerful compressions, yet simpler presentations, of complex solutions. They are more and more the basis for user/system interaction. The third important point is the extraordinary microinformatic progress that enables a large community of people who are interested in accessing numerous types of information to do so.

2.2   Databases : Formats and Standards

Indeed the generalization of systemic approaches, the growing use of models, the advantages of simulation, all led to the creation of many databases necessary for providing useful data at the various stages of prediction and management of systems.

For example, in conducting the vast programs of a national agency, in these tasks of an institute or in managing a technical program, important flows of information and data are established between all the partners involved in carrying out tasks. These flows bear on the transfer of data between the conceivers of industrial products (e.g. design exchanges), and from the 1980s, such exchanges, in industry, take place between automated sites of data transmission networks.

Today, these exchanges are primarily based on specific or neutral formats. In this book it is shown elsewhere that STEP is based on the concept of sharing data that are represented semantically for direct interpretation by the computer and/or the machine concerned. In order to ensure such transfers of data from one country to another, various norms in STEP (STandard for the Exchange of Product Model Data) were established in different countries.

This example highlights the importance of clearly structuring data description methods. We should mention here that such "structuring of descriptive methods" posits the existence of many "a priori" actions as well as of recommendations for using these methods. CALS (Continuous Acquisition and Life Cycle Support) is an initiative to improve relations and technical exchanges between subcontractors and military systems. In fact, it became clear that these elements of information are, in practice, useful not only to engineers as engineering information, but also as business information in decision support functions and, further, to develop a company culture. It was also found that standards and data descriptions have become essential features of communication among subdivisions in the systemic conduct of operations in an industrial organization. Thus, they are likely to be centered on process modeling and simulation.

2.3   Data Circulation : Communication and Navigation

Despite all efforts at rationalization carried out in industry and in program agencies, the circulation of information is not always excellent for two main reasons. One is the use of rather bulky informatic programs, developed before the advent of microinformatic graphic interfaces. The other are the too numerous and too varied access protocols proposed by the different specialized data banks whose indexing protocols for internal and external data are but little standardized. All this ST information is indeed "a priori" well defined. It therefore follows precise ST rules, but its access is complicated by the access codes imposed by the database administrators, most of whom often adopt their own indexing rules. There is also sometimes an absence of consensus as to basic classifications, despite the efforts of the scientific unions. Nonetheless, the specialized documentation networks, notwithstanding the aforementioned difficulties are to be congratulated for most often retaining <u>data validated by experts</u> acting in the author-editor-abstracting center chain.

2.4. Information Sharing : a must in Integrated Systems

The success of the global modelization of systems is significant but was gradually acquired and slowed down by factors involving computer development but also by inertia to change on the part of the actors themselves. Indeed the systemic approach nearly always implies open sharing of all information by many actors, and this can be difficult. Often time was lacking to train people differently and to accustom them to more openness for cooperative activities. The new generations of young scientists, engineers and managers work with computers normally, and the reorganization associated with systemic tasks and implying constant information from and to all actors is less of a problem therefore. Besides, times are ripe for such changes.

In fact, during these last decades, the need for and development of the necessary standards for communication have been perceived and achieved, and in specialized sectors more global and cooperative methods of action are taking place. The surprise was the irruption and success of Internet, suddenly creating an important breakthrough in the communication of information.

Indeed Internet with its simplified goals and the choice of a cocktail of measures to enhance communication and navigation appears as a potential source of new encouragement. What, however, is at the root of Internet's success, and how much of it can be used to strengthen the existing Specialized Information Systems?

3   INFORMATION SYSTEMS AND DOCUMENTATION SPACE : SIS AND WEB

A-The Web Space [8],[9]

In a limiting sense, one can consider that data and information constitute an essential expression of the resources managed in a specific system. In this same restricted sense, we shall look here at the usual Specialized Information Systems (SIS) that stem from the convergence of classical documentation systems and informatic methods. The sudden interest provoked by the little organized and little controlled Web space leads us to identify the reasons behind the development of the Web/Internet set.

3.1 The Web at the Start of Internet's Success [1],[2],[3],[4]

Appearing for the first time in 1969, Internet wove a spider web around the planet and federated many networks. It was primarily used by academics and researchers. Today its users can be counted by the millions throughout the world. The success of Internet is due mainly to the emergence of the distributed system of hypermedia information: the "World Wide Web". This technology makes it possible to navigate on the network in a most friendly way through the use of highly interactive graphical tools commonly called "Graphical Browsers".

Markup Languages. For the Web, the accepted format is the markup language HTML (HyperText Markup Language). This has become the standard for editing documents on the world wide network. The HTML format can be defined as a relative of the generalized markup format SGML (Standard Generalized Markup Language). This is a file in the ASCII format including structural marks of documents. Contrary to SGML, HTML defines the way in which the text is to appear on the screen. SGML indeed remains more general. Its format only defines the structure of the document in chapters, subchapters, titles, subtitles, but gives no indication as to the text. HTML therefore proposes a simpler structuring where the number of marks is limited and where the formats of the characters and the images are defined in advance. These limitations, or this simplicity, explain the "wherefore" of the proliferation on interpreting tools of the HTML format, such as Mosaic, Netscape, Cello, etc. The document created in this format is intended to be used in on-line consultation, i.e. via the connection to an information server. The HTML format further disposes of hypertext links enabling one to go from one document to another. These documents can be placed on the same server or on servers located at opposite ends of the earth.

Hypertext and Hypermedia. The concept of hypertext first appeared in 1945 when V. Bush, adviser to President F.D. Roosevelt, proposed the conception of a system named MEMEX (Memory Extended) to facilite access to large amounts of information by association of ideas. The term hypertext was invented by Ted Nelson in 1960 who defined its concepts as "the association of natural language with the computer's capacity to establish interactive links and dynamic displays of a non linear text". He imagined a network of cooperating machines providing access to an important amount of distributed data. However, the first person to implant hypertext ideas was Douglas Engelbart in 1965, by building a textual database that could be used in a multi-use network environment and enabled segments of files to link up by cross references. With the development of CD-ROM/CDI optical disks, whose storage capacity is greater than a magnetic tape, a new concept appeared, that of hypermedia , identical to that of hypertext, save that it includes, in addition to the text, multimedia resources, such as sound, images, graphics, video sequences, etc.

This technique combines three technologies heretofore separate: editing, information handling and broadcasting (in terms of animation). The definition of a multimedia system remains that of one capable of handling, in addition to the text, at least one of the following kinds of information: sound, photographic quality image and animated video image.

The HTML format broadens this concept still further, since the simple click of a mouse on an image or a word can refer one to a document stored on a server on the other side of the planet. To do this, the file specifies the access path or URL (Uniform Resource Locator) of the HTML document to be called up.

Originally conceived to describe documents of the same format on the Web, the HTML format has not ceased evolving to render consultation ever more interactive. Present versions include forms with acquisition fields, list boxes, buttons, tables, mathematical formulas. Further improvements are being developed for structuring of documents, e.g. of the text around an image, etc. The tools permitting interpretation of these new formats have themselves not stopped evolving; yet they remain limited compared with specialized tools. These evolution pathways are examined by the W3 consortium.Various versions of HTML format are already accessible, examples of which are : HTML 0.9, HTML 1.0, HTML 2.0 (and soon 3.0), HTML (Nescape) and SGML Hammer. All these tools are equally useful to those interested in electronic publishing.

Tools for writing HTML documents. With the ever growing craze for the Web, we see a proliferation of tools for the automatic generation of HTML pages such as HotMetal , HTML Assistant, etc. These are often based on dialogue boxes managing all the functions of the HTML format. Such tools are well adapted to creating complex pages. However, they become constraining if used for frequent updating of published information. This last requires the rewriting of the HTML document. In the present context, it is impossible to directly insert a portion of a text or a database field into a Web page. In a coherent publication system; data of all kinds must immediately be converted into HTML formats. This is a proposal made by the "Inter Notes Web Publications" where any Notes document is automatically converted into the HTML format. The user will no longer have to worry about updating HTML documents.The diversity of editing tools and their specificities pose real problems for adopting this system as a unique means of electronic publishing.

3.2   Exploring the Web

In order to deal with the information inflation on the Web and with the disordered nature of its space, several servers propose "guides for exploring the Web's resources". These tools can be simple thematic guides (starting point pages, subject tree) or else search engines enabling one to restore documents including one or more keywords. These last maintain databases (often WAIS) concerning the description of Web documents (keywords, titles, hyperlinks, etc.) and are updated by programs called "robots" that crawl along the Web looking for new documents. The highly automated creation of data banks in the Web space is a way of combating the chaos that can result from freely introducing documents with no elements of classification. Despite their usefulness, these servers, which thus group databases excerpted from the Web, have the same limitations as classical documentary research systems. Moreover, the absence of rigourous indexing rules induced by the democratization of information servers, substantially complicates the criteria for choosing which record to index. Their development is nonetheless an attempt to organize data gathering. Instead of a posteriori indexing of HTML documents, the Hyper-G graphical browser achieves similar results by working on the a priori structured Web space, as described in a paper above.

Access to External Resources. Web browsers are especially conceived to access Internet documents (Web, FTP, Gopher). For access to external resources such as specialized data banks, particular programs - also called scripts - are needed. A script is a small program that tells the server how to access a particular kind of information managed by various DBMS such as ORACLE, SYBASE, etc. The scripts are also called "gateways" because they constitute navigation bridges to a kind of information that the browser cannot otherwise reach. Since the Web is an on line transactional system allowing the user to supply services, the importance of the gateways is rapidly expanding. Standards are especially needed to enable browsers to research specialized databases. The CGI standard is being worked out; it specifies how scripts should be written so as to be compatible with graphic browsers such as Mosaic and Nescape.

A Generation of More Ambitious Browsers [5]. Today we see a new generation of browsers emerging, such as HotJava. Instead of static Web pages, we find dynamic pages that react to the least movement of the mouse. This technology, developed by SunMicrosystems, is revolutionizing the Web world. It was made possible only by introducing the concept of the object oriented environment. When a page is loaded onto the Web, it then contains a specific code that will explain the tasks to be performed on a given object. This approach gives rise to many possibilities, from the simulation of small models to the writing of more or less rich access interfaces to specialized databases.

B.Specialized Information Systems (SIS) and the Web

3.3 The SIS Present Status [10]

Systems diversity. The tendency to manage many situations by models and simulations led to organizing numerous specialized databases. The rapid evolution of informatics conditioned the choice of programming languages (FORTRAN, PASCAL, LISP, PROLOG, C, C++,...) and of management systems or DBMS, whose origins lie in different strategies and models (INGRES, ORACLE, SYBASE, ...). The worldwide distribution of methods used by sectorial databases led first to the creation of heterogeneous networks of bases, then gradually gateways were proposed to allow computers of different brands to communicate with each other and similarly, data banks managed by various systems. Thus, today, most informatic developments calling upon specialized data banks are grouped in various Local, or World Area Networks (LAN or WAN).

With regard to the graphic interfaces in these networks, the race for power of graphic stations has resulted in a wide variety of highly evolved stations and in the use of mini-networks using a local server, often under UNIX, and with microcomputers as clients. This evolution towards integrated ranges of hardware is paralleled by a corresponding software evolution and by the production of very diversified documentary products using recent popular tools such as CD-ROM and expert systems on microcomputers. The tendency is to work out more interactive computer-user documentation.

The present SIS are the result of gradually achieved progress in using informatics to approach problems of modeling, simulation and management in the spirit of systems theories, implying information management, optimized distribution and data sharing.
The limitations of successively used means were improved by choosing new informatic models based on languages and strategies (object oriented language and relational models), on the one hand and, on the other, a better adapted hardware organization (parallel computing and network distribution).

Gateways for Information Sharing in SIS. Given the difficulty of synchronizing the action of widely diverging system components, greater efforts were made to set up gateways or bridges, to use "agents" for carrying out navigation-type searching and to use visual display of programs for achieving graphs to visually improve the user-computer relationship.

In all these systems, communication aiming at data sharing, and sometimes at program sharing, was an important objective. It must be admitted that the diverse origins, the different objectives, the range of modeling methods, go far to explain 1° the many difficulties encountered 2° present limitations to greatly desired exchanges 3° the clumsy protocols required to go from one sector to another (gateways).

On the data level alone we often find different indexing for data banks dealing with the same documentary foundation but approached via different conceptual viewpoints. In other words, most knowledge, data and information are currently deposited and managed in that organized and controlled space called " Specialized Information", SIS, managed and consulted primarily by professionals.

Information Sharing in SIS spaces was easier to achieve in a single discipline or in an industry, either because of management imperatives or because of the necessary cooperation of many actors/experts in optimizing an industrial process or in design aid (many steps and pluriannual projects). On the contrary, information sharing is less successful in intersectorial exchanges such as those linking the very different kinds of data needed in environmental pollution studies dealing simultaneously with chemistry, hydrology and soil permeability. Present SIS are generally too compartmentalized and were developed with little thought of pluridisciplinary applications.

It is noteworthy that in these SIS systems, unlike Web (where users can be service providers), users are clearly defined as service consumers or as service producers.

In other contexts than the Web, SIS faced similar documentation problems and solved them with greater rigour according to activity sectors. In fact in the most specialized fields (economy or academia), the documentation standardization process has usually been slow due to conflicting expert views on complex information issues. In the Web such discussions were totally ignored, and the choice of lower indexing and marked up languages led to documentation limited to simpler problems.

3.4   SIS and Web Space Interactions

Opposing and/or Complementary Aspects. We have therefore two apparently distinct spaces, that of these SIS and the Web space. It is tempting to visualize two potential actions: one to improve the SIS functioning with the help of Web procedures, especially by hypertext communication, the other to broaden the consulting population of SIS through the curiosity and the growing level of Web consultants.

One can go further by asking through the Web, for contributions for creating Specialized Data Systems, usually reserved to experts in the SIS space. Consultation of a SIS data center through the Web implies an HTML interface for the SIS center and transmission through specific scripts. Such gateways are related to
either a simple graphic browser or a dynamic one like HotJava, which is not controlled by the server but handled by the local terminal.

Overlap, Extension and Limitations. The interest in Web and Internet technology in the world is a veritable onrush. However, the recent nature of this technology and the simplicity of its tools still limit the possibilities for integrating Specialized Information Systems in the lightly structured Web. Such real integration would require a security protocol and a range of tools compatible with the different languages, platforms, databanks and protocols. The network is too immense for this. Graphical browsers such as Netscape or Mosaic, or the "HotJava" technology are interfaces going in the direction of the Web's evolution with its multitude of servers and its total openness, but they are still very limited for adaptation to specialized systems.

The constraints in the generic nature of the Web and its HTTP protocol limit the current development of specific applications. An adaptation conforming to Web and to HTTP protocol is often inevitable because of the reduced functionalities of the graphic browser widgets and of the various access protocols of the specialized servers.

C   Scientific and Technical (ST) Data: Strategies and Management

3.5   Role and Management of ST Data

ST data are either isolated numerical data, sets, maps, graphics and even images. They are most often used as resources for projects, models or simulations, and they originate from different presentations. Hard or soft data, referring to their statistical validity, are more difficult to handle in the graphical interface navigation context than are textual data with which they can be associated in a document [7],[8].

Data, information and knowledge are terms often-analyzed. They are found, more or less closely linked, in studies of the systems for which they are the basic resources. They are valuable for structuring data and metadata. In the evolution following the multimedia upsurge centering on Internet, problems of data creation, management, circulation and use must be rethought. We will limit ourselves here to data description and data validation as important aspects in this context.

Data Description. Data description implies a certain number of operations, just like a text that must be decomposed before one can proceed to its analytical description, to which must then be associated indexing information. This latter, on the one hand, situates its contents with regard to various references and, on the other hand, contains the physical elements of its identity. Data description can be visual or arbitrary; its identity can be ambiguous; it can be determined according to a standardization, for instance. All the canonic values of a set of molecules can be seen as a non-ordered population or can be ordered within a hyperstructure (ordered space). Defining the representation of a molecule is important, but if the element description is too rigid, it is difficult to modify it in the same file. The file space can be ordered, but this organization is often linked to that of its elements. When the studied data can be acceptably fragmented, computerization can respect the organization operations, but at times there can be a conflict between the structuring of the file object and that of the file, according to the computer program chosen.

In structural chemistry, for example, a molecule can be perceived topologically, its structure can be concentric or linear, but it can also be built with the help of a grammar of cycles and substituents. To fragmentation, other global, local, geometric, electronic, orbital data can be added, and in general, only part of such a complex description is retained for a file. When two chemical databanks are to communicate with each other, this can involve referring back to a common description, or to an intermediate pivot format for transfer. Data fragmentation is an important operation that can be vital in certain CA Heuristic or CA Design uses, and in graphic display (where the interaction can depend on the basic data descriptors). It is clear that in drug design it is impossible to use direct information from a databank based on limited indexing and that missing structural information must then be introduced. For the same reasons, STEP is an excellent method for managing industrial descriptive data, although semantic description is not yet equal to syntactic progress, e.g. the semantic description of materials for a physical structure. This is a case where information is confidential and where sharing data implies economic agreement.

Data Validation. This aspect of data is essential and determines the absolute quality of a file or a database. Proposed new data may be false. Validation must, therefore, be carried out by compilation and verification before dissemination. Science and technology, both strong producers of data, need validation mechanisms. In the private sector, evaluations are often confidential, but in general for public data this work is carried out by experts acting as referees at various stages in the publication cycle. All these control mechanisms often slow down the production of new values. The publication cycle (including secondary publications) can often take from 12 to 24 months. In the Web space, these delays are minimal. The same is true in electronic publishing, but this is detrimental to the validation process, theoretically eliminated here. Various solutions are being studied, but it must be pointed out that some data collectors continue their validation function while using Internet.

3.5 MORE, a RSBE Transfer Project to Web [6]

The Repository Based Software Engineering (RSBE) project sponsored by the NASA Technology Utilization Division consists of two principal activities: research into repositories and operation of a public facility. A first repository mechanism, known as ASV3, was based on a model providing for an inheritance hierarchy of asset meta-classes with attributes chosen by librarians. This monolithic architecture required substantial installation work in a single DBMS (ORACLE) and implied broad consultation (1000 subscribers) that in turn required "substantial replication of system resources". With the same control, the system was redesigned to build a Web repository called MORE with visualization mechanisms using HTTP ISMAP protocols (2). In MORE 1.x metadata for a single environment resides on a single server. MORE 2.0 will enable the repository environment to seamlessly scan an arbitrary number of Web servers. This MORE database API, that was built using an object oriented approach, is considered an "unqualified success".

We purposely chose this example of the transfer of a large specialized DB from the SIS environment to the Web. One should, however, be cautious and realize that the repository of software programs can be easily centered in well identified subcore topics located on special Web servers. Their users are usually all computer professionals or experts. On the contrary, for some DB, all the data must remain accessible on a central core, as is the case, for instance, for the millions of compounds in the Chemical Abstract Service [11]. This is no doubt due to the diversity of its users from widely diverging backgrounds. Nevertheless, the CAS has foreseen an HTML Web connection to its mainframes.

Central Databases and Frequently Asked Questions (FAQ). In the Web space, there is usually a large audience of curious or non professional users whose information needs are relatively simple. The most frequent Word method is one for organizing "hot" files that almost act as services. In chemistry, for instance, there are 12 million known compounds, but less than 5000 occur regularly in our daily activities and in our inquiries. The hot list of queries by the public at large probably contains several hundred if not less. Such a screening system transferred onto the Web from a SIS core database could answer the public's needs. A FAQ file based on keywords is already on the Web.

3.6   Interoperability

In some sectors, ST communication will remain difficult, if not well-nigh impossible. In fields where many teams do either parallel work or work on different subjects, and exchanges take place by computer messages, it is important to establish norms and standards very early. One good example concerns the control of online resources for biomedical and biotechnological information. This is examined hereafter in a very clear article by Lois Blaine. She describes the efforts made in the United States for setting up a rational genomic database whose producers "pledge to develop and suscribe to standards regarding syntax, semantics and management/curation issues".

A CODATA Task Group is already working internationally on some of these aspects, but it was felt urgent to improve communication between the many actors of the US Genome Data Community (Informatic Summit 1993) . The Genome Database (GDB) is active in developing all the necessary computer tools for achieving its goals: a common communication language and a common schema description language. Good collaboration and exchanges from all over the microbial world helped carry out this vast SIS project.

Meanwhile "a less ambitious method of linking data resources is the use of HTML and the Web". Thus far, the ATCC, the largest service of culture collection in the world, is accessible via the Web. Work to complete these links is underway.

Although interoperability, seen as the capacity to search and analyze data from various and disparate databases simultaneously, can be essential within the specialized Bioinformatics networks, the Web space is also a very instrumental medium. Both approaches can thus combine to achieve a dynamic new database to serve as a multidimensional spreadsheet for formulating and testing hypotheses. Indeed, if testing hypotheses is the objective, this can imply using complex models requiring more information than can be found in the databases consulted. In fact, interoperability problems must be taken into account in line with the possible levels of information transfer in the field concerned. The choices, that stem both from the chosen models and from the precision of the information, are influenced by the knowledge and the objectives of the sector studied. It can prove fatal for the development of a database to start too precipitately.

ST Public Project Management on the Web. Certain public projects must be transparent both to the public and to the various geographically distant actors. The CODATA FRANCE Committee is currently carrying out such a binational action in environmental studies. The Web makes it possible to manage this by sub-committees. In order to arouse wider interest, software was developed to create thematic word associations allowing interaction with a user who is interested but not trained in this project. A visual and interactive help program is mouse driven. In addition to this initiation, it is possible to generate sectorial guides, by an original hypertext procedure, in order for such a user to efficiently consult the Web about this CODATA project and related information.

4   CONCLUSION

Indeed the Web technologies lead to a non structured network of hypermedia documents that differ from current databases in that active references serve as starting points for surfing through the Net. This "horizontal" structuring is different from the multilevel structured organization of SIS databases, isolated or circulated in specialized networks.

Integrating both these technologies in a common universe could result in an extremely complex distributed hypermedia system, since it would involve associating two distinct types of organization: one very flat and poorly structured and the other highly structured (usually with tree hierarchies). Today the W3 consortium suggests two attempts at a solution: defining new protocols and defining new standards for writing gateways.(3,4)

Such attempts are well worth while, although it is difficult to deal with the complexities of some situations while maintaining the advantages of a too highly organized simplicity. Markup tools do not cope easily with higher complexity, and one should remember that real systems tend to resist excessive reduction. Nonetheless, one must consider highly probable an evolution leading to various types of SIS-Web super hybrid systems (SHYS) that will be partly field or discipline oriented.(12) Exploratory endeavors in this field should be encouraged.

Most future SHYS will probably combine both centralized and decentralized forms of data quality labeling and reliability assessment, and several coexisting levels of compatible data standards allowing for various types of input, including those of the public at large. These SHYS should be endowed with navigation tools allowing interactive access to modelization programs. These services will be directed either towards lay persons or towards specialists through special assistance tools such as icons, guides or user friendly "agents".

All in all, the Web can be credited for having so far influenced the newly emerging cyberspace by providing a strong impetus for greater flexibility in ST data handling, easier sharing of information and far better communication at all stages of computer aided or design strategies.

KEYWORDS

Web, hypertext, hypermedia, HTML, SIS, data validation, ST data, information sharing, integrated systems, interoperability, FAQ, agent.

REFERENCES

[1]   Andreessen M., A Beginner's Guide to HTML, National Center for Supercomputer Applications, Univ. of Illinois, http://www.ncsa.uiuc.edu/demoweb/html-primer.html.

[2]   Berners-Lee T., (ed) HyperText Mark-up Language, CERN, http://info.cern.ch/hypertext/WWW/MarkUp/MarkUp.html.

[3]   Berners-Lee T., The World Wide Web Initiative, CERN, http://info.cern.ch/hypertext/WWW/TheProject.html.

[4]   McCool R., The Common Gateway Interface, National Center for Supercomputing Applications, University of Illinois at Urbana-Champaign, http://hoohoo.ncsa.uiuc.edu/cgi/

[5]   The HotJava Browser, Sun Microsystems, http://java.sun.com/

[6]   Eichmann D., Integrating Structural Databases into the Web: the MORE system, Research Institute of computing and Information Systems, University of Houston, http://rsbe.jsc.nasa.gov/eichmann/WWW94/MORE/MORE.html

[7]   Krol E., The Whole Internet User's Guide & Calalogue by O'Reilly & Associates, Inc (1992).

[8]   Dougherty D. , Koman R., The Mosaic Handbook for Microsoft Windows, O'Reilly & Ass, Inc.

[9]   Pfaffenberger B., World Wide Web Bible, MIS Press (1995)

[10]   New Perspectives in Scientific Complex Data Management, CODATA Bulletin, Vol 22,4 (1990)

[11]   American Chemical Society Web Server, http://www.acs.org/

[12]   Westbrook J.H., Kaufman J.G., Cverna F., Electronic Access to Factual Materials Information: The State of the Art, MRS Bulletin, 40-48, Aug.(1995).

ONLINE ELECTRONIC PUBLISHING : DEVELOPING INFRASTRUCTURE FOR THE ELECTRONIC READER

Barbara E. KIRSOP[1], Andy EDWARDS[1] and Sidnei SOUZA[2]

[1] *Bioline Publications, Stainfield House, Stainfield, Bourne, Lincs, PE10 0RS, UK [bio@biostrat.demon.co.uk]*
[2] *Base de Dados Tropical, Campinas, SP. Brazil [sidnei@ftpt.br]*

ABSTRACT

The technological advances in global networking and data searching and retrieving provide the infrastructure for the development of online electronic publishing. Journals, conference proceedings, technical documents and newsletters may all be made available through academic or commercial networks, speeding access and reaching regions of the world where such material is limited. One development, Bioline Publications, uses the Internet with access by WWW, gopher and e-mail for the distribution of documents of importance to bioscientists.

RESUME

Les progrès récents dans les réseaux globaux, dans les procédures de recherche et d'extraction de données procurent l'infrastructure nécessaire à l'édition électronique "en ligne". Par le biais de réseaux universitaires ou commerciaux, l'accès rapide jusqu'aux régions isolées du monde mais dotées cependant de moyens électroniques sera ouvert aux journaux, actes de conférence, lettres d'information et documents techniques. Bioline Publication est un outil d'actualité qui utilise Internet, WWW, gopher et le courrier électronique pour assurer la distribution de documents essentiels aux scientifiques de la biologie.

1   INTRODUCTION

The advent of faster, easier and more generally available access to information linked to the Internet means that the storage, distribution, location and management of bibliographic information is becoming revolutionized. It is taking advantage of the new technology now available to all sectors throughout most regions of the world, and seems destined to change the reading habits of the scientific community.Journals, reports, conference proceedings, specialist newsletters and other professional documents can now be delivered directly to the PC of the scientist. A number of access routes exist to suit all levels of technical sophistication - from World Wide

Web, gopher and telnet to e-mail searching/requesting for those without full Internet connectivity - and lead to various levels of information. Text documents and associated graphics files may be delivered in a number of forms, from ascii and compressed graphics formats to full hypertext formats with different styles and fonts, embedded graphics and transparent links to other resources on the Internet, easily made by clicking highlighted words or phrases.

A number of bibliographic systems have been developed in which the networking environment has been deployed. Some provide abstracts of material, others tables of contents, while yet others provide full text and graphics of documents. The latter may either be electronic versions of already printed publications, or increasingly may be online-only publications. In the disciplines of mathematics and physics, online-only journals are already established and similar initiatives are underway in the biosciences. Publishers of scientific material have been considering ways in which they can take advantage of the new technology, yet retain their commercial interests. Some consider electronic publication to be a supplement to printed publications, forming an alternative distribution mechanism that may be more attractive to a section of their readership and thus reach new markets. Electronic publishing has a number of advantages and also some disadvantages both from the points of view of the provider and the user. One major advantage is that the costs of printing and postal distribution are saved through electronic distribution. The advantages for scientists of cheaper journals is obvious, and is particularly important in countries with economic difficulties (see Bioline Publications, below). Since scientists must themselves make some effort to access the material online and must learn how the system works and adapt to new ways of obtaining information, a high cost service for personal subscribers is unlikely to be attractive at this stage.

The delivery of material direct to the laboratory terminal also has advantages in facilitating immediate access to information of importance to the bench scientist. For this means of access to replace visits to the library, a critical mass of material on specific topics needs to be available in the new form. It is unlikely that library services will be ever be replaced, but complementary services offering 'niche area' material are likely to succeed in meeting the needs of specialist groups of individual laboratory scientists.

Electronic distribution eliminates the delays met through shipping hardcopy material to remote regions. This is a considerable benefit, since publications can reach research scientists as soon as the material becomes available following completion of the peer-review and editing processes. Some have criticized the rapidity of distribution, fearing it will lead to a lowering of publishing standards, but there seems no reason why the same standards applied to printed journals should not be applied to the electronic journals. The need for scientists to publish in quality journals, to be cited and to be included in the abstracting services are important factors that must be met by electronic publishing services. Where the system duplicates existing printed journals, these criteria are already met. With online-only journals, appropriate steps must be taken for citation and abstracting in order to meet career development demands. The disadvantages arising from the fact that the potential readership is often unfamiliar with networking procedures is one that must be taken into account when setting up an electronic publishing service. At the present time there exist large sectors of the potential readership that are unable to take advantage of networking services. This may be because of a lack of time to learn new systems, the lack of adequate support, an inability to connect to the appropriate networks, or unawareness of opportunities. It can be assumed, however, that these difficulties will disappear as new generations of network-competent scientists appear, and as networks spread to regions currently not serviced. Already, training courses (online and offline) are being organized and many manuals exist. A recent online workshop on the use of the Internet had 25,000 subscribers from nearly 60 countries - and was the third such online training course.

Although large areas of the world do not as yet have full Internet connectivity, many are able to use e-mail systems. It is therefore important that services are accessible by a number of routes if usage is to be universal and scientists are not to be disadvantaged by technical limitations.

For online electronic publishing to be broadly acceptable to the international scientific community, therefore, it must take into account the following factors :

1. Use of a global network such as the Internet which must be accessible by a wide range of access routes

2. Cost, which should be less than the printed equivalent since scientists must use their time and effort to access the system and since budgets are currently being reduced in many Institutes and University departments

3. Comprehensive coverage - perhaps by focusing on a specific area of science

4. Material should be available in a timely fashion

5. Material should be formally identified, to allow citation and abstracting

6. Material should be offered in a widely used form that will be acceptable to a wide readership. Technical support and training must be made available.

2   BIOLINE PUBLICATIONS

One initiative, Bioline Publications, is collaborating with publishers (commercial and otherwise), editors and authors, to deliver online full text and graphics of scientific journals, reports, conference proceedings and newsletters of interest to the bioscientists (focusing on biotechnology, biodiversity, microbiology, bioinformatics).

The system uses the Internet and is accessible by WWW, gopher, telnet and E-mail. A number of supplementary services are linked to the system. These include a library of freeware/shareware software that is useful to users (e.g. compression and coding programs, graphics viewers, communications tools), links to other bibliographic sites, News and a List (Bulletin Board) that are used to maintain close links with the readers and inform them of system upgrades and new material on the system.

All abstracts and summaries are available to all Internet users without cost or need for registration; subscription is necessary only for the delivery of the full text and graphics of ordered documents. Subscriptions to the electronic versions of published commercial journals are substantially less than those for the printed versions. Collaborating publishers have reduced the price of the annual subscriptions for the electronic version by between 30-60% for personal subscribers. There are no delivery charges. *Early in 1995, material on the system will be available for purchase as single documents as well as by annual subscription. This is likely to prove beneficial to scientists in such multidisciplinary fields as biotechnology and biodiversity, where papers of interest may appear in a range of journals, yet an annual subscription to all could not be justified. At present all requests are delivered by e-mail to the user's electronic address (or the site address in the case of multiple subscriptions). *Soon, the system will offer on-screen viewing for WWW users as an alternative means of obtaining the documents. This will allow hypertext links to figures in papers, and allow the use of different fonts and styles to improve the appearance of material.

The statistics available to Bioline Publications provide extensive information on the way that scientists use the system and on the popularity of different journals on the system. Information on which sites have accessed the system and which papers have been requested most frequently by subscribers can be determined. Analysis of such data has the potential for informing about the trends in usage of scientific material and will be valuable for those interested in designing information exchange systems that provide the greatest benefit to the scientific community.

Bioline Publications is a joint initiative between the Base de Dados Tropical (BDT) that provides the Internet site, a growing number of publishers, and the administrative and editing office in the UK. The interest shown in this initiative has been very great and the numbers of sites and countries watching developments and now beginning to subscribe is encouraging. The numbers of journals available through the system is now 22 (as at mid-January 1995) and the *first online-only journal, Biosafety, begins electronic publication shortly. The number of reports grows steadily and 19 Newsletters, both public domain and commercial, are available on the system, together with the first books (available chapter by chapter). Similar initiatives are being set up by others in different scientific disciplines, optimizing the new technology, and allowing scientists easier access to more bibliographic material at lower cost. The electronic infrastructure - the highway - exists; new and exciting applications appear almost daily, together with software for searching and locating information. The consequences of these developments will be considerable in terms of improving information transfer among scientists and aiding the more equitable distribution to scientists worldwide.

KEYWORDS

Electronic publishing, online journals, Internet, web, gopher

ANNEX: List of material available through Bioline Publications:, January 1995

[1] JOURNALS

AGBIOTECH NEWS AND REVIEWS; BINARY; BIOCONTROL SCIENCE AND TECHNOLOGY; BIODIVERSITY AND CONSERVATION; BIOMETALS: BIOPOLICY INTERNATIONAL; BIOTECHNOLOGY AND DEVELOPMENT MONITOR; BIOTECHNOLOGY LETTERS; BIOTECHNOLOGY TECHNIQUES; ECOTOXICOLOGY; ENVIRONMENTAL VALUES; FOOD AND AGRICULTURAL IMMUNOLOGY; NANOBIOLOGY; THE GENETIC ENGINEER AND BIOTECHNOLOGIST; TRANSGENIC RESEARCH; TROPICAL BIODIVERSITY; WORLD JOURNAL OF MICROBIOLOGY AMD BIOTECHNOLOGY

Available in early 1995:
Oswaldo Cruz Memorias; Avian Pathology; British Poultry Science;
Journal of Nutritional Medicine; Toxicology Modeling; Biosafety

[2] REPORTS

BIOTECHNOLOGY :

EEC Documents
EEC Council Directive 90/219/EEC on the contained use of genetically modified microorganisms
- EEC Council Directive 90/220/EEC on the deliberate release into the environment of genetically modified organisms
- EEC Explanatory notes on above
- EEC Council Directive 90/679/EEC on safety at work
- EEC Amendment to above
- EEC Communication on Biotechnology Policy 1991
- EEC Biotechnology after the 1991 Report - a Stocktaking Note
- EEC Progress Report 1992: Pre-normative Research in Biosafety
- EEC Report 1993:'The Global Perspective 2010: the case for biotechnology'
- EEC 1993 Research Reports on Biosafety (BRIDGE projects)
- Council of Europe Report 1993 ADOC 6780 - developments in
Biotechnology and the consequences for agriculture
US Documents -
- NIH Guidelines for Research involving Recombinant DNA molecules with Appendices
- US report on national biotechnology policy
Regulatory documents
- Grouping of Biological Agents, BG Chemie, Germany
- Information Centre for European Culture Collections 1993

Instructions for shipping non-infectious and infectious biological substances
- European Culture Collections' Organisation 1994 Issue of Instructions for
shipping infectious, non-infectious and genetically modified microorganisms.
General documents
- Forum for Industrial Microbiologists (FIM) Opinion Paper on
the Future of Microbiology and the needs of pharmaceutical industries (1994)

BIODIVERSITY :- Biodiversity Convention, UNEP/Nairobi Conference Report, UNEP/Norway Conference Proceedings, UNEP Expert Panel Reports I-IV, Green College Oxford Conference Report: IPR and indigenous rights and conservation, UK Darwin Initiative (Biodiversity), WWF Position Paper on the Convention on Biological Diversity (October 1993), WRI Reports: The United States needs a national biodiversity policy; ,Biodiversity Indicators for Policy Makers, ATSAF Circular (Tropical and Subtropical Agricultural Research, Microbial Diversity and the 1992 Biodiversity Convention (FIELD), WCMC Policy Document: The Biodiversity Information Clearing , House Mechanism (1994)

CULTURE COLLECTIONS (see also Newsletters)

- European Culture Collections' Organisation - holdings and services
- WFCC Guidelines for the Establishment and Operation of
Collections of Cultures of Microorganisms

CONFERENCE REPORTS

- 1st Slovene Congress on Microbiology, October 1993,   Abstracts
- International Congress on Culture Collections Abstracts,
Beijing October 1992, Abstracts
- USAID Latin America/Caribbean Regions Biosafety Workshop
- Biotechnology '94 Conferences (Biochemical Engineering,
Industrial Immunology, Applied Biocatalysis, Fermentation Physiology)

[3]   NEWSLETTERS

Public domain:

- AgBiotech, Canada; Biodiversity Coalition Newsletter; BioLink, USA; Biorep Newsletter; Bio/Technology/Biodiversity Bulletin; Centraalbureau voor Schimmelcultures, Netherlands; European Biotechnology , Information Service (EBIS); European Centre for Animal Cell Cultures (ECACC);European Tropical Forest Research Network (ETFRN); Federation for European, Microbiological Societies (FEMS); The Genetical Society; Information Centre for European Culture Collections (ICECC); International Council for   Scientific Unions (ICSU) Science International;International Organisation of Palaeobotany Newsletter; Oleae Newsletter; Polychaete Newsletter; UK ,Federation for Culture Collections (UKFCC); World Federation for Culture Collections (WFCC)

Commercial: Environmental Health Briefing - weekly newsletter

[4]   BOOKS
- WRI Biodiversity Prospecting
- WFCC's 'The Biodiversity of Microorganisms and the Role of
Microbial Resource Centres' - a WFCC (1994) publication

WWW LINKS TO OTHER BIBLIOGRAPHIC RESOURCES FOR BIOLOGISTS
AVAILABLE ON THE INTERNET:
Microbial Germplasm Network (USA, Oregon), Genethon (France), ICGEB (Trieste, Italy),
ERINYES Newsletter (Australia)

Technical developments marked * was implemented recently.

A WORKBENCH FOR BIBLIOGRAPHIC OR FACTUAL DATA HANDLING

Jacques DUCLOY, Jean-Charles LAMIREL and Emmanuel NAUER

CNRS/CRIN - Centre de Recherche en Informatique de Nancy, Campus Scientifque, Bât.Loria, BP 239, Vandoeuvre lès Nancy Cedex, France

ABSTRACT

DILIB (Document and Information LIBrary) is a workbench for Scientific or Technical Information and Document Engineering. It has been designed in order to make investigations on heterogeneous sets of data or to build Information Retrieval Applications. Its kernel is a toolkit whose basic part consists in a SGML tree handling library and which contains basic elements for building Information Retrieval Systems. We present two aspects of its utilization: building WWW hypertexts from bibliographic databases, and developing an experimental IRS system, NOMAD, based on a symbolico-connectionist approach.

RESUME

DILIB (Document and Information LIBrary) est une plate-forme dédiée à l'ingénierie de l'Information et du Document Scientifiques et Techniques et plus précisémment pour les investigations documentaires et la construction de systèmes de Recherche d'informations. Le standard SGML y est utilisé pour unifier les données et les interfaces avec les outils constituant cette plate-forme. Nous présentons deux aspects de son utilisation : la construction d'hypertextes Internet/WWW et le développement d'un système expérimental : NOMAD, basé sur une approche symbolico-connectioniste.

1   INTRODUCTION

In the framework of the CRIN and INRIA Lorraine laboratories we have built DILIB (Document & Information LIBrary), a workbench dedicated to polyvalent engineers (or teams), expert in Information Science and well versed in computer and data processing techniques... This workbench must primarily be used for developments with a very short life cycle, such as prototyping a new Information Retrieval System by continual approach, or investigating among multiple sets of heterogeneous information in order to produce synthetical documents.

We use the main results of some experiments which were carried out in the framework of INIST [DUC91-1]. The SDOC application (Scientific DOCumentary database), developed in the framework of the KWICK[1] system [KWI90] was designed to produce conceptual organization maps of given scientific fields from a set of information; the target retrieval system was based on the hypertext technique, and the building process on co-word analysis. The NEURODOC [DUC91-2] project with similar objectives used neural techniques to build concept network. Finally, the STID [SCH 92][ROY 92] application was designed to assist an information specialist in the indexation of bibliographic records. This workbench was also used in some applications oriented towards library management or database production (for example, editing catalogues with various frames, or computing a set of records to obtain statistical results). For all these experiments, SGML [ISO 86], with its symbolic mark-up, proved to be very convenient for handling information coming from all main sources of information: from traditional cataloguing formats such as USMARC or UNIMARC [DUS 91] to bibliographic information currently used in laboratories such as BIBTEX [LAM 86].

We introduce DILIB with a first example: the generation of a hypertext which uses Internet [KRO 92] facilities. Then, we give a general idea of the conversion of bibliographic data to SGML, and a general overview of the main tools of DILIB. Another example deals with an investigation using infometric techniques. Finally we present NOMAD, an experimental IRS system based on a symbolico-connectionist approach whose information storage and retrieval module is based on DILIB.

2 PRODUCING AN HYPERTEXT FROM A BIBLIOGRAPHIC DATABASE

At the present time, a popular target of DILIB is the automatic generation of hypertexts from a simple set of bibliographic data, for example the bibliographic base of papers issued from CRIN (2000 records). Records are coded according to BibTeX format, and appear as follows :

```
@INPROCEEDINGS{crehange89a,
        DATE = {1988},
        CRINNUMBER = {88-R-101},
        AUTHOR = {M. Cr\>e}hange and G. Halin,
        TITLE = {Machine Learning Techniques for Progressive Retrieval in an Image Database},
        KEYWORDS = {retrieval system, image database, expert system},...
```

They are currently printed like this :

```
ref:      crehange89a
title:    Machine Learning Techniques for Progressive Retrieval in an
          Image Database
author:   Créhange M., Halin G. ,...
```

---

[1] an ESPRIT project funded by the EEC

Records are indexed with a controlled lexicon and this database has no thesaurus. For any request with this classical system, the user must supply pertinent key-words; it is quite the same with a product like WAIS if he wants to use full text query features. To make the query easier, we have provided a hypertext interface, browsing through an automatically built-up thesaurus. We use WWW and Mosaic as hypertext tools. The first generated page of the WWW session contains a list of clusters and begins by :

CRIN - PUBLICATIONS
List of Clusters
> acoustic-phonetic decoding - speech recognition
> expert system - image database
> FIP - fieldbus
> rewriting - termination

Each cluster is identified by an association of two key-words. Each association is hyperlinked to a corresponding page which contains details of the given cluster which is composed of a list of key-words, a list of internal associations and a list of external associations. For example, the second cluster of the list has the following aspect :

expert system - image database
List of keywords

> [106]   expert system
> [29]   image database
> [12]   retrieval system

Internal Associations

> [16]   expert system - image database
> [10]   expert system - retrieval system
> [9]   image database - retrieval system

Relationships with other clusters

> acoustic-phonetic decoding - speech recognition
> artificial intelligence - knowledge-based system
> database - software engineering

The numbers between square brackets are the indexing frequencies. Clicking on a key-word or on an internal association generates an elementary query on the data base, on an external association provides access to another cluster. For this application and starting from an initial set of records, the following steps are required: converting original records into SGML, creating an inverted file with a «kwd» field for the clusterization algorithm, creating association files and cluster files, building HTML pages from clusters. All these steps are carried out with DILIB tools.

3   ADAPTATION OF INPUT FORMATS

The use of DILIB tools requires data to be coded in SGML format. So we must either use data from the SGML world or convert them. SGML (ISO 8879-1986), which was designed as a transfer format for printing electronic documents, is actually of much more general use, since all it does is to lay down flagging rules to describe tree-like structures, in which each node is identified by a tag (or «generic identifier» in the SGML standard).

Some experiments on the use of SGML in documentary fields were carried out from the very origin of this standard. For example, the EEC's FORMEX [EC85] project proposes a DTD that uses the information contained in a CCF [PGI 88] record. Many working groups are currently defining other DTD for bibliographic applications, for example MAJOUR[EWS91] by the EWS (European Workgroup on SGML). However, most available bibliographic data are coded with traditional formats. So we worked on minor adaptations of these formats, allowing the use of SGML tools, without requiring major changes. Most of the formats currently used in documentary applications can be easily transformed into SGML mark-up. For instance, it is very easy to define an equivalent SGML structure for BibTeX format, and the previous example becomes :

```
<doc type="inproceedings">
    <ref>crehange89a</ref>
    <crinnumber>88-R-101</crinnumber><category>4</category>
    <author><e>M. Cr&eacute;hange</e><e>G. Halin</e></author>...
```

Most documentary organisations have chosen ISO 2709 [ISO 81] based formats, such as CCF, UNIMARC, USMARC, for the exchange of data and as a basis for their internal information structure. Basic ISO 2709 is a two-level (field and subfield) structure, tagged with numerical or alphabetic digits, and it is relatively easy to define an equivalent SGML structure, using original tags. For example, the beginning of a CCF record such as :

```
001     0 0     157028
201     0 0     00@ALegislative study - ...
210     0 0     00@AEtudes Legislatives ... Agriculture@Lfre
```

could be marked as follows :

```
<record>
<f001>157028</f001>
<f201 dir="00", ind="00"><sA>Legislative study - ...
<f210 dir="00", ind="00"><sA>Etudes Legislatives ... Agriculture</sA><sL>fre</sL>
```

Once this general schema of adapting ISO 2709 to SGML has been worked out, only two converters need be written to convert any kind of MARC format to its equivalent SGML document and vice-versa.

4   MAIN TOOLS OF DILIB

A first set of tools is used to help in converting heterogeneous data into SGML. Two main levels (character set and data structure) are taken into account. The character set recommended on the workbench is based on SGML entity mechanism (and annex D of the ISO standard). Each character is represented by a symbolic chain bounded by an ampersand and a semicolon. For example, the French character «à» is represented by «`». DILIB provides commands to make this conversion. Concerning data structure level, in the previous chapter, we gave some information on the conversion of ISO 2709 to SGML. We also provide some tools to convert other formats into SGML (generally this work can also be done by using public parsers like SGMLS). Once data have been converted, they can be handled by various tools. A common problem consists in locating a particular element in a document. In order to solve this problem in a generic way, we use a path mechanism close to that of Unix. A path is composed by a string of tags separated by solidus characters. For example, let us consider the following record :

```
<doc><title>London by night</title>
  <author><f>John</f><l>Smith</l></author>
  <author><f>Paul</f><l>Templar</l></author>...</doc>
```

An example of a valid path is «doc/title» which gives access to text element «London by night», another example is «doc/author/f» which points to the set of author first names: «John, Paul». With some extensions (introducing conditions on contents), this mechanism is currently used to design parameters for DILIB Unix tools. For example, if we want to select records whose titles contain «London», we can use the following SgmlSelect command :

```
SgmlSelect -g doc/title#?London? < mySetOfRecords
```

Another part of the workbench consists in an Information Retrieval System in kit form. We have chosen to define some basic access mechanisms very close to the Unix file system. On this basis, we have defined other items such as inverted files whose records are also coded into SGML form :

```
<index><kw>usmarc</kw><freq>223</freq><list><e>0010</e><e>0532>/e>...
```

All these commands are written in C, and we have also developed a set of C functions, whose kernel is an SGML tree handling library.

5 CLUSTERIZATION TOOLS

All the internal data as inverted files can be handled by DILIB. This facility has been used to develop most of the infometric modules. For example, with an inverted file we can first build association files (always using a toolkit command) which look like this :

```
<assoc><ti><kw>usmarc</kw><f>223</f></ti>
  <tj><kw>SGML</kw><f>300</f></tj>
  <fij>15</fij><list><e>000035</e>...</list></assoc>
```

where «fij» is the frequency of co-occurrences of the key-words «usmarc» and «SGML». This association file can be used to build a cluster file which is also a set of SGML documents, one per cluster. Each cluster is made of a group of words with their inter-relations. The construction of clusters is carried through thanks to a classification based on a file of associations describing the relations existing between the keywords symbolizing the document of the database.

The method of clusterization carried through thanks to DILIB is that of «single link». The principle of the method is the following: the algorithm of clusterization works by consulting the file of associations between words in decreasing order of significance. The clusters are thus built in a successive way by putting into chains associations with common descriptive elements. The size of each cluster is limited to the group with the most significant associations used to build it. The group of remaining associations is used in an additional way to create links between the various clusters.

Some samples of DILIB results are available at the following WWW URL :

http://www.loria.fr/~ducloy/ingenist.html

6   EXAMPLE OF INFOMETRIC APPLICATION: EVOLUTIONS OF THE VARIOUS THEMES BELONGING TO A DOCUMENTARY FUND

The main interest of clusters is that they allow for automated characterization of the emergent themes of a documentary database and for showing their evolution. This processing is constructed through several levels:

- the clusterization of the database in order to bring out the main themes of the fund.
- the computation of the outline from a cluster: clusters being complex objects since they have both internal data (words and inter-relations) and external ones (relations to other clusters), we have chosen to transform them into simpler objects called «outlines». An outline is thus made of a list of elements in two parts (a word with its modulation) coming from the concepts of the cluster.
- the division of the fund into several parts, according to the years of publication.
- the computation of the representativeness of the outlines into each part thanks to a weight function

The application of this method on the database of written documents published by the CRIN allowed us to analyze the evolution (successive weight of those themes through the various sections in the year) of the themes on which our laboratory has carried out research during the last ten years.

7   THE DILIB TOOLKIT IN RESEARCH FIELDS: THE NOMAD SYSTEM EXAMPLE

The DILIB toolkit has proven very useful for managing documents in the sophisticated IRSs. It has been used successfully in the NOMAD [LAM 94] system described hereafter.

The NOMAD system is a documentary database interrogation system based on a symbolico-connectionist approach. NOMAD makes use of the synthesis capabilities and flexibilities inherent in this type of approach to increase its processing power as compared to existing systems while proposing new operating modes directly accessible to a large number of users. NOMAD manages multiple synthetic type views on its documentary contents in the form of neural topographies acting as case-memories as well as elaborate thematic browsing tools. NOMAD manages a session memory based on the neural model of the novelty detector with the following three functions: cumulative recording of user need, managing user contradictions and proposing new orientations. NOMAD also has extended learning capabilities, enabling it to improve its performance in the long term.

The whole kernel of the NOMAD system has been written in SMALLTALK. In its preliminary version, the NOMAD system worked with small documentary databases (approx. 100 documents).

The function of the DILIB toolkit used with this version was to convert the database references from their original format into SGML, which is easier to manipulate. The NOMAD system is presently in a test phase on a documentary database of 25000 references extracted from the INRIA documentary fund.

With databases of this size, it is necessary to use the on-line capabilities of the DILIB platform as a documentary server. The fact that SGML structures were provided as results by the DILIB toolkit made it easier to build the interface between the NOMAD system and the toolkit by devising in SMALLTALK access function to these SGML structures.

CONCLUSION

Obviously, to use this toolkit efficiently, one has to know how to manipulate Unix commands and to write C programs. This point may be considered restrictive, but it can be balanced with increased flexibility. For example once an Information Retrieval system has been set up, flexibility of such a toolkit allows many possibilities for new developments or improvements in various directions: specific adaptations to a particular field, performances, end-user facilities.

Today, a few hours are sometimes sufficient to treat a large amount of information in order to build a WAIS service on the INTERNET network, using a low priced workstation and some freeware components. If an information specialist wishes to benefit from this new situation, he must become an information engineer who integrates technological culture (and especially computer science), in the same way as an alchemist became a chemist by using mathematical tools (and now software tools as well).

KEYWORDS

Information engineering, SGML, hypertext, Internet, clustering techniques.

REFERENCES

[DUC91-1] Ducloy J., Grivel L., Lamirel J.-C., Polanco X., Schmitt L., INIST's Experience in Hyper-Document building from bibliographic Databases, Proceedings of RIAO'91, Barcelone (SP), Apr. (1991).

[DUC91-2] Ducloy J., Lelu A., Construction d'hyperdocuments à l'aide de procédés neuronaux, Proceedings of Génie Linguistique 91, Versailles (France) (1991).

[DUS91]   Dusoulier, N., Ducloy, J., Processing of data and exchange of records in a scientific and technical information center. Formats : what for? UNIMARC/CCF Workshop, Florence (Italy) (IFLA/UNESCO), (1991).

[EC85]   EC - FORMEX - Formalized Exchange of Electronic Publications. Office for Official Publication in the European Communities - Luxembourg, (ISBN 95-825-5399-X) (1985)..

[EWS 91]   European Workgroup on SGML: MAJOUR (Modular Application for Journal) , STM: Scientific Technical and Medical Publishers, Amsterdam (1991).

[GUI 89]   Guittet J., Combining CCF and SGML to exchange scientific and technical information, Proceedings of the first CCF Users Meetings, Unesco/IBE, Geneva, (PGI-90/WS/4, Apr. (1989).

[ISO 81]   ISO 2709 - Format for Bibliographic Information Interchange on Magnetic Tape (1981).

[ISO 86]   ISO 8879 - Standard Generalized Markup Language (SGML) (1986).

[KRO 92]   Krol E., The Whole Internet User's Guide and Catalogue, O'Reilly & Associates, Sebastopol (1992).

[KWI90]   KWICK - ESPRIT II Project nr 2466 Technical Annex, Document Id: KWICK: BullIt:TA:0002, by KWICK Consortium, July (1990).

[LAM 86]   Lamport L., LaTeX: A document Preparation System, Addison Wesley (1986).

[LAM 94]   Lamirel J.C., Crehange M., Application of a symbolico-connectionist approach for the design of a highly interactive documentary database interrogation system with on-line learning capabilities Proceedings of CIKM 94, Gaithersburg (USA) to be published.

[ROY 92]   Royauté J., Schmitt L., Olivétan E., Les expériences d'indexation à l'INIST Proceedings, 14th International Conference on Computational Linguistics, 1058-1063, (1992).

[SCH 92]   Schmitt L., Olivétan E., Landi B., Royauté J., Ducloy J., STID: Une Station de Travail pour une Indexation Assistée, Proceedings, 12ème Conference Internationale d'Avignon, June (1992).

[PGI 88]   UNESCO, PGI & UNISIST CCF: The Common Communication Format, Second Edition, Paris (PGI-88/WS/2) (1988).

Chapter 2

OBSTACLES TO A FREE OR FAIR CIRCULATION OF SCIENTIFIC DATA

A FEW FACETS OF THE KALEIDOSCOPE OF SCIENTIFIC INFORMATION

André HECK

Strasbourg Astronomical Observatory, 11, rue de l'Université, F-67000 Strasbourg, France. E-mail: heck@astro.u.-strasbg.fr, URL: http://cdsweb.u-strasbg.fr/~heck

ABSTRACT

The recent dramatic information technology evolution has brought major modifications in the way information is handled with new techniques and new tools. This paper will question a few clichés and deal with a number of newly resulting problems and challenges, especially ethical, legal and educational ones. The long-term impact of interdisciplinary approaches should be emphasized in the global Information Technology (IT) evolution and web-like telecommunications.

RESUME

L'évolution spectaculaire des technologies de l'information a entraîné des modifications majeures dans la gestion de l'information à l'aide de nouvelles techniques et de nouveaux outils. Cet article traite de la validité de quelques "clichés" ainsi que de quelques problèmes et défis résultants, notamment aux plans de la légalité, de l'éthique et de l'éducation. Il est important de souligner le rôle de l'impact des approches interdisciplinaires dans l'évolution globale des technologies de l'information future dont celle des systèmes de communications tels que le web.

1   INTRODUCTION

The ultimate aim of scientific investigations is to contribute to a better understanding of Nature. To this purpose, together with theoretical studies, we carry out experiments and/or observations to obtain data that will undergo treatments and studies leading to the publication of results[1]. The whole procedure can include several internal iterations or interactions between the various steps as well as with external fields (instrumental technology, ...), with other scientific disciplines and with information-handling methodologies.

In the following pages, the concept of information will cover the experimental and observational material, the more or less reduced data extracted from it, the scientific results, as well as the accessory material used by the scientists in their work; (bibliographical resources, increasingly important yellow-page services, and so on).

It is common to speak nowadays of *information technology (IT) revolution.* We prefer the more realistic concept of *IT evolution*, as we do not know whether or when the process will stop. As far as communication is concerned, many consider we are currently living a period which is as important for mankind as the XVth century that saw Gutenberg's invention of the movable-type printing process.

In a recent book, Peter F. Drucker (1993) predicted a power shift from the entities with financial resources towards persons or organizations who will have, not necessarily the knowledge itself, but who will know how to access it and to handle it. At a shorter term, financial wizard George Soros declared in his keynote address at a recent Internet Society conference that he considered the current connectivity a critical component for the Open Society which was the basis for political and economical stability as well as organizational success and self-fulfillment in the XXIst century (Rutkowski, 1994).

The previous reference itself is a good example of the changes occurring nowadays in communication: it is indeed pointing, not to a classical contribution on paper, but to an electronic document available through new tools and, last but not least, on-line shortly after the *Networld+Interop '94* conference in Tokyo where it was given as a keynote address on 29 July 1994.

---

[1] Publication is to be understood here as public announcement (Webster, 1976). No implicit assumption is made as to the medium used.

2   THE IT EVOLUTION

The recent years have seen a dramatic progress in computer capabilities, data reduction, communications, desktop and electronic publishing, and, more generally, information handling. The substance of libraries and the rôle of librarians are also significantly changing. The distinction between the formal and the so-called 'grey' literature is everyday more difficult to make as both are taking similar electronic shapes. The formal 'invited papers' are becoming multimedia presentations.

The structure of information itself is becoming different: beyond the classical quasi-linear layout of publications on paper, there are more and more frequently sets of *documents* with hypertext links (see e.g. Nielsen, 1990 & Landow, 1992), the structure of which can be closer adjusted to the authors' own mental structure.

Information as a whole now exists in an increasingly distributed way. Mankind should now definitively be protected from the consequences of a disaster such as the burning of Alexandria's libraries in the IIIrd century AD. If data centres have seen their rôle evolving and if they tend now to act more as a hub towards distributed specialized repositories of different types of data and material (rather than, as in the past, holding as much as possible themselves and carrying out the integration work on their own location), this is largely due to the fact that the IT evolution has brought in major modifications as to hardware and connectivity as well as new tools (client/server facilities, resource discovery packages, ...) and concepts (hypertext/hypermedia, virtual libraries, ...).

From its origin as part of a US government project (ARPA research project on inter-networking in the early 1970s), the Internet has become the major network linking nowadays millions of machines and tens of millions of people around the planet. Today, little of the Internet is controlled directly by governmental bodies and there are already impressive listings of commercial companies on the 'web'[2] . It is obvious that the accumulation of an estimated 20-30 million people on Internet (Rutkowski, 1994) is an appealing market!

Developed at CERN (see e.g. Berners-Lee et al., 1992 & 1994; White, 1993), the World-Wide Web (WWW) actually allowed for the first time Internet users to reach the various types of services accessible via this network (ftp, gopher, telnet, ...) through a consistent and abstract mechanism. Based on a hypertextual language (HTML - see Berners-Lee & Connolly, 1993), WWW calls on a specific protocol (HTTP - see e.g. Berners-Lee, 1994a) for a rapid transfer mechanism based also on Universal (or Uniform) Resource Locators (URLs) providing the electronic addresses of documents accessible on the Web (see e.g. Berners-Lee, 1994b). These URLs are already heavily used as references in this chapter. More flexibility (figures, tables,

---

[2] See e.g. the URL: http://tns-www.lcs.mit.edu/commerce.html.

forms, footnotes, margins, additional special characters, ...) will result from the use of HTML+ [3] and further versions.

The development of tools such as Mosaic at NCSA (e.g. Hardin, 1994) made it much easier to move ('navigate') happily from one document to another through virtual libraries on the Web, as well as to give access to already existing services. The distributed information is there (see e.g. Christian, 1994), and it is up to us to make the best use of it at the maximum of its current and future possibilities. More generally speaking, each document or 'page' connecting itself on the web contributes to the enlargement of the virtual libraries and we are everyday closer to the original Ted Nelson's (1981) vision of a virtual encyclopaedic library (Xanadu project).

The publications of the *Association for Computational Machinery (ACM)* and the proceedings of the meetings organized by its various Special Interest Groups (SIGs) are precious sources of information on the IT evolution and the various related issues. The meetings sponsored by the ACM's *Special Interest Group on Hypertext and Hypermedia (SIGLINK)* and *Special Interest Group on Information Retrieval (SIGIR)* are particularly recommended.

In astronomy and related space sciences for instance, a series of conferences and books testify this evolution: see e.g. Albrecht & Egret (1991 & 1995), Heck & Murtagh (1993), and (Egret & Heck, 1994, 1995).

3   THINK ABOUT IT TWICE

This section will be devoted to restate a few commonly misunderstood points, beginning with electronic publishing. First, there is still a confusion between desktop and electronic publishing. The former can be understood as a way of producing locally through relatively sophisticated software packages and laser printers high-quality printed material ready for reproduction by a publisher with the traditional camera-ready technique. The latter term rather concerns the electronic submission of material straight to the publisher who will work directly on the electronic files and get the paper, journal, or book ready for being printed through a succession of computer-assisted steps.

The popularization of hypertextual structures has added new degrees of freedom. Unfortunately many people nowadays have still too classical an approach, seeing nothing more in electronic documents than an electronic version of a traditional publication on paper. This leads to semantically conflictual expressions such as 'electronic preprints' ! It is also interesting to note that a journal on paper was

---

[3] See e.g. the URL: http://info.cern.ch/hypertext/WWW/MarkUp/HTMLPlus/htmlplus_1.html and Raggett (1994).

launched a few years ago by Wiley with the title *Electronic Publishing* while other commercial publishers are already heading at full steam to take advantage of the new hypertext techniques (Dougherty, 1993).

To the frequent question *'Do we still need the classical publishers?'*, our answer is *'Yes'*, simply because we still see the new IT media as complementary to the traditional ones. Of course, there are quite a few valuable arguments raised against it (see e.g. Berners-Lee, 1992 & Heck, 1992), especially at a time when library costs are spiraling upwards as opposed to the electronic material where the costs are widely distributed and where there is apparently a reduction of the overall invested energy and manpower. There are also quite a few arguments in favor such as the expertise (and the means) by commercial publishers to protect copyrighted works. But how often has this procedure actually been applied in the past and do we really need it in the future?

It is a fact that creators, authors, contributors, and so on, are worried by the fragility of their work under electronic format (making illicit copying easier, etc. - in this respect, see e.g. Samuelson, 1994), but this fear is basically linked to the aspect of recognition. This, and more generally ethical behavior, will have to be adapted to the new communication practices (see below). It is probably unfair to consider as competitive the classical journals (thus the traditional libraries) and electronic information (thus the virtual libraries), since the hypertextual structure of the latter, its distributed nature as well as its various digitized media make it primarily complementary to the former ones. One must be careful before burying too quickly the 'classical' publishers, the traditional journals and our beloved librarians.

The CD-ROM is another case of a sometimes misunderstood technology. Its biggest advantage is its compactness and the following example is well known: the F-18 aircraft required some 300,000 pages of documentation which is equivalent to a storage volume of about 68 cubic feet of paper. This could be put on a 0.04 cubic feet CD-ROM. But this medium is a frozen repository of information compared to permanently updated databases available on-line. And it requires quite an exercise to be consulted: to switch on the computer, to get the CD drive running with the ad hoc software, and so on, not to speak of standards. Here again, it is important to stress that the CD-ROM is a complementary technique, and not a panacea to replace classical documentation including journals.

It is actually surprising that new journals are being issued on this medium when connecting facilities are multiplying everywhere, including the wireless ones. For classical journals structured along the traditional quasi-linear layout, the eyes and the hands remain particularly efficient tools for scanning them. This is why people still often prefer searching through journals or books, rather than switching on computers, sliding in CD-ROMs or floppies, and keying codes and identifiers. This is not necessarily guided only by habits and inertia, but more often motivated by a better efficiency and handiness.

In a very interesting essay, Moore (1991) investigated the adoption life cycle of new technologies, pictured them as bell-shaped curves divided in zones corresponding to various behaviors (innovators, early adopters, early majority, late majority, and laggards), and pointed out cracks between these zones. The largest one, the 'chasm', appears to separate the early adopters from the early majority. This is where hypertextual techniques are currently emerging from[4] and where other techniques such as pen computing (Meyrowitz, 1992), virtual reality (see e.g. Rheingold, 1991) and others are still waiting for better times.

Thus new technologies are not always immediately adopted, and this adoption does not necessarily undergo a smooth process. It is also interesting to see how some tools or products laboriously and expensively developed for solving urgent needs at a specific time are then used much more successfully by a subsequent technology.

In a keynote address at *ECHT '92*, Ritchie (1992) brilliantly explained the remarkable technological achievements made at the canal age to bring water and barges over bridges and through tunnels because of the then pressing needs of transportation of ore and other goods. All this technology was subsequently much more efficiently exploited by the railway.

4   YELLOW-PAGE SERVICES

The concept of *yellow-page services* is now commonly used in a scientific context. Reference products have tuned themselves to the new capabilities brought in by the IT evolution. New reference products naturally derived from the new media available.

In astronomy and related space sciences, several resources provide the accessory information needed by present-day research, besides bibliographical information. The *Star*s Family* products have been described at an earlier CODATA· conference (Heck, 1994) and are organized around three sets of master files: data on organizations and services; lists of acronyms, abbreviations, contractions and symbols; database of personal WWW pages of essentially astronomers and space scientists. See Heck (1995) for an update and the references quoted therein.

AstroWeb (Jackson et al., 1994) is a new WWW resource providing hyperlinks (URLs) to astronomy resources available on Internet and using i.a. the Mosaic client tool. These links allow transparent access to information provided by WWW, gopher (Anklesaria, 1993), anonymous ftp, WAIS (Fullton, 1993), Usenet News, and Telnet services.

---

[4] Hypertext - a term coined by Nelson (1967) - has been around for quite some time already. See e.g. Smith & Weiss (1988) and the subsequent papers of that special issue of the *ACM Communications* on hypertext they edited.

5   MAINTENANCE AND QUALITY

The maintenance process of information resources such as databases must continuously be improved from lessons learned with time and by using new tools available. Generally speaking, information has to be collected, verified, de-biased, homogenized, and made available not only in an efficient way, but also through operationally reliable means (it becomes useless if plugged into a confidential network or reachable through deficient routers). Redundancies have to be avoided; precision is, and details can be, extremely important. Last but not least, the continuous political evolution of the world has also to be taken into account, and one must be permanently alert to practical aspects such as restructuring of postal codes, telephone area codes, and so on.

Professional file construction techniques are nowadays mandatory. These, however, cannot lessen the extensive background, unrewarding and very careful work which is indispensable for the compilation of a valuable resource. One can never stress enough the importance of this obscure daily work consisting of patiently collecting data, checking information and updating the master files. If scientists have a natural tendency to design projects and software packages involving the most advanced techniques and tools, there is in general less enthusiasm for the painstaking and meticulous long-term maintenance which builds up the real substance of the databases. This has also to be carried out by knowledgeable scientists or documentalists and cannot be delegated to unexperimented clerks.

Efficient working procedures have to be worked out and may vary from one person to another depending on working abilities, intellectual structure and education, and so on. Once again maintaining a database is a very demanding tedious task, a time-consuming and endless everyday occupation requiring memory, aesthetic feeling, as well as pragmatism and acumen towards current and future needs of users.

Information retrieval *per se* is raising a number of evaluation issues[5] The fashion is now shifting towards designing and experimenting quality control processes. This might be a very serious matter or a big joke. Until further evidence is brought up, we believe that the best quality assurance (accuracy, homogeneity, exhaustivity, ...) has to be achieved when collecting and entering the data themselves. None of the algorithms currently available has really convinced us of their absolute necessity and satisfactory efficiency.

Here again, developing such processes is an appealing challenge for scientists, but most of the algorithms designed work statistically. For a database user, it does not matter much whether the material queried is accurate up to 95% or 98%. The user

---

[5] See e.g. Harman (1992) and the subsequent papers of the corresponding special issue.

wants to find the piece of information he/she is looking for, and, if found, this has to be accurate. If what he/she is looking for is not available or is wrong, this is what will be remembered. All these considerations are obvious if a telephone book or database is taken as a model for yellow-page services .

6   PLENTY OF WORK ON HAND

This explosion of documents on the web is not a bed of roses. New facilities and new possibilities naturally involve new questions and new problems. Some of the WWW servers have already reached a quite fair degree of maturity. Others are still a bit in a wild stage by lack of structure and homogeneity or simply because they offer, let us say it frankly, a significant amount of rubbish of little interest. Although quite a few features have been adopted *de facto* by the developers of documents on the web, there is a definite need for a WWW *ethical charter*. It could concern quite a number of features from the substances of the documents themselves to their aesthetical presentation and a number of recommended functionalities..

Each document should be 'signed' in some way and contacts for comments should be provided, if possible involving dynamic e-mail facilities (but please do not forget also to indicate the full name of the organization with its address, phone and fax numbers, and so on; an access map is also quite welcome). The multiplication of large pictures and icons should also be discouraged and limited to what is really essential for the sake of information retrieval and network efficiency. The fashion of putting unrelated material, especially pictures of wives, girlfriends, actors, actresses or top models is an insult to the persons querying the pages in hope of some interesting information (or, at the very least, it is a ridiculous waste of time for the user). People should also remember that humour is not always exportable.

Hypertext itself is too often badly used. Also only well-tested documents should be put on line. It is easy to create working directories on which Mosaic (for instance) can be run locally. URLs should not be changed unless absolutely necessary and, in such cases, links should be provided from the obsolete ones to the new ones.

Since tools such as Mosaic make it so easy to download the original files, crediting the sources appropriately becomes critically important. It is actually smarter and more elegant to insert a hyperlink to the original document since then it will point always to the freshest version of the file.

This brings us to *security* issues, involving monitoring, restricted access, confidentiality and so on. Away from governmental policies (such as the Clipper chip project in the US that is raising substantial controversy), there is no golden rule on security issues: it is up to each local 'webmaster' to put the appropriate securities according to the material concerned. Some resources require appropriate clearance (password, account number and so on); others will be only partially retrievable in a specific query (such as large copyrighted databases); finally, other documents are freely accessible and usable, conditioned to a minimum of ethical behavior (see above).

Legal aspects (copyright, electronic signatures, ...) are also extremelely important and jusrist are busy setting up reference for the computerized material. Particulary in this case, there might be variations from country to country when the law already exists. However, with the world globalization of electronic communications, one can expect, and hope for, a quick harmonization of the various references and procedures. One such matters, refer to Samuelson (1993) and to her very interesting regular column '*Legally Speaking*' in the *ACM Communications*.

Last, but not least, there are non-negligible *educational aspects* to be taken into account as the introduction and training of young and not-so-young people to the new technologies within the various communities. This is true not only for scientists, but also for librarians and documentalists who will see their rôle significantly changing within their institution and who will be increasingly dealing with virtual material.

7   A FEW LAST COMMENTS

It would be dangerous __ and pretentious __ to play here the game of guessing the long-term impact of the IT evolution. What is sure is that technological progress will play a key rôle in future orientations. But these are still too fuzzy and all predictions are risky. Two years ago, the WWW was unknown while today it allows a daily cyberspace navigation [6] on a planetary scale. Who would still dare plan computer technology and information handling a lustrum ahead? It is more than ever time for managers to rely on members of their staff gifted with intuition.

We might, nevertheless, have to reassess thoroughly the process of *evaluation* applied for financing research and that conditions the need for *recognition* (which is currently based essentially on traditional publications) for getting positions (grants and salaries), acceptance of proposals (leading to data collection), and funding of projects (allowing materialization of ideas).

The whole IT evolution emphasized the need for multidisciplinary approaches and that is where meetings organized by ACM, CODATA, SIAM[7], and others, are valuable forums. It is also clear that the advent of the web makes interdisciplinary communications much easier, more emulative and more inspirational. One must however be cautious with encyclopaedic tendencies resulting from the IT evolution

---

[6] For the literary navigation style, the '*cyberpunk*' school, refer e.g. to Gibson (1986 & 1993).

[7] Society for Industrial and Applied Mathematics

and, even within a specific scientific discipline, one must refrain from engulfing enormous amounts of energy and manpower in oversized endeavors with questionable return.

KEYWORDS

Information technology, hypertext, multimedia, electronic publishing, databases, World-Wide Web.

REFERENCES

[1]   Albrecht M.A., Egret D., Databases & on-line data in astronomy, Kluwer Acad. Publ., Dordrecht, xiv + 274 pp. (ISBN 0-7923-1247-3) (1991).

[2]   Anklesaria F., McCahill M., The Internet gopher, in Intelligent Information Retrieval: The Case of Astronomy and Related Space Sciences, Heck A., Murtagh F.(eds) Kluwer Acad..Publ., Dordrecht, 119-125 (1993).

[3]   Berners-Lee T.J., Electronic publishing and visions of hypertext, Physics World, June (1992).

[4]   Berners-Lee T.J., Hypertext transfer protocol (1994a) (see also the URLs: http://info.cern.ch/hypertext/WWW/Protocols/HTTP/HTTP2.html

        & ftp://info.cern.ch/pub/www/doc/html-specs.ps

        & ftp://info.cern.ch/pub/www/doc/html-specs.txt)

[5]   Berners-Lee, T.J., WWW names and addresses, URIs, URLs, and URNs (1994b) (see the URL: http://info.cern.ch/hypertext/WWW/Addressing/Addressing.html).

[6]   Berners-Lee T.J., Connolly D., Hypertext markup language (1993) A representation of textual information and metainformation for retrieval and interchange, CERN Internal Draft (see also the URLs :

        http://info.cern.ch/hypertext/WWW/MarkUp/MarkUp.html

        & ftp://info.cern.ch/pub/www/doc/html-specs.ps

        & ftp://info.cern.ch/pub/www/doc/html-specs.txt).

[7]   Berners-Lee T.J., Cailliau R., Groff J.F., Pollerman B., World-Wide Web : The information universe, in Electronic Networking: Research, Applications and Policy, 52-58 (1992), see also the URL: http://info.cern.ch/hypertext/WWW/TheProject.html

[8]   Berners-Lee T.J., Cailliau R., Luotonen A., Nielsen H.F. , Secret A., The World-Wide Web, Comm. ACM 37-8, 76-82 (1994).

[9]   Christian C., The National Information Infrastructure Tested, in Astronomical Data Analysis Software and Systems III, (eds). Crabtree, D.R., Hanisch, R.J.& Barnes, J., Astron. Soc. Pacific Conf. Series 61, (1994), (see also the URLs :

        http://niit1.harvard.edu/~carolc/utils/cmsi_adass/section3.1.html

        & http://niit1.harvard.edu/~carolc/utils/cmsi_adass/cmsi_adass.html).

[10]   Dougherty D., Forging the business of hypertext publishing, Hypertext '93 Tutorial 12, Seattle, 42 pp, (1993).

[11]   Drucker P.F., Post-capitalist society, Harper Business, New York, (ISBN 0-88730620-9) (1993).

[12]   Egret D., Heck A., WWW in astronomy and related space sciences, in Second Internat. WWW Conf., Chicago, (Oct 1994). Weaving the Astronomy Web, Vistas in Astron. 39, 1-126 (1995)

[13]   Fullton, J., WAIS, in Intelligent Information Retrieval: The Case of Astronomy and Related Space Sciences, Heck A., Murtagh F. (eds) Kluwer Acad. Publ., Dordrecht, 113-117 (1993).

[14]   Gibson W., Neuromancer, Grafton, London, 318 pp. (ISBN 0-586-06645-4) (1986).

[15]   Gibson W., Virtual light, Viking, London, 296 pp. (ISBN 0-670-84890-5) (1993).

[16]   Hardin J., Human collaborations technologies for the Internet - NCSA Mosaic and NCSA Collage, in Astronomical Data Analysis Software and Systems III, Crabtree D.R., Hanisch R.J., Barnes J. (eds) Astron. Soc. Pacific Conf. Series 61, (1994).

[17]   Harman, D., Evaluation issues in information retrieval, Information Processing & Management, 28, 439-440 (1992).

[18]   Heck, A., Desktop publishing in astronomy and space sciences, World Scientific, Singapore, xii + 240 pp. (ISBN 981-02-0915-0) (1992).

[19]   Heck A., The Star*s Family, in New Data Challenges in Our Information Age, Glaeser P.S., Willward M.T.I (eds), CODATA Proc. Series 2, B110-B113 (1994).

[20]   Heck A., The Star*s Family: An example of comprehensive yellow-page services, in ip Databases & On-Line Data in Astronomy II,. Albrecht M.A., Egret D.(eds) Kluwer Acad. Publ., Dordrecht, (1995).

[21]   Heck A., Murtagh F., Intelligent information retrieval: the case of astronomy and related space sciences, Kluwer Acad. Publ., Dordrecht, iv + 214 pp. (ISBN 0-7923-2295-9) (1993).

[22]   Jackson R., Wells D., Adorf H.M., Egret D., Heck A., Koekemoer A., Murtagh F., AstroWeb— A database of links to astronomy resources (announcement of a database), Astron. Astrophys. Suppl. (1994), (see also the URLs:

        http://cdsweb.u-strasbg.fr/astroweb.html

        & http://meteor.anu.edu.au/anton/astronomy.htm

        & http://fits.cv.nrao.edu/www/astronomy.html

        & http://ecf.hq.eso.org/astro- resources.html

        & http://stsci.edu/net-resources.html).

[23]   Landow G.P., Hypertext: The convergence of contemporary critical theory and technology, Johns Hopkins Univ. Press, Baltimore, xii + 242 pp. (ISBN 0-8018-4280-8) (1992).

[24]   Meyrowitz N., Pen computing: The new mobility of interactive applications, ECHT '92 Tutorial Milano, 36 pp. (1992).

[25]   Moore G.A., Crossing the chasm, Harper Business, New York, xviii + 224 pp. (ISBN 0-88730519-9) (1991).

[26]   Nelson T.H., Getting it out of our system, in Information Retrieval: A Critical Review,. Schechter G. (ed), Thompson Books, Washington, 191-210 (1967).

[27]   Nelson T.H., Literary Machines, Mindfull Press (1981).

[28]   Nielsen J., Hypertext and hypermedia, Academic Press, San Diego, xii + 264 pp. (ISBN 0-12-518410-7) (1990).

[29]   Raggett D., A review of HTML+ document format, in First Internat. Conf. on the World Wide Web, (1994) (see also the URL:

        http://wwwl.cern.ch/PapersWWW94/dsr.ps).

[30]   Rheingold H., Virtual reality, Simon & Schuster, New York, 416 pp. (ISBN 0-671-69363-8) (1991).

[31]   Ritchie I., The future of electronic literacy: Will hypertext ever find acceptance?, ECHT '92 Keynote Address, Milano & private communication (1992).

[32]   Rutkowski A.M., The present and future of the Internet: Five faces, in Networld & Interop '94 Conf. (1994) (see also the URL: http://info.isoc.org/interop-tokyo.html).

[33]   Samuelson P., Intellectual property protection, Hypertext'93 Tutorial 21, Seattle (1993).

[34]   Samuelson P., Copyright's fair use doctrine and digital data, ACM Comm. 37-1, 21-27 (1994).

[35]   Smith J.B., Weiss S.F., Hypertext, ACM Comm. 31, 816-819 (1988).

[36]   Webster Third New International Dictionary, Merriam Co., Chicago, lxxxvi + 3136 pp. (ISBN 0-87779-106-6) (three volumes) (1976).

[37]   White B., WorldWideWeb (WWW), in Intelligent Information Retrieval: The Case of Astronomy and Related Space Sciences, Heck A., Murtagh F. (eds) Kluwer Acad. Publ., Dordrecht, 127-133 (1993).

ICSU POLICY ON ACCESS TO DATA AND INFORMATION

Michael A. CHINNERY

National Geophysical Data Center, 325 Broadway, Boulder, Colorado 80303, U.S.A.

ABSTRACT

In response to a mounting concern among scientists in many fields that scientific data needed for research are becoming harder to obtain, the International Council of Scientific Unions established an Ad Hoc Committee on Data Issues to explore the problem and make recommendations for future ICSU action. The Committee restricted its review to environmental data, where it is clear that the concept of free exchange of scientific data is being attacked by some commercial and nationalistic interests. This paper discusses the conclusions of the Committee, which stress the urgency of this issue. ICSU needs to fight to preserve access to environmental data for research scientists in all countries.

RESUME

En réponse à une préoccupation croissante du monde scientifique groupant de nombreux secteurs d'activités et constatant que les données scientifiques utiles aux recherches deviennent plus difficiles à obtenir , le Conseil International des Unions Scientifiques a établi un Comité Ad Hoc sur les problèmes de données en vue d'explorer ce domaine et de faire des recommandations pour une action future ICSU . Le comité a limité son analyse aux données de l'environnement, domaine où il est clair que le concept de libre échange de données scientifiques est attaqué à présent par divers intérêts commerciaux et nationalistes . Cet article présente une discussion des conclusions du Comité , qui souligne l'importance de ce sujet . ICSU devrait se battre pour préserver l'accès aux données de l'environnement à tous les chercheurs scientifiques de tous les pays .

1 INTRODUCTION

Current policy of the International Council of Scientific Unions (ICSU) in the area of access to scientific data consists of a resolution approved at the 1988 ICSU General Assembly. "Noting that :

1. The success of international cooperative programmes in science depends on an unprecedented sharing of scientific data and information;

2. ICSU has a longstanding commitment to the free circulation of scientists and access to scientific data and information; and

3. Processes of data and information handling and dissemination are rapidly becoming technically more sophisticated and potentially more expensive for those who provide and use these services;

Recommends all ICSU members to support the fundamental principle of open exchange of data and information for scientific purposes by strongly urging public and private organizations in all countries to facilitate access to scientific information and data needed to address the research objectives of ICSU programmes; and further recommends that the Executive Board establish a mechanism to monitor the implementation of this principle and take action on problems that may arise."

In February 1993, ICSU established the Ad Hoc Committee on Data Issues, with the following charter :

1. To propose a revised ICSU policy on data issues that covers broadly and effectively the needs of scientists in the ICSU family,

2. To encourage and stimulate pilot data projects, and

3. To build on the spirit and substance of the meeting of the informal group (CODATA,FAGS,WDC and IGBP-DIS) that met in Paris in September 1992, and the actions in Beijing in October 1992 recording CODATA's support and continuing interest.

The Ad Hoc Committee on Data Issues decided to limit its initial considerations to issues of environmental data policy. This was partly a result of the membership of the committee, and partly because there have been some very interesting developments in environmental data policy during the last few years. This provides a good example of the complexities that arise in data matters, where we find more and more conflict between the needs of the scientific research community, national economic and security interests, and the interests of the commercial sector.

2   EXISTING ENVIRONMENTAL DATA POLICY

Many organizations have issued statements of environmental data policy. Perhaps the most interesting was a statement of United States Policy, which was issued by the Executive Office of the President in July 1991: "The overall purpose of these policy statements is to facilitate full and open access to quality data for global change research. They were prepared in consonance with the goal of the U.S. Global Change Research Program and represent the U.S. Government's position on the access to global change research data.

1. The Global Change Research Program requires an early and continuing commitment to the establishment, maintenance, validation, description, accessibility, and distribution of high-quality, long-term data sets.

2. Full and open sharing of the full suite of global data sets for all global change researchers is a fundamental objective

3. Preservation of all data needed for long-term global change research is required. For each and every global change data parameter, there should be at least one explicitly designated archive. Procedures and criteria for setting priorities for data acquisition, retention, and purging should be developed by participating agencies, both nationally and internationally. A clearinghouse process should be established to prevent the purging and loss of important data sets

4. Data archives must include easily accessible information about the data holdings, including quality assessments, supporting ancillary information, and guidance and aids for locating and obtaining the data

5. National and international standards should be used to the greatest extent possible for media and for processing and communication of global data sets

6. Data should be provided at the lowest possible cost to global change researchers in the interest of full and open access to data. This cost should, as a first principle, be no more than the marginal cost of filling a specific user request. Agencies should act to streamline administrative arrangements for exchanging data among researchers

7. For those programs in which selected principal investigators have initial periods of exclusive use, data should be made openly available as soon as they become widely useful. In each case, the funding agency should explicitly define the duration of any exclusive use period"

3 RECOMMENDATIONS FOR AN ICSU POLICY FOR ENVIRONMENTAL DATA

The Committee felt that the above statement should be a good starting point for the development of an ICSU Policy.

However, the Committee recommended that ICSU work towards a data policy that would be applicable to a wider range of environmental research than global change, important as this is. In form, this policy should consist of a modified version of the above U.S. statement designed for the international environmental community.

It is very important that this policy address the range of data types to which it should apply. A statement that requests that all environmental data be made easily available to all researchers is probably unreasonable because of commercial and national security (including economic security) issues. An attempt must be made to separate the needs of global environmental research from the legitimate requirements of individual nations and the commercial sector. It might be possible to base this separation on spatial resolution. Thus, high resolution observations of the environment are often closely related to commercial and national interests, and have limited application to the study of global processes. However, lower resolution and gridded data are generally much less sensitive, and are very useful for regional and global research.

Once the types of data needed for global research have been defined, the ICSU position must be that these data must be made easily available to global researchers in all nations. The term "easily" must be defined in a useful way. Many organizations   rely on phraseology like "full and open exchange". While this is a valid philosophy, it disregards the definition of an infrastructure that will accomplish the exchange, and the mechanisms that will be needed to evaluate and improve the exchange. It is possible, for example, that the ICSU World Data Center System could have an important role in these tasks.

One of the biggest impediments to the accessibility, or free and open exchange, of environmental data is cost. The U.S. Policy Statement gave an approach based on the idea of the "lowest possible cost". That may be satisfactory for developed nations with easily convertible currency, but even a small cost in "hard" currency can be an insurmountable barrier for scientists in developing nations. ICSU needs to develop innovative approaches to this problem, using traditional free data exchange along with new concepts such as data "grants" to individual scientists, and the establishment of data "libraries" that will service different parts of the world.

4   FUTURE OF ICSU ACTIVITIES RELATED TO DATA ACCESS

The Ad Hoc Committee concluded that significant problems related to access to scientific data arise within the ICSU Unions and Special Committees, and that these are expected to get worse in the future. It recommended that consideration of these problems should be a continuing task for ICSU, and should be assigned to a group that has a stable responsibility and accountability within the ICSU structure. There are several ways that this could be done, including establishing an ICSU Standing Committee on Data Issues. While this might eventually be necessary, the Committee did not recommend this solution at present. Instead, the Committee recommended that the task be assigned to CODATA. The charter of CODATA is very broad and could easily include the formulation of ICSU data policy. Approved by the Executive Board of ICSU, a CODATA Working Group on Data Access was established during 1994.

KEYWORDS

ICSU, data policy, data access, data exchange, environmental data, global change data.

Issues in the Transborder Flow of Scientific Data

Shelton ALEXANDER[1] and Paul F. UHLIR[2]

[1] Dept. of Geosciences, The Pennsylvania State University, University Park, PA 16802, USA
[2] National Research Council, 2101 Constitution Avenue, Washington, DC 20418, USA

ABSTRACT

The US National Committee for CODATA is conducting an interdisciplinary study of international access to scientific data. The primary focus is on data in electronic forms, a topic of increasing complexity and importance in scientific research and international collaboration. The study is characterizing the technical, legal, economic and policy issues that have an impact -- whether favorable or negative -- on access to data by the scientific community. Special attention is being given to the specific conditions inherent in the transborder transfers of electronic scientific data among the academic, governmental and private sectors. The study is also identifying and describing those barriers that have the most adverse impact in each of the discipline areas within CODATA's purview -- the physical, astronomical, biological and geological sciences -- and across those disciplines, using representative examples. Finally, it is attempting to identify trends that are likely to have significant discipline-specific and interdisciplinary impacts on the use of scientific data, particularly in electronic forms, and will suggest approaches that could help overcome both generic and specific barriers to access in the international context. Because of the broad nature of this topic it is important to maintain an appropriate focus on key issues and this will be done in part through the use of representative case studies. The study will be completed by the fall of 1996.

RESUME

Le Comité National des Etats-Unis conduit une étude interdisciplinaire sur l'accès aux données scientifiques. L'aspect principal porte sur les standards électroniques, sujet d'une complexité croissante mais essentielle au plan de la collaboration internationale. L'étude vise à définir les questions techniques, légales, économiques, et politiques qui influent, de façon favorable ou négative, sur l'accès aux données par la communauté scientifique. Il sera porté un intérêt particulier aux conditions spécifiques inhérentes aux transferts, au-delà des frontières, des données scientifiques électroniques dans les secteurs académiques, gouvernementaux et privés. L'étude vise à identifier et à décrire les barrières qui ont les impacts les plus importants dans les champs d'activités de CODATA, tels que les sciences physiques, astronomiques, biologiques et géologiques, et ceux qui traversent ces disciplines. L'examen de ces *cas est conduit à partir de cas représentatifs. L'objectif est de tenter d'identifier les tendances propres aux disciplines et aux thématiques interdisciplinaires qui ont un impact sur l'utilisation de données scientifiques, en particulier sous forme électronique et qui peuvent suggérer des approches autorisant le franchissement de barrières spécifiques et génériques pour accéder au contexte international. En raison de l'étendu de ce sujet il faut réellement maintenir un intérêt approprié sur les "thèmes-clés".   Ceci sera fait, en partie, à l'aide d'études de cas représentatifs. L'étude sera complétée pour la fin de l'année 1996.*

1   INTRODUCTION

Scientists commonly encounter difficulties in gaining access to data relevant to their research because of both technical and non-technical barriers. The issues related to adequate access to the mounting volumes of data in all scientific disciplines--particularly data in electronic forms--have been a topic of considerable concern in recent years. The integration of multidisciplinary data on an international basis to address problems such as global environmental degradation or disease epidemics raises new and even more challenging problems in this regard.

Consistent with the charter of CODATA international, the U.S. National Committee (USNC) for CODATA is concerned with all types of quantitative data resulting from experimental measurements or observations primarily in the physical, biological, geological, and astronomical sciences. Particular emphasis is given to data management problems common to different scientific disciplines and to data used outside the field in which they are generated. The general objectives are the improvement of the quality and accessibility of data, as well as the methods by which data are acquired, managed, and analyzed; the facilitation of international cooperation among those collecting, organizing, and using data; and the promotion of an increased awareness in the scientific and technical community of the importance of these activities. The USNC/CODATA is organized and operated within the U. S. National Academy of Sciences (NAS) and its operating arm, the National Research Council (NRC).

One NRC study, Sharing Research Data, published by the Committee on National Statistics in 1985, provided a comprehensive analysis of the issues related to broadening the access to social science research data. Many of the conclusions and recommendations set forth in that report are equally relevant in the context of natural science research, although this was not expressly addressed. The focus of the 1985 study, however, was primarily on the sharing of data within the U.S., rather than on an international basis.

A seminal work on Scientific and Technical (S&T) data access and dissemination in the international context, Study on the Problems of Accessibility and Dissemination of Data for Science and Technology, was published by a CODATA task group in

1975 (CODATA Bulletin 16). This report provided an excellent overview of the problems associated with the transborder flows of S&T data at that time. However, the focus of that study was mainly on analog data in hard copy formats rather than on the large and growing volumes of digitized data in electronic formats that now support scientific research activities. Therefore, this 1975 study, while still relevant in some respects, is substantially outdated because it did not expressly address the problems inherent in the transborder flow of electronic S&T data.

A more recent attempt to examine the barriers to data access at the international level was made by CODATA in conjunction with the International Council for Scientific and Technical Information (ICSTI) through an informal survey in 1990. The survey solicited comments from approximately 70 producers, distributors, and users of scientific databases on barriers to data access in the following categories:

1. Restrictions on transmission of scientific data/information across national boundaries.

2. Impediments resulting from pricing policies and differing national practices regarding subsidies for database development.

3. Special problems of academic scientists who face high prices for data that have high commercial importance as well as basic research interest.

4. Barriers that might result from efforts of database owners to protect their intellectual property from unauthorized redistribution or other illegal practices.

5. The particular problems of developing countries.

The survey identified several barriers, but did not provide details on the nature and extent of these problems. However, from this study and other experiences within the scientific community it is evident that access to scientific data continues to be restricted by technical, legal, economic, and policy constraints on both a national and international basis. The constantly increasing use of computers and telecommunications networks in the creation, maintenance, and dissemination of scientific data significantly changes the context in which these constraints on effective access apply. These problems also are exacerbated by the emergence of a global economy where competitiveness among technologically advanced nations leads to increased emphasis on the real and perceived value of scientific data and intellectual property to national interests. Scientists in developing countries commonly have additional or different concerns from their colleagues in the wealthier nations, leading to asymmetries in research relationships and related transfers of data. Apparent solutions to problems in one context may not be appropriate or applicable in another.

During the five years that have elapsed since the CODATA/ICSTI survey, the USNC/CODATA has held several seminars in conjunction with its regular meetings to gather background information on these issues from government policy experts and knowledgeable individuals in the international scientific community. A session on the "Social, Political and Legal Aspects of Databases" was also held at the October 1992 International CODATA Conference in Beijing.   These preliminary investigations have made it clear to the USNC/CODATA that a broad study on the transborder flow of scientific data, with a primary focus on data in electronic forms, could help bring the problems and challenges in this area into sharper focus. In addition, the committee has been encouraged to do this study by the agencies that provide its core support.

2   PRESENT STUDY

The USNC/CODATA study now in progress has undertaken a study of technical, legal, economic, and policy issues that impact the transborder flow of scientific data, with a special emphasis on data stored and transmitted in electronic formats (e.g., on the Internet). Because of the study's interdisciplinary focus, the standing committee has augmented its existing expertise in the natural sciences with experts in the legal, economic, and policy aspects of international transfers of scientific data.

The study will be performed by two panels with sub-panels organized according to a matrix of disciplines (physical, astronomical, biological, and geological sciences) and issues (technical, legal, economic, and policy).   Each discipline area will be represented by 2-3 experts (including the panel and sub-panel chairs). The panels of 11-12 individuals will meet separately in sub-panels as well as together. The same individuals will constitute both panels but in different groupings on sub-panels. This matrix approach will enable the discipline panel to take a cross-cutting issue persepective, and the issue panel to take a multidisciplinary perspective.

The study will be performed under the following Terms of Reference:

- Outline the needs for data in the major research areas of current scientific interest that fall within the scope of CODATA--the physical, astronomical, geological, and biological sciences.
- Characterize the legal, economic, policy, and technical factors and trends that have an influence--whether favorable or negative--on access to data by the scientific community.
- Identify and analyze the barriers to international access to scientific data that may be expected to have the most adverse impact in discipline areas within CODATA's purview, with emphasis on factors common to all the disciplines.
- Recommend to the sponsors of the study approaches that could help overcome barriers to access in the international context.

The panels will hold three meetings. Following the panel's initial meeting, input will be solicited from: other units at the National Research Council, including the

Committee on Geophysical and Environmental Data and the various U.S. National Committees to ICSU, with significant involvement in these issues; other CODATA National Committees and Task Groups; other ICSU Scientific Unions, Associates, and Interdisciplinary Bodies; national, foreign, and international professional societies in the relevant disciplines; government agencies and intergovernmental bodies involved in scientific research; and other individuals, groups, and institutions. This major fact-finding activity will be supplemented by extensive research, as well as by follow-up interviews. The study members also will be encouraged to take advantage of opportunities to obtain additional inputs at international scientific conferences. A questionnaire has been designed to elicit specific information from these various sources; it is focused on the following issues:

1. Barriers to Data Access. The objective here is to assess the adverse impacts that various restrictions on access to scientific data have had and to identify trends that may be important.

2. Pricing of Data. Several detailed questions are asked of users concerning whether they get most of their data free (for the cost of reproduction) or must pay and what pricing policies they have encountered. They also are asked to assess the impact of data costs on their research and identify trends, new media, and other technological advances that may affect the cost of data they use in the future. For suppliers of data for scientific research, questions are asked concerning their type of organization, what kinds of data they provide, media used for distribution, pricing policies (including whether they offer special prices for research/academic users), and what factors most influence their pricing policies.

3. Protection of Intellectual Property. Here the objective is to determine what legal and technical protections from unauthorized uses of scientific data currently exist, how they are implemented and enforced, and what the positive and negative impacts of these protections are.

4. Less-Developed Countries. Respondents are asked to describe the principal problems associated with transferring data into and out of less-developed countries and to suggest ways to alleviate these problems, especially by the international scientific community.

5. Electronic Networks. Respondents are asked whether the rapid growth of electronic networking, such as the Internet, has affected the way data of importance to them are accessed or distributed internationally, and if so, to cite examples and give opinions on what the impact of future growth in electronic networks on their activities is likely to be.

6. Other Technical Issues. The objective is to identify technical issues or new developments other than electronic networks that affect access or dissemination of scientific data internationally and to determine trends that are likely to be important over the next decade.

7.   Scientific Data for Global Problems. Opinions are solicited on the role of
        international scientific data for addressing global problems both now and in
        the future and on steps that can be taken to enhance the availability of these
        data
8.   Other Issues. Respondents are invited to identify and discuss other relevant
        issues or give examples of successes in transborder flow of scientific data that
        would be appropriate to consider in the study. Suggestions of other
        institutions or individuals that should be contacted with regard to the issues
        in the questionnaire are also requested.

Readers are invited to send responses on any or all of these issues to:

Paul F. Uhlir, Director,
U.S. National Committee for CODATA, National Research Council,
2101 Constitution Avenue, N.W., Washington, D.C. 20418, U.S.A.
(Telephone: (202) 334-3061; Internet: BITS@NAS.EDU).

To be useful in this study responses should be received by January 1996.

The results of the fact finding and research will be reviewed at the second meeting, in
the fall of 1995, and a significant portion of the drafting of the report will be done at
that time. The study members also will identify any additional research and writing
assignments that may be necessary. The members will convene one more time to
complete the report, which will be reviewed by the USNC/CODATA at its spring
1996 meeting. A report will be published in the fall of 1996.

KEYWORDS

Transborder scientific data flow; electronic data; international access; technical, legal,
economic, policy issues; scientific data; trends affecting access.

Legal and Economic Aspects of Data Production and Transfer

George PAPAPAVLOU

European Commission, Direction General XIII, Bât. Jean Monnet, 2920 Luxembourg, Luxembourg

Abstract

Information is one of the economy sectors which will become a leading one controlling the growth, competitiveness and employment of the European Union. Legal and economic aspects are closely interlinked. Legal solutions related to security of information, data and authors' rights must be seriously taken into account within international developments supported both by technical and organizational initiatives .

Resume

L'information est un des secteurs économiques qui passera vraisemblablement très vite en tête des efforts communautaires pour accroître la croissance et la compétitivité de l'Union Européenne. Les aspects légaux et économiques sont étroitement liés . Les solutions légales relatives à la sécurisation et aux droits des intervenants doivent recevoir l'appui intensif d'initiatives techniques et organisationnelles de préférence par des actions conduites au plan international .

1 Introduction

Tackling all legal and economic aspects of data production and transfer cannot be accomplished in a paper of any length, but requires a work the size of an encyclopedia. In this limited presentation, one has to be selective: what data are we talking about? which are the main legal issues concerned? how do they relate to economic aspects? again, this cannot be done exhaustively. What follows should be taken as an introduction rather than an analysis of the issues concerned. My presentation will be better understood if I first provide the context of our work in the European Commission. We have been in charge of the programmes IMPACT and IMPACT 2, which over the last eight years have been contributing to the creation of a single, competitive and fast-growing European information market.

The kind of data we deal with are data collected and provided as information products and services, mostly but not exclusively in electronic form, for professional users or for the public at large. DG XIII is concerned with data in many other forms, be it public and private libraries, technology transfer information, information on R&D projects in the E.U., or questions concerning linguistics, telecommunications, information and computer technology or security aspects. There are important economic and legal issues involved in all these fields.

2   INFORMATION MARKET : LEGAL ISSUES

As I am in charge of a sector that deals with the legal issues of the information market, this article will focus on those. Most of them are valid to a larger or smaller extent, both for the other fields I mentioned and certainly for scientific data that form an important part of the information services addressed to professionals.

The crux of the matter can be summarized in seven statements.

1.   Legal and economic aspects are very closely interlinked.
2.   In the past much attention was given to technology infrastructure and not so much to information content. This seems to be changing now.
3.   The information sector is one of the fastest growing economic sectors and is counted upon to become the spearhead of the European Union's effort to achieve high rates of growth, competitiveness and employment.
4.   This will be possible if the different legal issues concerned are successfully dealt with.
5.   These issues are mainly intellectual property rights, access to information rights, protection of personal data, fair competition, consumer protection and legal aspects of information security.
6.   Legal solutions are required, in the first place, in most cases. Technology has reached a point, however, in which legal solutions may no longer be enough. They have to be supported by technical and organizational initiatives.
7.   Last but not least, legal and other solutions, cannot be at national, nor even at the European level; they have to take international developments seriously into account.

3   ECONOMIC ISSUES : THE INFORMATION SOCIETY

That economic and legal issues are closely interlinked hardly needs any further elaboration. Whatever investment is put into creating an information product, it will hardly ever be recovered, let alone give profit, unless unauthorized usage and reselling is protected against or unless legal regulations, for example concerning personal data protection or public morals, allow its commercialization or unless consumers feel confident about using this product. More on all these later. At this stage we should note that the European Commission's White Book on Growth, Competitiveness and Employment, the recommendations of the senior personalities group chaired by Commissioner Bangemann and the conclusions of the heads of state or government European Council meeting in Corfu, all have as a central theme the creation of the so-called Information Society.

4   THE BANGEMANN GROUP REPORT : INTELLECTUAL PROPERTY RIGHTS (IPR)

Thus, the current and expected role of the information sector is more than adequately stressed. I quote only a few phrases from the Bangemann group report: "Throughout the world, information and communications technologies are generating a new industrial revolution already as significant and far reaching as those of the past.... The first countries to enter the information society will reap the greatest rewards. They will set the agenda for all who must follow. By contrast, countries which temporize, or favor half-hearted solutions, could, in less than a decade, face disastrous declines in investment and a squeeze on jobs."

As regards overall expectations, the report summarizes them as follows:

- A more caring European Society with a significantly higher quality of life and a wider choice of services and entertainment.
- New ways for the content creators to exercise their creativity as the information society calls into being new products and services.
- New opportunities for Europe's regions to express their cultural traditions and identities and, for those standing on the geographical periphery of the Union, a minimizing of distance and remoteness.
- More efficient, transparent and responsible public services, closer to the citizen and at lower cost.
- For European business and SMEs, more effective management and organization, access to training and other services, data links with customers and suppliers generating greater competitiveness.
- For Europe's telecommunications operators, the capacity to supply an ever wider range of new, high value-added services; and finally,
- New and strongly-growing markets at home and abroad for the products of the equipment and software suppliers, the computer and consumer electronic industries.

A few figures will illustrate the information sector's economic potential (and I speak of the information content services only), but also the need for urgent action in the light of international competition. Between 1986 and 1990, turnover in the European electronic information services has been growing annually between 20-30 % (there was a relative slackening to 13% in the last of these years, due to specific short-term circumstances). Between 1980-91 the number of databases and hosts worldwide rose from 400 d/b and 59 h to over 5000 d/b and 730 h. Although world production and distribution of databases is very much concentrated in the highly developed economies of North America and the European Union, the differences between these two are still striking. North American figures of databases, database producers and hosts are nearly double the European figures. This is basically because of linguistic, technical and regulatory barriers that still keep the European market fragmented. A lot has been done over the last few years at the initiative of the European Commission to overcome this fragmentation, but a lot more remains to be done. Here it should be stressed that large scale projects very similar to the European Union's Information Society project and called National Information Infrastructure are in progress in the U.S. and in Japan and that interconnection of these will be on the agenda of the next G7 meeting.

The Bangemann Group report has made, and the European Council has accepted, a number of recommendations relating to full liberalization of networks and services, interconnection and interoperability, promotion of joint public/private sector ventures, measures to foster a critical mass for investment and to secure a worldwide dimension for the information society.

5   IPR IN THE INFORMATION SOCIETY

The report also focuses on a number of legal issues, on which we have been working for some years, but which acquire a new dimension as a result of these political but also current technological developments.

First, protection of intellectual property rights. In the information and communications technologics fields, the Commission proposed and the Council adopted in 1991 a directive on the legal protection of computer programmes. It also proposed (and the amended version dates from 4 October 1993) a directive on the legal protection of databases. Intellectual property rights concern of course first and foremost the authors of databases who should be encouraged to continue their creative work. They also concern authors of copyrighted works that are included in these databases, competitors in the market, who should not be faced with unjustified monopoly situations; and users (including consumers) who want access to a choice of reasonably priced database services. A particular complication concerns those databases which do not meet the criteria of form originality that would entitle them to copyright protection. The proposed directive has taken all these interests and problems into account. First, it applies to all databases. To those databases which do not meet the copyright criteria, but also to those who do, it gives a separate right against unauthorized copying. In this way, the large majority of databases that are important not because of their form (the selection and arrangement of data), but because of their information content and the effort and money invested, will also be protected.

Discussion on this draft directive at Council working group level is progressing, so that adoption by the Council may reasonably be expected for 1995.

The Information Society prospect, especially the globalisation of markets and networks, raises many new IPR questions, both legal and non-legal. These include (among many others).

    a.   The scope of protection, until now traditionally extending to a given national territory;

    b.   Identifying the location in which an infringement has taken place and the national law which should apply to that infringement;

    c.   Existing intellectual property rights (patents and copyright) over many elements (standards, interfaces) which are essential to the interoperability of the networks;

    d.   Technical protection devices (ex: the Commission co-funded CITED project) for the identification, monitoring and exploitation of IPRs - these are useful, even necessary, for authors but should not undermine other existing interests (competitors, users) or impede the free flow of data on the information superhighways;

    e.   Exploitation of IPRs through collective management; this is increasingly important since in certain cases (e.g. multimedia) there are many thousands of rightholders concerned for creating a single new product;

    f.   Moral rights will be of increasing importance, as regards reproduction and adaptation of works, given the ease with which digitized works can be manipulated;

    g.   Works created with computer assistance, especially products derived from expert systems and artificial intelligence, may create problems for the traditional understanding of IPR concerning exclusively creations by a human author.

For all these issues the Commission is launching a large scale consultation exercise that will include publication of a Green Paper on "IPRs in the Information Society", in order to assess the need for possible new proposals.

6   ACCESS TO PUBLIC SECTOR INFORMATION

Access to information is a very wide issue that, from a legal viewpoint, includes basic human rights, consumer protection, intellectual property, privacy and confidentiality, competition and penal law aspects. Here I will contain myself to a specific issue, that of access to public sector information. The public sector, in the context of its tasks, is the biggest producer of information which interests both the citizens and the private sector and in particular private sector information providers who add value and resell it. In the U.S.A. there is a Freedom of Information Act which gives a basic right of access to all these interested parties, regardless of vested interest or intended use.

There is also a very detailed federal government policy, which covers issues like tarification, format and presentation. This combination of law and policy has had a substantial influence on the U.S. information market. In the E.U., some countries have only access laws, some have only policies, some have both (but not related to each other) and some have neither. There is one E.U. Directive giving right of access to environmental information, and there are guidelines for improving the synergy between the public and private sectors in the information market. It is clear that if government is to become more transparent and an information society created at European level, this situation has to be improved and cover, if possible, the whole range of public sector information. We are now studying possible action options and will arrive at basic proposals by next year.

7   PERSONAL DATA PROTECTION

Personal data (or privacy) protection has until recently been an underestimated issue considered to be basically a human rights question. It may largely be so, but its economic aspects are considerable. The more personal information processing and communication possibilities are expanded, the more risks appear for privacy and, therefore, the more there is need for sufficient legal protection. This is now generally accepted. Protection should be equivalent within the European Union, otherwise there may be barriers to information flows between Member States and market distortions in favor of Member States having low level or no protection, and thus encouraging operations that in other Member States would be impossible or would require special procedures.

Moreover, particular attention should be given to personal data transfers to countries with no sufficient data protection in order to avoid circumvention of national laws and creation of unfair competition advantages in these countries. The European Commission has proposed a draft Directive for personal data protection (the amended version dates from 15 October 1992), negotiations on which are now reaching completion and should result in adoption by the Council in 1995.

Furthermore a sectoral draft directive on personal data protection concerning ISDN (RNIS) networks and mobile telephony has also been proposed, since it has been established that the general directive must be followed by special initiatives on specific sectors. Other sectoral initiatives may thus follow later. As with intellectual property, legal instruments must be supplemented with technical measures that will facilitate control of personal data processing. Traditional control systems of registering personal data with national supervisory authorities will not be enough, given the current and expected rate of personal data processing and communication internationally. In the scientific field personal data are not often relevant, but there are some very striking exceptions, for example genetic information or information on AIDS.

Fair competition principles are fairly simple and well-known. Basically there should be no abuse of dominant position in a given market. In the information field, the situation is somewhat complicated by laws concerning media concentration and pluralism, which put certain conditions for media ownership. All these provisions may have to be re-examined in the light of developments basically in North America and, subsequently, in Europe. Telecommunications, cable TV and publishing companies join forces to provide multimedia information products and services internationally. Competition and pluralism issues may now have to be seen at global rather than regional or even national levels.

8   CONSUMER PROTECTION AND SECURITY SYSTEMS

Consumer protection issues are relevant and have already been touched upon in relation to intellectual property, access, privacy and competition law. There are other consumer related issues: transparency with regard to information content and tarification; liability in cases of damage caused by erroneous information, poor service. Such issues need to be tackled, especially for public information services where there are no contract relationships between the providers and users.

In a global context where all citizens, professionals, scientists, business and public bodies anywhere in the world with a PC can access all publicly available information sources, it is important that appropriate security systems be established to prevent unauthorized access, abuse and eventual damage to the accessibility, integrity and confidentiality, as the case may be, of the information concerned. Encryption is one possible security measure. The increased use of encryption will protect from hacking into the system in order to avoid payment or to obtain confidential information. On the other hand, governments may need powers to override encryption for the purposes of fighting crime and protecting national security. A European solution is needed which will provide a global answer to this problem, both dissuading potential hackers and clarifying conditions for state interference.

CONCLUSION

Although it has been very active on the technical and organizational side of information security, the European Commission has so far maintained a low profile as regards the legal aspects, since delicate penal law issues are involved. Important work has been undertaken by the OECD and, especially, the Council of Europe in Strasbourg. The Commission will, however, re-examine the situation in the light of the Bangemann Group recommendations and the Corfu summit conclusions.My last point will concern the need for international cooperation. Global networks and services require global legal approaches. Beyond the measures to be taken by the European Union, appropriate solutions will have to be found internationally. There are four multilateral bodies where these issues may be discussed, the GATT, (now the WTO) the World Intellectual Property Organization, the Council of Europe, the OECD, and there are bilateral discussions with our commercial partners. The Commission has been active in all these fora with a view to ensuring that the European Union gets a fair share of Information Society benefits.

KEYWORDS

Information society, intellectual property, access, personal data, encryption, IPR.

Author's postscript. The personal data protection directive was adapted (24 July 1995); the legal protection of databases directive has reached the stage of a common position; a broad-ranging green paper on IPR in the Information Society was published by the Commission and a new four year programme, INFO 2000, was proposed by the Commission including an action line on access to public sector information.

Guidelines of a European Meteorological Services Policy on Data Exchange

Bartolomé ORFILA

European Climate Support Network INM, Apdo. 285, Madrid 28040, Spain

Abstract

The European Meteorological Services have a long history of successful international data exchange that is expected not only to continue but also increase. Some practical limitation to this exchange has existed in the past and will continue because the volume of data exchange must be restricted to that financially justified. In the frame of WMO, this subject is widely considered and, following their resolutions and guidelines, the European Meteorological Services are adopting the corresponding data exchange policies to be followed by them and by those organizations such as the ECMWF, EUMETSAT, ECSN and ECOMET.

Resume

Les Services Européens de Métrologie (EMS) ont une longue histoire internationale d'échanges de données dont il faut espérer le maintien mais aussi l'intensification. Quelques limitations pratiques de ces échanges ont existé dans le passé et se maintiendront en raison du volume des échanges de données dont on cherche à limiter l'importance pour des raisons financières justifiées. Dans le cadre du WMO, le sujet est largement débattu, à partir de ses résolutions et de règles proposées, les services (EMS) ont adopté des politiques d'échanges de données à suivre pour leurs actions. Elles sont également retenues par d'autres organisations telles que ECMWF, EUMETSAT, ECSN et ECOMET.

1   Introduction

Meteorological Services have a long history, in some cases extending over 150 years, of successful international data exchange on a global basis. This exchange of data started long before the World Meteorological Organization (WMO) was funded and reiterated the guiding principle of free exchange of certain data between all WMO members.

The wish and intention of the European Meteorological Services participating in the European Centre for Medium Range Weather Forecasts (ECMWF), European

Organization for the Exploitation of Meteorological Satellites (EUMETSAT and European Climate Support Network (ECSN) is that the exchange of data shall not only continue but also increase. The increase is necessary because of the growing need for all nations of the world to understand weather and global climate and because increased quantities of data are essential in order to achieve this understanding. In order that data exchange may continue to grow it is essential to safeguard and increase the relevant databases.

2   RATIONALE FOR A EUROPEAN METEOROGICAL SERVICES POLICY ON DATA EXCHANGE

Although the Meteorological Services have for more than a century practiced the free and open exchange of data, that practice has always been subject to practical limitations. It has never been the case that all data are exchanged. Each national service provides data as agreed internationally, through WMO or bilateral agreements, serving international needs. Each service invariably generates additional observational data needed for local purposes and does not exchange them internationally. Similarly, derived products, including analyses and forecasts, are usually tailored for national use and only a selection are subject to international exchange. This approach is expected to continue since the volume of data exchange must be restricted to that needed by the participants. There are good practical reasons for this restriction, one of which is that the transfer of unnecessary data cannot be justified financially.

In recent years there have been important new developments which affect the practice of data exchange. Three are stressed as of particular concern to European National Meteorological Services in formulating their data policies.

a.   The first is that the nature of observational data and other products has changed out of all recognition over recent decades. Originally observations made in one particular national territory, were of greatest interest for that individual territory and of lesser importance for neighboring areas. Similarly forecasts were until quite recently regional in nature. Now there are satellites which observe the entire world and are not restricted to one territory and at many centres forecasts are made on a global basis. This development, together with the growing importance of global change research and climate monitoring, makes it also necessary to re-examine the rationale and practice of date exchange.

b.   The second development is that certain developments in meteorology are so expensive that European nations have come together to share resources in specific fields. They share the high cost of research and operations in medium range forecasting through funding of the ECMWF. They also share the cost of obtaining satellite data through participation in the EUMETSAT. This voluntary cooperation immediately raises an important problem. If any country not a member of ECMWF or EUMETSAT can receive all their data freely, the motivation to belong to either organization and pay the large membership contributions vanishes, with the result that probably the programmes would eventually collapse. EUMETSAT and ECMWF data policies must therefore include sufficient motivation for contributing to their programmes, to ensure that they continue to enhance the global database. The rights and benefits of membership must be worth the financial contribution.

c. The third development is the growing tendency towards commercial meteorological activities, both in the public and private sectors. By tradition the public sector not only provides a service to the user community, it also maintains the system and the database on which the service is based. By contrast the private sector has no obligation to maintain the system or the database. Certain National Meteorological Services NMSs are under tremendous pressure to ensure that services are provided on a fully commercial basis and that income is used to offset costs. They cannot expect to receive any income if they can be subject to competition from entities which use all of the data but do not contribute to the costs of the database and which can therefore provide services at much lower prices. Therefore the commercial issue must be addressed if the global database is to be maintained and increased.

3   WMO RESOLUTIONS ON DATA EXCHANGE POLICY

The way to face this new situation, that is more general and not limited to the European National Meteorological Services, has been widely discussed in many forums and specially, in the last two years, by WMO. So, in its WMO forty sixth Executive Committee meeting, held in Geneva in June 1994, the following set of resolutions were approved. They will be submitted to the decision of the next Congress in June 1995.

1. WMO policy on the exchange of meteorological and related data and products.(Resolution 17/1)

2. A proposed new practice for the exchange of meteorological and related data and products. (Resolution 17/2)

3. WMO guidelines on commercial activities to protect the cooperative and supportive relations among NMSs in facing different national approaches to the growth of commercial activities in some countries. (Resolution 17/3)

The resolution on WMO policy reads,

"As a fundamental principle of the World Meteorological Organization (WMO) and in consonance with the expanding requirements for its scientific and technical expertise, the WMO commits itself to broadening and enhancing the free and unrestricted international exchange of meteorological data and products"

The data and products exchanged under the auspices of the new practice will be identified as Tier 1 and Tier 2 information. The complete requirements of WMO Members for meteorological and related data and products to sustain their WMO Programme activities will be met by the combined exchange of Tier 1 and Tier 2 information.

Within the practice:

1. The NMSs of each WMO Member shall identify a set of meteorological and related data and products which it will make available for distribution internationally to other Members without charge and with no restrictions or conditions on the use to which the data and products are put. These data and products will be referred to as Tier 1 data and products and will be defined by each Member taking into consideration guidelines approved by Congress.

2. A further set of meteorological and related data and products, to be referred to as Tier 2 data and products, may be identified by the NMSs of each WMO member and made available for distribution internationally to other Members. Tier 2 data and products will be made available without charge but only on the condition that they not be re-exported by the receiver for commercial purposes, directly or subsequently, to the territory of the Member or of the group of Members forming a single legal territory, that produced them.

In addition to the above Tier 1 and Tier 2 sets of data and products distributed to Members to sustain their WMO Programme activities, other meteorological and related information may be exchanged on a bilateral or multilateral basis between NMSs according to agreements between the parties. These data and products are exchanged outside the international exchange of Tier 1 and 2 data and products.

4　　CASE OF THE EUROPEAN METEOROGICAL SERVICES : ECMWF, EUMEMSAT AND ECSN

For the European NMSs, the decisions on the distribution of these other data rest on the Directors of the NMSs and in the Councils and Board of the three aforementioned Institutions. They are reflected in framework agreements. The case of the ECSN, for instance, follows the next guidelines.

" To the furthest possible extent, the Members of ECSN will undertake to make quality controlled and, if possible, homogenized data and products available for climate research at the most favorable terms and under conditions described in the corresponding model licensing agreement to entities involved in the climate research projects and those producing climate databases for non-commercial climate research, recognized by ECSN."

5   ECOMET

On the other hand, to tackle the commercial aspects several European NMSs are proceeding to create a new organization, called ECOMET which is expected to be formally launched early in 1996. Its objectives are:

   a.   The creation of a unique European-wide meteorological market.

   b.   To maintain and develop the free exchange of meteorological data sets and products within the framework of WMO.

   c.   To expand the availability of meteorological information for the European Private Sector.

   d.   To have all users contribute to the meteorological infrastructure cost.

ECOMET is seen as a mechanism that brings advantages and economic benefits to several groups:

   •   to National Meteorological Services, by providing a legal and fair basis on which to operate commercial services;

   •   to the private sector, by giving guarantees of easy and continuing access to the necessary basic data and information on which their services depend;

   •   to taxpayers, through recovery of some of the high meteorological infrastructure costs;

   •   and most importantly to the customers, by increasing the range, and improving the standard of services.

CONCLUSION : RECENT DECISIONS

The WMO congress held in June 1995 ratified the policy described under 3 above. Tier 1 data receives now the name of "essential" data and Tier 2 the name of "additional" data. The congress also endorsed that no restrictions be applied in the use of essential and additional data for research and education purposes.

In December 1994, the ECMWF Council approved the rules governing the distribution and dissemination of ECMWF real time products. For non real-time products the rules approved by the Council in November 1980 are still in force.

The EUMETSAT Council held in November 1994 approved the conditions of real time access to EUMEMSAT high resolution images (HRI) data outside the EUMEMSAT Member States and, throughout 1995, has made good progress in preparing an update of the 1991 approved EUMEMSAT data policy for non-NMS users in the Member States.

In July 1995, the ECSN Board approved the ECSN recommandations for the availability and provision of Members' data and products for Climate Research within Member States.

KEYWORDS

Meteorological services, data exchange policy, commercialization, WMO, ECOMET, EUMETSAT, ECMWF, ECSN.

REFERENCES

[1]   Douglas A., Devernet F., Hoenson R., Potential economic benefits from the introduction of ECOMET. Conference on the economic benefits of Meteorological and Hydrological Services. WMO/TD/N_ 630, Geneve (1994).

[2]   ECSN guidelines on a data exchange policy. Decision of the Fourth ECSN Board meeting held in June (1994).

[3]   Eumetsat Data Policy as agreed by the 15th Eumetsat Council, EUMETSAT, Darmstadt (1991).

[4]   Resolution 17/1, WMO policy on the exchange of meteorological and related data and products. EC-XLVI WMO Executive Council, Abridged Report and Resolutions, Geneve (1994).

[5]   Resolution 17/2, Proposed new practice for the exchange of meteorological and related data and products. EC-XLVI WMO Executive Council, Abridged Report and Resolutions, Geneve (1994).

[6]   Resolution 17/3, WMO guidelines on commercial activities, EC-XLVI WMO Executive Council, Abridged Report and Resolutions, Geneve (1994).

[7]   Resolution 40, WMO policy and practice for exchange of Meterorogical data and related data and products including guidelines on relationships in commercial meteorogical activities, C9-XII WMO Congress, Abridged Report and Resolutions, Geneve (1995).

[8]   Resolution of the ECMWF Council Rules governing the distribution and dissemination of the ECMWF real-time products, Reading, Dec. (1994)

[9]   Resolution EUM/C/94/Res.I Conditions of Real Time access to EUMEMSAT HRI data outside the EUMETSAT MEMBER STATES, EUMETSAT, Darmstadt (1991)

[10]   ECSN Decision of the Sixth Board meeting Recommendations for the availability and provision of the Members' data and products for Climate Research within Member States, Madrid, July (1994)

Chapter 3

DISTRIBUTED DATA AND INFORMATION NETWORKS

INTEGRATED GROUND-BASED AND REMOTELY SENSED DATA TO SUPPORT GLOBAL STUDIES OF ENVIRONMENTAL CHANGE[1]

Richard. J. OLSON, Robert. S. TURNER and Charles. T. GARTEN,Jr.

Environmental Sciences Division Oak Ridge National Laboratory Oak Ridge, Tennessee 37831 U.S.A.

ABSTRACT

Global studies of environmental change require integrated databases of multiple data types that are accurately coordinated in terms of spatial, temporal and thematic properties. Such datasets must be designed and developed jointly by scientific researchers, computer specialists, and policy analysts. The presentation focuses on our approach for organizing data from ground-based research programs so that the data can be linked with remotely sensed data and other map data into integrated databases with spatial, temporal, and thematic characteristics relevant to global studies. The development of an integrated database for Net Primary Productivity is described to illustrate the process.

[1] Research sponsored by the National Aeronautics and Space Administration under Interagency Agreement DOE No. 2013-F044-A1 under Martin Marietta Energy System, Inc., contract DE-AC05-84OR21400 with the U.S. Department of Energy.

RESUME

Les études globales des changements de l'environnement imposent l'accès à des bases de données intégrées de données à caractères multiples, qui sont coordonnées de façon rigoureuse et portent sur les propriétés spatiales, temporelles et thématiques. De tels ensembles de données doivent être conçus et développés par des chercheurs scientifiques, des experts informatiques et analystes planificateurs. L'article est centré sur notre approche pour organiser les données à partir de recherches fondamentales de façon à pouvoir relier ces données effectuées au sol avec celles obtenues à distance et autre données cartographiques dans des bases de données intégrées regroupant des caractéristiques spatiales, temporelles et thématiques propres aux études globales. Le développement d'une base de données intégrées pour "Net Primary Productivity" est décrit pour illustrer le processus de création.

1   INTRODUCTION

Data centers routinely archive and distribute large databases of high quality and with rigorous documentation but, to meet the needs of global studies effectively and efficiently, data centers must go beyond these traditional roles. Global studies of environmental change require integrated databases of multiple data types that are accurately coordinated in terms of spatial, temporal and thematic properties. Such datasets must be designed and developed jointly by scientific researchers, computer specialists, and policy analysts. The presentation focuses on our approach for organizing data from ground-based research programs so that the data can be linked with remotely sensed data and other map data into integrated databases with spatial, temporal, and thematic characteristics relevant to global studies. The development of an integrated database for Net Primary Productivity (NPP) is described to illustrate the process.

2   DISTRIBUTED ACTIVE ARCHIVE CENTERS (DAACs)

The United States Government has initiated the U.S. Global Change Research Program to develop a predictive understanding of the global environment. A pivotal part of the program is the National Aeronautics and Space Administration's (NASA) Mission to Planet Earth with the Earth Observing System (EOS). The NASA Earth Observing System Data and Information System (EOSDIS) manages data from satellites and field measurement programs.

EOSDIS is composed of nine Distributed Active Archive Centers (DAACs) that provide data to the global change research community, policy makers, educators, and interested members of the public.

Each DAAC focuses on an Earth science discipline and specializes in one or several types of data and data products, which are often associated with specific NASA flight missions. The DAACs became operational in July 1994 to form a physically distributed archive and distribution system linked through a system-wide information management system.

3   OAK RIDGE NATIONAL LABORATORY DACC

The mission of the Oak Ridge National Laboratory (ORNL) DAAC is to archive and distribute data pertaining to the Earth's biogeochemical dynamics, specifically data acquired from ground-based measurements of biological and chemical interactions among the elements that comprise the Earth system.

The ORNL DAAC provides (1) an information management system that is integrally linked to the other DAACs, (2) a data archive and distribution system, (3) a user services function, (4) value-added products that summarize and synthesize biogeochemical dynamics data from around the globe, and (5) the capability to provide guidance and support for data management, data quality assurance, and data integration for field experiments.   Preparing data entails acquisition, quality assurance, documentation, and archiving to produce complete packages of data and metadata for distribution.

Data available through the ORNL DAAC include data from ground-based, NASA-funded projects as well as data generated by other agencies in the United States and other countries. Current and future holdings include data from the First ISLSCP Field Experiment (FIFE), the Oregon Transect Ecosystem Research (OTTER) Project, the Boreal Ecosystem-Atmosphere Study (BOREAS), and the Carbon Dioxide Information Analysis Center (CDIAC).

The FIFE project collected data to understand the biophysical processes controlling the exchanges of radiation, moisture, and carbon dioxide between the land surface and the atmosphere; to develop and test remote-sensing methodologies for observing these processes at a pixel level; and to help understand how to scale the pixel level information to regional scales commensurate with the modeling of global processes.

The OTTER project estimated major fluxes of carbon, nitrogen, and water in forest ecosystems using an ecosystem-process model driven by remotely sensed data.

The BOREAS project investigates the interactions between the boreal forest biome and the atmosphere.

The CDIAC provides access to information related to atmospheric trace-gas concentrations and global climate change. The preponderance of the CDIAC data deal with historic and atmospheric carbon dioxide and methane concentrations and historic weather and climate readings from throughout the world.

4   INTEGRATED DATABASES

Environmental data are collected by a variety of agencies and organizations for specific mission-oriented requirements.   To be useful for assessing global environmental issues, it is necessary to assemble and organize selected data into integrated databases.   Scientists use integrated data to study across systems, parameterize models, verify model output, and conduct regional assessments. Decision makers require ready access to information on a variety of topics to develop policy and often do not have the time to wait for the completion of definitive scientific studies.   Educators need easy access to information for teaching. To meet these user needs, the ORNL DAAC goes beyond the traditional data center role to design and compile integrated databases that meet the needs of these users. Integrated databases are packaged datasets with an organizing framework; that is, each component dataset conforms to a common set of characteristics, including :

1.   **Spatial** - both extent of coverage (e.g., Europe) and resolution (e.g., countries or common pixel size),

2.   **Temporal** - both extent of time period (e.g., 1980s) and resolution (e.g., annual averages or totals), and

3.   **Thematic** - general level of detail (e.g., if land cover is classified into a few major types then soils would be aggregated to major categories).

Defining the framework involves working with the data user community to incorporate their needs for the integrated database. The iterative design process must often reflect diverse user needs, unknown future needs, and data availability. Although the design and resulting database may not meet all users' needs, it usually will provide users with an initial data resource that can be expanded for more specific needs.

Integrated databases usually reside in a single database management system with tools for retrieval, report generation, analysis, display, geographic information systems (GIS), and export functions.

Metadata document the source of each data component, describe the data collection and processing, and define data characteristics. Compiling the integrated database may require an extensive effort for each component, including acquiring data, reformatting, performing QA checks, converting to common units of measure, assigning common code values, resolving problems with the data generator, aggregating or extrapolating data to common spatial and temporal units, and documenting sources of data and processing (see Carter and Diamondstone 1990). The processing and packaging of the data add value to the original component data sets in terms of consistency, completeness, documentation, and availability for secondary use of the data.

5   TERRESTRIAL NET PRIMARY PRODUCTION DATABASE

Data on spatial patterns of terrestrial net primary production (NPP) and on rates of carbon accumulation are essential for a fuller understanding of the potential extent and impacts of global changes. NPP is the amount of organic matter synthesized per unit of area of the Earth's surface per unit of time. The spatial pattern of mean NPP varies greatly over the Earth from 0 g dry mass/m^2 per year in extreme deserts to 3000 g dry mass/m^2 per year in swamps and marshes. Uncertainty in the current estimates of carbon storage in the Earth's vegetation and soils may account for the carbon that currently is unaccounted for in the global carbon budget.

Potential uses of a NPP database are the calibration and validation of remotely sensed patterns and model predictions of terrestrial productivity associated with global change. Successful remote sensing of terrestrial carbon dynamics requires the development of methodologies and models that relate the spectral properties of plant canopies to ecosystem processes like NPP. Ground-based measurements of NPP are essential for meeting the challenge of scaling up from small ecosystem studies to large regional scales. To meet these needs, the ORNL DAAC is working with several groups to design and develop an integrated NPP database, including the ORNL DAAC User Working Group and modelers participating in the 1994 Model Inter-Comparison Workshop for Global Terrestrial Net Primary Productivity.

A major recommendation from that workshop was to develop common datasets to parameterize the global models. The NPP database will provide in situ measurements from terrestrial ecosystems for merging with remote sensing measurements from aircraft and satellite platforms. For example, the Pathfinder Advanced Very High Resolution Radiometer (AVHRR) Land Data Set at Goddard Space Flight Center contains NDVI (normalized difference vegetation index) data from satellites. A recent study used a parametric approach to combine estimates of canopy absorption efficiency of incoming solar radiation from NDVI data with estimates of conversion efficiency to calculate the production of organic matter (Ruimy et al. 1994).

The estimates of conversion efficiencies for broad biomes were obtained from the literature. Although the modeled results generally agreed with previous estimates of NPP, significant differences appeared in the spatial patterns. The authors identify the lack of available data as one source of uncertainty in their results.

In recognition of the need for this type of data, the International Union of Forest Research Organizations (IUFRO) has initiated an international cooperative project to coordinate data formats of studies of woody plant productivity. The NPP database will be compiled from the scientific literature and from regional thematic maps. Information in the database will include (when available from published sources) the following: physical location, time of study, elevation, annual precipitation, plant community type, biome, country or political division, principal investigator or author, reference or publication, plant biomass, NPP, associated measurements (e.g., leaf-area index, solar radiation, plant nitrogen), soil type, and funding agency. Distinctions will be made between aboveground, belowground, and total plant carbon stores. The initial emphasis will be on acquiring data from major terrestrial biomes from published compilations such as Cannell (1982) and DeAngelis et al. (1981).

CONCLUSION

The NPP database will be available from the ORNL DAAC. Scientists needing data sets for global analysis, methods development, or simulation modeling are encouraged to make full use of resources available from the DAAC. In addition to data that are being gathered for specific EOSDIS goals, environmental scientists also have an opportunity to archive their data in the ORNL DAAC. The staff at the ORNL DAAC will work with scientists entering data and metadata into the system. Contributors will be acknowledged as data base "authors." Individuals wishing to contribute data or to learn more about the data center can inquire by e-mail at ornldaac@ornl.gov, by phone at 615-241-3952, or by FAX at 615-574-4665.

KEYWORDS

Database, integrated data, environmental, global change, assessments, archive centers.

REFERENCES

[1]   Cannell M.G.R., World Forest Biomass and Primary Production Data, Academic Press, London (1982).
[2]   Carter G.C., Diamondstone B. I., Directions for Internationally Compatible Environmental Data, Hemisphere Publishing Corp., New York (1990).
[3]   De Angelis D.L., Gardner R.H., Shugart H.H., Productivity of Forest Ecosystems Studied during the IBP: The Woodlands Data Set, in International Biological Programme 23, Dynamic Properties of Forest Ecosystems, Reichle D.E. (ed) Cambridge University Press, Cambridge London, pp. 573-672 (1981).
[4]   Ruimy A., De Dieu G., Saugier B., Methodology for the Estimation of Terrestrial Net Primary Production from Remotely Sensed Data, J. of Geophysical Research, 99:5263:83 (1994).

CRITICAL FACTORS FOR THE USE OF PUBLIC DATABASES

Arild JANSEN and Pål SORGAARD

Finnmark College, University of Oslo and Norwegian Computing Center[1] , Norway

ABSTRACT

In spite of the increasing importance of information technology, there are several example of failures. Systems are built with unrealistic assumptions about individual and organizational behavior. Public databases are important mediators of information. We use a media metaphor for databases to derive a model where we can identify a series of conditions for the well-functioning of public databases. These conditions are not easily met in practical work with such databases. One should therefore be careful with ambitions regarding the design, use and impact of information technology.

RESUME

En dépit de l'importance croissante des technologies de l'information, on connaît quelques échecs. Les systèmes sont bâtis avec des hypothèses non réalistes de comportement des individus ou des organisations. Les banques de données publiques sont d'importants médiateurs de l'information. Nous avons utilisé une métaphore médiatique pour les bases de données afin de développer un modèle pour lequel on puisse identifier une série de conditions pour un bon fonctionnement de ces banques de données. Ces conditions ne sont pas aisèment trouvées dans la pratique de telles bases de données.

1   INTRODUCTION

CODATA addresses the issues of data and knowledge in a changing world, and is specifically concerned with how our environment can be improved, and how modern

---

1 Contact addresses: Arild Jansen, Dept. of Information Technology, Finnmark College, Follums vei 1, N-9500 Alta, Norway; arild@hifm.no.

Pål Sørgaard, Department of Informatics, University of Oslo, PO Box 1080 Blindern, N-0316 Oslo, Norway; paalso@ifi.uio.no.

information technology can contribute to increased awareness of environmental issues when important decisions are made. We fully share these concerns. It turns out, however, that having relevant data in some database does not guarantee the use of these data in actual decision-making. In this paper we will explore some reasons why public databases are not always used as intended. Some conclusions may seem pessimistic, but the aim is a constructive one: successful application of information technology requires attention to a broad range of issues beyond the purely technical ones.

The use of information systems, and information technology in general, has increased rapidly in the Western, industrialized world in past years. There is a broad range of application areas. Intuitively, the potential of the technology is large, and as prices continue to fall, more and more applications become feasible. We address use, and especially lack of use, of databases in the public sector. We do not discuss interfaces and detailed design (where there might be a lot to do), but we focus on the organizational and to some extent political context where information systems are being used.

Public information is a necessary part of a democracy. The Norwegian parliament has laid down a set of principles for an information policy of the Norwegian public administration. This policy states as its goals: "to provide the citizens and the businesses real access to information about public activities and about personal rights, obligations and possibilities. Equal access to information is a basic prerequisite in ensuring everybody equal opportunities to participate in democratic processes" [12]. It has the potential to provide everybody with the same access to public information, and can thus play an important role in the implementation of this policy. We must, however, realize that the capabilities to manage the technology, and to get access to information are not equally distributed [13]. Appropriate attention to this question is needed if we want databases to support such democratic goals.

In the literature, there is a broad range of analyses of the role of information and information systems.

In a thought provoking paper, Feldman and March present an analysis of how information may act as a *signal and symbol* to the surroundings [6]. It may be more important to *appear as a user* of information than actually to *use it*. By requesting information (not necessarily using it), decision makers maintain an image (to themselves and to their surroundings) as rational decision makers. Feldman and March further note that people are seldom criticized for demanding too much information, whereas the failure to obtain information that turned out to be relevant for a case is considered a major mistake.

Cohen, March, and Olsen use a ``*garbage can"* metaphor in their analysis of decisions in organizations [5]. They see a decision as a result of a suitable mix of problems, solutions, participants, and choice opportunities. They reject the rational view of decisions as generation of alternatives, examination of consequences, followed by optimal choice between these alternatives.

Bøgh Andersen views databases as a kind of *communication medium* [2]. The medium is not a simple channel from sender to receiver operating in real time, but in essence, what goes on is communication between a group of senders and a group of receivers. Clearly, aggregation and other operations on the data further blur the identity of the senders, but this does not reduce the validity of the analysis.

Often, it is quietly ignored that people have their own interests, and that they therefore do not necessarily share all data, nor do they always make their utmost effort to provide correct data to the information systems. Ciborra has applied the transaction cost theory to the field of information systems to get a framework where *opportunistic behavior* is explicitly recognized [4]. In a related vein, Orlikowski has analyzed the use of a groupware tool and identified a contradiction between the support for sharing information supported by the tool and the highly competitive environment at the work place she analyzed [11].

In the Finnish Knowledge and work project there was a deliberate focus on how information systems were used in real work [9]. In the study of a storehouse it was shown that the system did not align well with the work as it was performed. The workers therefore had to do rather advanced circumventing actions in order to get the system to behave as they wanted [8]. In many cases this involved entering ``wrong'' data into the system, and keeping track of the discrepancies of the system's beliefs and the real state of the warehouse.

2   THE CHAIN OF MEDIATION

Data, collected at the source, have a long way to go before they become information which is perceived, interpreted and understood by the user. Several processes are involved, from the acquisition of data at the source, via the retrieval of a report from a database, transport through a network, and lastly, to the interpretation of the data by the user in the context of his/her specific problem area.

One important key to understand these processes is to distinguish between *data, information* and *knowledge*.

By data, we mean the physical representation of information, e.g. as carvings in a rock, the printed words in a book, or the bits in a computer. Information is organized data, as meaning, facts or figures communicated and interpreted by people, while knowledge is something which is processed, digested and internalized by a human recipient or an intelligent software. Weizenbaum claims that data becomes information *in the light of a hypothesis,* and says "the way knowledge is put into a computer clearly reflects someone's hypothesis" [14]. He goes further by saying: "What happens with the organization of knowledge in the computer is that the organization itself, that is the whole system, very rapidly becomes incomprehensible. This is because a large scale organization's data, information and knowledge is a function of its history, and its history gets lost in the very act of its construction" [14, p. 51].

One way of modeling the flow of information between the source and users is the ``information mediating chain''2 [12], as shown in Figure 1.

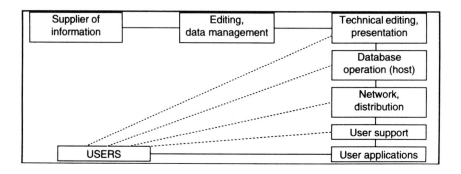

Figure 1. Information mediating chain

Using this model we may define functions as *data production* (the production or collection of data wherever they emanate), *editing and management of data* (the structuring and manipulation of data for specific usage, in accordance with given standards and the intended use), *technical (computer-based) handling of data* (operation, maintenance and provision of access to the database), *network distribution* (the physical dissemination of data), and *information mediation* (the provision of requested data in an appropriate format for the user).

The model is an "ideal" structure. In real life, one actor may have more functions. The essence of the model is that the distance (geographic and/or organizational) between the data producer and the user may be considerable, and that they do not even necessarily know of each other.

3   SHORT EXAMPLES

3.1   The "wheel"

The health sector in Norway may illustrate some of the problems related to managing data collection and flow between various actors in the public sector. The data

---

2 The model was originally developed by professor Jon Bing in a report on citizens' rights to public information to the Ministry of Administration in 1988. It has been further developed by Statskonsult, within the programme on National infrastructure for IT.

producers are service providers (nurses, doctors, health administrators) at the local level. The users are mainly government agencies, which collect data using a large number of forms. The purpose is to get information about health conditions, level and quality of service provision and resources used. The data are collected, aggregated and stored in national data bases, where they can be retrieved by users in government agencies for management and control of municipalities. Furthermore, the aggregated data are conveyed back to the local authorities, to be used as bases for local planning processes. The system of data exchange is organized like a "wheel" as shown in Figure 2.

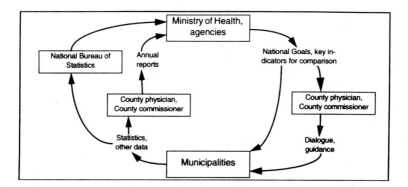

Figure 2. The control and information wheel in the health sector in Norway

The aim of the wheel is to "contribute to the fulfillment of national objectives and main priorities at a local level, and to assist decision making by local authorities. This means that the system should be designed to help practical work at the local level" [10].

Originally, a number of problems were experienced with the manual system of data collection and reporting:

- The standards for data collection did not conform to local organizational structures,
- The data reporting processes took time, and provided little help for local administrations in their planning and control work, and
- Even when data quality in the first place was good, data quickly got outdated.

The results were poor quality data and double sets of files to maintain data of local interest (thus increasing the burden of reporting data to central agencies.) As a consequence an improved system for data exchange was implemented. The basic idea was to simplify the data collecting procedures and to speed up the return of data back to the local level, using IT in the acquisition, transfer and presentation of data.

Positive experiences have been reported, in particular in areas where data are standardized, e.g. epidemiological data, where comparison between different districts are fruitful.

In an investigation of the need for information in the local health administration, it is, however, reported that a large amount of the existing statistics and guiding data are not felt to be very useful. In particular, the planning of medical service provision is based on other information sources than centrally defined priorities, typically on locally produced data from both formal and informal sources [7].

The basic problem is the difference between the perspectives of:

• The local health personnel, whose primary concern is to provide better services with limited resources (data collection is mainly felt as a burden, not a help),
and
• The centrally located civil servants whose main goal is to get data that can support their planning, monitoring and control work.

The success of the new IT-based wheel will depend on to what extent one manages to provide the local level with more relevant and more timely data than before. There will always be contradictions between the needs of the local and central levels, but adequate compromises may be found.

3.2   Use of environmental data

Norway's environmental administration is organized in a Ministry of Environment, several directorates, and county environmental offices. All of these are central government bodies. After a trial period of four years, it was decided to add a municipal level to the environmental administration. This took effect in 1992. Today, each municipality has a head of environmental issues, hereafter referred to as municipal environmental officer MEO.

There are several databases within the Norwegian environmental administration. These are used only infrequently by MEOs. In interviews with MEOs and with database owners we experienced the following problems.

1. Often a database contains very specialized data, which makes little sense unless interpreted in the appropriate context. Such databases may be available to those working in a special field in a directorate, but they are not prepared for use by MEOs, although they sometimes contain data of interest for them.

2. A lot of useful information is available only in unstructured and informal ways, sometimes only as tacit knowledge, e.g., knowledge about stock of game, fish, etc.

3. Many databases are too coarse to be used by MEOs. They only contain a few figures for each municipality, thus they cannot be used for issues internal to each municipality. They may, however, be used to compare the municipality with the rest of the country. In this way an MEO can get support for assigning priorities to

different areas, e.g. by concluding that acid rain is or is not a problem for his or her municipality.

4. MEOs must be generalists, and will therefore only be infrequent users of each individual database. The threshold for learning a new database is therefore high, and since the databases tend to have different interfaces, an MEO can never become fluent in many of them.

As a fifth problem, we have the impression that it is more rewarding for a bureaucrat within the government's environmental administration to initiate and create a database, than to see that it is actually used and maintained. In our experience many database projects are silently forgotten and the data slowly deteriorate into uselessness.

4   A MODEL FOR DATABASES AS COMMUNICATION MEDIA

The examples presented illustrate several problems related to the use of databases, issues like common definitions of data, demands for data with little sensitivity for their production costs (c.f. [6]), lack of incentives for reporting and sharing data (c.f. [4, 11]), non-rational decision-making (c.f. [5]), too slow and improperly edited data back to end users, etc.

We feel that the idea of understanding computers as communication media (c.f. [2]) is a good starting point for this discussion. Databases are, however, media with special properties. They have collective senders and receivers, they work asynchronously, and functions like editing and distribution may take place several times. This means that the distance between senders and receivers can be very large, not only in distance, but also in time and context.

Based on this perspective on databases we raise a number of questions or issues which together constitute an extension of the information mediating chain [12] presented above.

1. Data in a database are concerned with some phenomenon or collection of phenomena. Do we have an agreed-upon delimitation of the universe of the database. For example: what is a meaningful unit of health care? We have a problem of *existence and definition*.

2. Given a phenomenon, it is not obvious that it can be observed, that it can be measured properly, and that data can be extracted. This applies to many phenomena in the environment (e.g., some actions causing pollution) and in health care (e.g., actions taken by individuals which affect their future need for health care). If we also consider cost, the problem of *measurement* increases further.

3. The data must be reported and entered into the database. This is often felt as a little rewarding job, and the systems are often built up so that those who report data (or their organizational unit), have small or no benefits from the successful operation of the system. There have been some examples of this in health care, and the authors have seen several examples in Norwegian public administration. We refer to this as the problem of *incentive to record and update data*. The development of ``the wheel" is an example of a system where the central level tries to achieve better data by improving the relevance of the system to the local level.

4. The quality of the data should be verified, or at least be reasonably well known. We have observed lack of use of data due to poor quality. In a confidential investigation of tax-related data we identified the following aspects of data quality: timeliness, accuracy of identity, formal correctness (according to rules set), completeness, and accuracy. The problem of *data quality* is, in general, related to the use of the data. As an example, data collected for statistical purposes may not form a good basis for taxation of individuals.

5. Databases need competent *database management*. The data must be structured and stored in ways which ensure consistency and retrievability. The data must be stored in a safe way; we need procedures for backup and recovery, etc.

6. The data need *processing* to form a basis for obtaining information. Obvious examples are aggregation, calculation of statistics, creation of time-series, etc.

7. There is an obvious need for *physical distribution* of the data, typically through a network, but mailing printed reports and floppy disks are also examples. The purpose of the distribution is to make the data accessible to users and to value-added suppliers of data. Clearly, physical distribution may take place before and after several of the other functions mentioned here.

8. The data need *editing and presentation* in ways appropriate for their intended use. This may involve construction of special interfaces and views to the database, combination of ``one's own" data with data from other sources, designing reports, tables, diagrams, and other means which serve to illustrate the data.

9. There must be a *demand* for and an actual *acquisition* of the data. Somebody has to ask for and actually obtain the data, in whatever way they are available.

10. Finally, the data may be subject to *actual use*, i.e. a decision is based on the data, an action is taken in accordance with the data, etc. As said above, it is not obvious that this happens, although the data have been acquired.

All these questions are relevant for the use of most types of data, but may be particularly important for public data, where we in general find weak connections between the source (sender) and the user (receiver).

To sum up, our model deals with three levels: real world assumptions, computer based systems [1], and technical issues, see Figure 3.

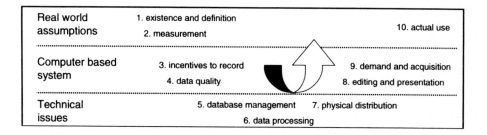

Figure 3. Model of databases as media

5   CONCLUSION

The model for databases as communication media presented in this paper provides concepts which can be used in an analysis of why public databases work as intended or not. Specifically it recognizes the possibly different interests and incentives of various groups involved in providing, maintaining and presenting the data.

The model can be used to suggest practical advice to providers of public databases. As an illustration, we would propose the following suggestions for the examples given from health care and environmental administration.

1. In order to get good data quality, make sure that the system is useful for those persons and organizational units which have the burden of providing the data. The central health care administration should therefore go further in making the "wheel" (see section 3.1) useful to local administrations. One way of doing this is to develop and provide computer applications supporting local administrations in their work, and make these applications able to collect and report the necessary statistics to the central level.

2. In order to ease use of the data, more emphasis should be put on editing and presentation, i.e. by presenting data in a format useful to end users. Separate access mechanisms for different kinds of data should be avoided. World Wide Web [3] can be used to provide easy to use and fairly universal access to the data.

3. Given the tendency to artificially inflate the demand for information, critical investigations of the actual use of the information should be made. Based on such investigations some databases may be eliminated, and efforts may be concentrated on databases where there is active and real use.

Beyond the issues mentioned here, this paper also encourages a discussion of issues like distribution and pricing of data, stimulation of value added distributors, etc. We have not had room to discuss these issues, but they too support the relevance of selecting a media perspective on databases.

KEYWORDS

Public databases, information mediating chain, information wheel, knowledge

REFERENCES

[1]   Andersen N. E., Kensing F., Lundin J., Mathiassen L., Munk-Madsen A., Rasbech M., Sørgaard P., Professional Systems Development, Prentice Hall, Business Information Technology Series, UK (1990).

[2]   Andersen P. B., Semiotics and informatics: Computers as media, Taylor G, In Information technology and information use, Ingwersen, Rajtery, Pejtersen M. (eds) 64-97 (1986).

[3]   Berners-Lee T., Cailliau R., Luotonen A., Nielsen H. F., Secret A., The World Wide Web, Communications of the ACM, 37(8) 76-82 August (1994).

[4]   Ciborra C. U., Information systems and transactions architecture, International Journal of Policy Analysis and Information Systems, 5(4) 305-324 (1981).

[5]   Cohen M. D., March J. G., Olsen J. P., People, problems, solutions and the ambiguity of relevance, In Ambiguity and Choice in Organizations, March J. G. , Olsen J. P. (eds) 24-37, Universitetsforlaget, Oslo-Bergen-Tromsø (1976).

[6]   Feldman M. S., March J. G., Information in organizations as signal and symbol, Administrative Science Quarterly, 26,171-186 (1981).

[7]   Grimsmo A., Ford N., Informasjonssystesmer i Helse- og Sosialplanleggingen, (In English, Information systems in Health Administration), Tidsskrift for Den norske Lægeforening, 112 (29) (1992).

[8]   Hellman R., A fictitious HIS-reconstruct of an inventory information system, Computers in Industry, 11, 301-310 (1989).

[9]   Nurminen M. I. ,Kalmi R., Karhu P., Niemelä J., Use or development of information systems: Which is more fundamental?, In System Design for Human Development and Productivity: Participation and Beyond, Docherty P., Fuchs-Kittowski K. , Kolm P., Mathiassen L. (eds) 187-196, Amsterdam North-Holland (1987).

[10]   Styrings- og, Informasjonshjulet for Helse- og sosialtjenestene i kommunene (In English, The Control and Information Wheel for the Health and Social services in Municipalities), Publ. I-9/92, Ministry of Health, Oslo (1992).

[11]   Orlikowski W. J., Learning from Notes: Organizational issues in groupware implementation, Turner J., Kraut R. (eds) CSCW'92, 362-369, Toronto, October 31 to November 4 ACM Order Number 612920 (1992).

[12]   Organisering og styring av formidling av offentlig informasjon (In English, Organisation and management of mediation of Public Information). National Infrastructure for IT, Project 5, Statskonsult, Oslo (1992).

[13]   Söderquist T., Knowledge is Power, Proceedings of Knowledge and Communication in the Computer Age, Forchheimer C. (ed), Linköping, Sweden, Nov.(1987).

[14]   Weizenbaum J., On the Status of Knowledge in the Information Society, In Proceedings of Knowledge and Communication in the Computer Age, Forchheimer C. (ed) Linköping, Sweden, Nov.(1987).

The NASA Astrophysics Data System: a Heterogeneous Distributed Data Environment

Michael J. KURTZ, Guenther EICHHORN , Stephen S. MURRAY,
Carolyn STERN-GRANT, and Alberto ACCOMAZZI

Harvard-Smithsonian Center for Astrophysics, 60 Garden Street, Cambridge, MA 02138, U.S.A.

ABSTRACT

The NADS Astrophysics Data System (ADS) is a distributed information system which provides access to archive, catalog and bibliographic data in astronomy. Because of recent technical and budgetary developments the ADS has become a smaller project and changed its focus. While continuing to provide access to certain archives and databases the ADS will substantially expand its already extensive bibliographic service to include the whole text of articles from the major journals in astronomy; it will thus become a major digital library.

RESUME

Le système de données astrophysiques (ADS) de la NASA (NADS) est un système d'information distribuée donnant accès aux archives, catalogues et données bibliographiques de l'astronomie. Pour des raison techniques et budgétaires ADS est revu comme un projet plus restreint avec une finalité modifiée, tout en continuant à assurer l'accès à certaines archives et bases de données l'ADS accroitra fortement son service bibliographique déjà important pour inclure les textes complets des articles des journaux essentiels d'astronomie; il deviendra de fait une bibliothèque digitalisée importante.

1   RECENT CHANGES TO THE ADS PROJECT

The U.S National Aeronautics and Space Administration (NASA) has for many years supported several methods of remote data access to space science data. Beginning in 1989 NASA has supported a fully distributed data distribution system for astronomical data, based on proprietary networking software provided by Ellery Systems Incorporated; this system is the Astrophysics Data System. The NASA Astrophysics Data System (ADS) has recently had a substantial change in focus, brought about by NASA budget constraints, and by the rapid success of the World

Wide Web, which has rendered some of the distributed networking work of the ADS redundant. [1]

The new ADS will be a substantially smaller project, with its primary purpose to provide bibliographic services to the NASA astrophysics community (which is in essence all astronomers) via the internet, specifically via the World Wide Web. Secondarily we will provide WWW access to a distributed collection of catalogs, to a few data archives, and will provide certain utility services.

2   THE CURRENT ADS ABSTRACT SERVICE

The NASA ADS Abstract Service is now one of the most used data services in astronomy. Currently about 40,000 queries are made per month and about 500,000 bibliographic entries (references and abstracts) are returned. Use is still increasing rapidly.

The ADS Abstract Service provides sophisticated query and retrieval capabilities to the NASA STI abstract database for the categories Astronomy, Astrophysics, Lunar and Planetary Exploration, Solar Physics, and Space Radiation. These comprise over 200,000 abstracts from 1975 to the present.

One may query the database by author name, words in the title, keyword (assigned by the NASA STI staff), or by natural language match with words in the abstract. An extensive synonym list, created by Joyce Watson, makes the exact choice of words in a natural language query not so critical (for example spectroscope is a synonym of spectrograph, but not of spectrophotometer). [2]

In addition the Abstract Service can merge data from the SIMBAD data service in Strasbourg with the data from NASA STI to give the ability to search the literature for particular facets of particular astronomical objects. Examples are: search for the joint occurrence of the galaxy M31 in SIMBAD and papers in STI containing the words "globular cluster" to get a list of the few dozen papers on the M31 globular cluster system (out of several thousand on M31 and on globular clusters); search SIMBAD for M87 and STI for "black hole" to get all papers on the black hole at the center of M87.

The first figure shows a simple query, papers by the first author on redshift surveys. Figure 2 shows the first few papers corresponding to the query; notice the "Available Items" column, this shows what is currently in the database. For the first article nothing shows, indicating that just the bibliographic reference exists; the second article shows an "F" indicating the full text of the article is on-line as a bitmapped image, shown in Figure 3. The next two articles have an "A" meaning that the abstract is available, and the bottom article also shows a "D" which means that data tables from that article are available on-line. Figure 4 shows the abstract as returned by the system, notice that options exist to obtain the on-line data and to perform an additional search of the database using this abstract as a query.

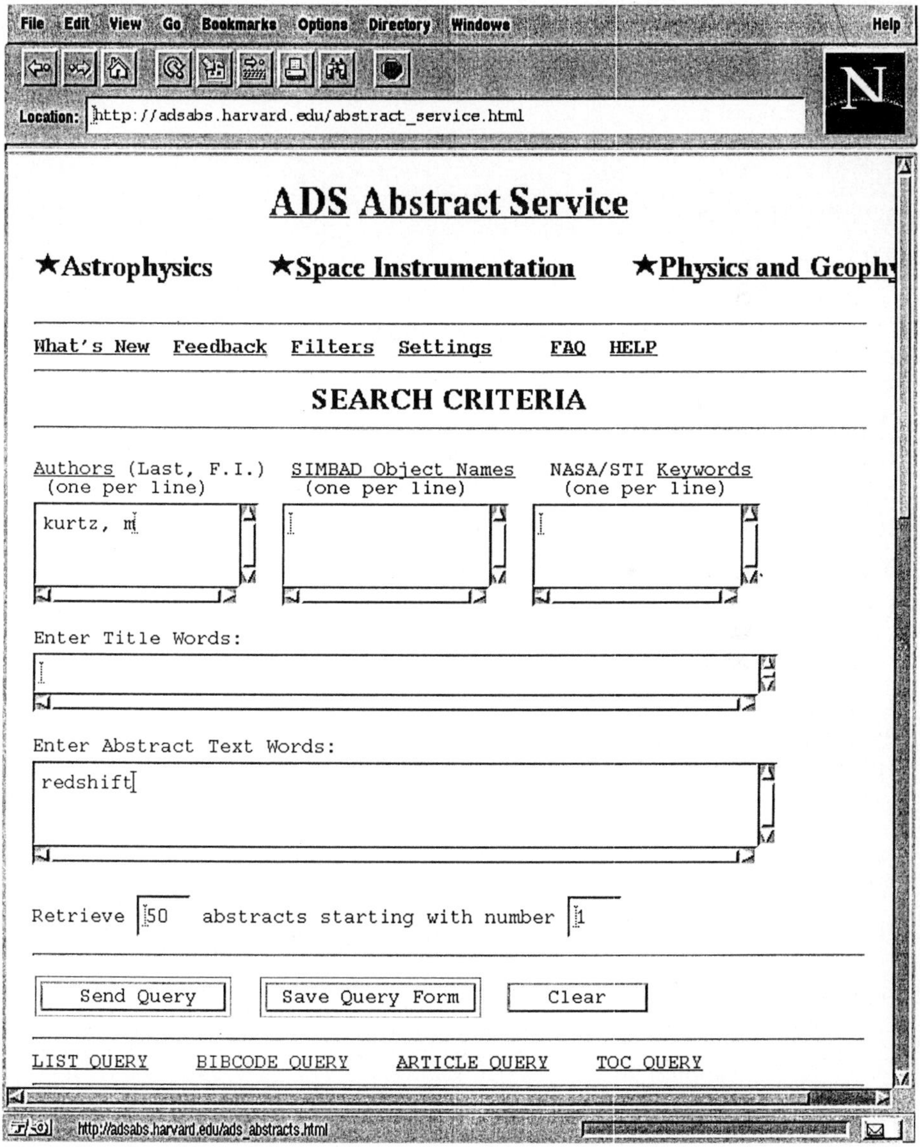

Figure 1. A typical query to the ADS Abstract Service, asking for the first author of these articles on redshift survey

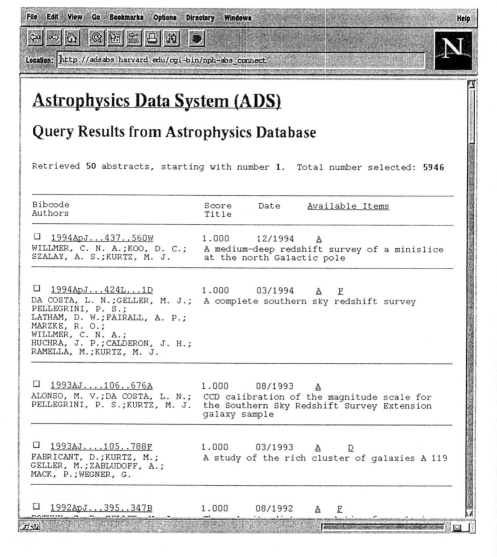

Figure 2. The result of the query in Figure 1., described in text

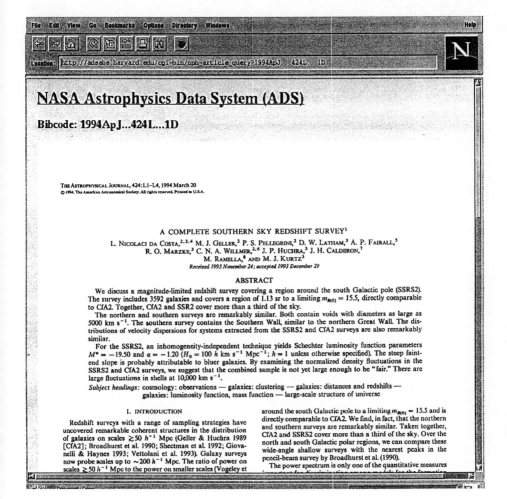

Figure 3. A screen readable first page of the second paper in the list in Figure 2.; note that printable PostScript versions are also available.

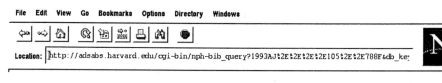

ADS Astrophysics Abstract Service

▸ **Find Similar Abstracts**
▸ **Data links**

Title: A study of the rich cluster of galaxies A 119
Authors: FABRICANT, DANIEL; KURTZ, MICHAEL; GELLER,
                      MARGARET; ZABLUDOFF, ANN; MACK, PETER; WEGNER,
                      GARY
Affiliation: AD(Harvard-Smithsonian Center for Astrophysics,
                      Cambridge, MA) AE(Michigan-Dartmouth-MIT
                      Observatory, Tucson, AZ) AF(Dartmouth College,
                      Hanover, NH)
Journal: Astronomical Journal (ISSN 0004-6256), vol. 105, no.
                      3, p. 788-796.
Publication Date: 03/1993
Origin: STI
Category: Astrophysics
NASA/STI Keywords: ASTRONOMICAL PHOTOMETRY, GALACTIC CLUSTERS, HEAO 2,
                      RADIAL VELOCITY, RED SHIFT, X RAY IMAGERY,
                      BRIGHTNESS DISTRIBUTION, CHARGE COUPLED DEVICES
Bibliographic Code: 1993AJ....105..788F

Abstract

We use Einstein Observatory X–ray images, galaxy photometry, and galaxy redshifts to study the cluster of galaxies Abell 119. We report 60 new radial velocities, as well as new photographic and CCD photometry. We find corresponding evidence for substructure in the projected galaxy distribution and the X–ray surface brightness profile. A multiple clump model, in which galaxies trace the condensations in the dark matter, reproduces the main features of the photometric and X–ray data. The galaxy velocity histogram of A 119 is Gaussian (with the exception of a superposed foreground group), but the velocity data do not sample the subclumps adequately.

Find Similar Abstracts:

Use: ☐ Authors

Figure 4. The abstract for the fourth paper in the list in Figure 2., notice the built-in ability to access data tables from the paper, and to find similar papers.

3   THE FUTURE ADS BIBLIOGRAPHIC SERVICES

With the new direction for the ADS the Abstract Service will expand substantially to become a true digital library.

Two important changes, which will not be discussed here, are: we will double the size of the database by including those categories from the STI Abstracts which concern building space instrumentation; and we will include the citation histories for articles in our database, by purchasing that information from the Institute for Scientific Information.

We will permit abstracts to be submitted into the system by anyone (we will decide if the data is relevant to us), in particular we will accept original author abstracts from journals and from editors of conference proceedings. We will only take abstracts of documents which are in their final form, this is not intended to be a preprint service. We will also accept notes from authors of articles abstracted in our service, errata will probably be the main use of this feature. These notes will be linked to the abstract. Perhaps the most important change will be the addition of access to the full text of journal articles, which will first be done for articles from journals owned by the American Astronomical Society, and in collaboration with their on-line journals project. We expect to be able to provide current papers in the Astrophysical Journal Letters, and papers from the Astrophysical Journal and the Astronomical Journal after a time lag of about one year to protect the subscriber base of these journals.

The papers will be provided as images of the actual paper pages of the journal. We will provide two versions, a 75dpi grey scale image which can be viewed on computer screens using WWW browsers such as Mosaic, and a 600dpi bitmap version which would be sent as a Postscript file to send to a printer. No ASCII version of the articles will exist, or be sent; we will not send the results of an OCR program to end users, as the data cannot be guaranteed accurate.

The AAS On-line journals project expects within three years to have an all digital version of the ApJ Letters; when this happens we will likely discontinue the creation of bitmapped images of paper pages, and have the service point directly to the digital version.

Another extension of the current service is to link on-line data tables taken from journal articles with the abstracts of the articles. This has already been done, with the data tables being kept on-line by the Centre de Donnees astronomiques de Strasbourg.

We are also using the abstracts as a basis for a hypertext information system. We are connecting the names of authors and the names of astronomical objects to a number of information sources, such as a list of e-mail addresses for author names or a list of the basic observational data for object names.

Now named the NASA ASIAS (Astrophysics Science Information and Abstract Service), the ADS bibliographic service already is used as much as the five largest libraries in astronomy put together; with the additional services listed here it will continue as one of the premier digital libraries in the world.

4   ACCESS

Access to the ADS Abstract Service is via:

http://adsabs.harvard.edu/abstract_service.html

General access to the ADS is via

http://adswww.harvard.edu/ads_services.html

Recent articles on the ADS may be found at

http://adsdoc.harvard.edu/pubs/

KEYWORDS

Astronomy, information systems, information retrieval, digital libraries.

REFERENCES

[1]   Good J. C., In Astronomical Data Analysis Software and Systems I, (eds) Worrall D. et al., San Francisco : Astronomical Society of the Pacific, p. 35 (1992).
[2]   Kurtz M. J. et al, In Astronomical Data Analysis Software and Systems II (eds) Hanish R. et al., San Francisco : Astronomical Society of the Pacific, p. 132 (1993).
[3]   Eichhorn G. et al, In Astronomical Data Analysis Software and Systems IV (eds) Hanish R. et al, San Francisco : Astronomical Society of the Pacific (1993).
[4]   Accomazzi A et al, In Astronomical Data Analysis Software and Systems IV (eds) Hanish R. et al, San Francisco : Astronomical Society of the Pacific (1994).

Computer Networks with Episodic Links and the Use of Portable Computers

Jean-Charles PROFIZI

University of Savoie - L.G.I.S, 73340 Le Bourget du Lac, France

ABSTRACT

Our study is focused on optimization of information exchanges in computer networks using episodic links. It results in improved availability on "traveling" sites as well as fixed ones, provided their interdependence is precisely assessed. To that end , the description of the virtual architecture and the operating conditions for the network is reflected by binary relations of a topological, functional or dependency type , applied to objets : computers , software , data and users. This approach leads to study of a multi-agent system and induces adaptation to that context of cooperative applications and their data. It is aimed at the design of "intelligent processes" that would leave free initiative in interaction up to each site , within an evolutive environment .

RESUME

Notre étude porte sur l'optimisation des échanges d'informations dans des réseaux d'ordinateurs à liaisons épisodiques. Elle engendre une amélioration de la disponibilité des sites "nomades", et également statiques, moyennant une évaluation précise de leur interdépendance. A cet effet, la description de l'architecture virtuelle et des conditions d'exploitation du réseau se traduit par des relations binaires de nature topologique, fonctionnelle ou de dépendance appliquées à des objets : les ordinateurs, les logiciels, les données et les utilisateurs. Cette démarche conduit à l'étude d'un système multiagents. Elle induit l'adaptation, à ce contexte, des applications coopératives et de leurs données. Elle vise à la conception de "processus intelligents" laissant , à chaque site , la libre initiative de ses interactions dans un environnement évolutif .

1 INTRODUCTION

Not long ago, "computer network" was only used for groups of computers in fixed positions and linked together by permanent links that were confided to either private or public data transmission networks. That gave rise to their name of "static networks".

The efforts at research made in the field of computer networks seem to be focused on two distinct, and yet complementary, centres of interest :

•The first aims at improving performances, reliability and flexibility in use of those static networks. The future "electronic highways", in charge of carrying information intended for multi-media, will form a privileged inter-site link.

•The second aims at opening up another alternative, by giving a more important role to portable computers. If we take advantage of their specificity, they can be considered as totally independent sites, especially as their performances have gradually tended to resemble those of fixed computers. That in turn has given rise to the term of "mobile computer networks".

Our work is oriented towards that second centre of interest and concerns the creation of general computer networks based on "episodic links". To that end, we have been concerned with the problems raised by optimization of exchanges in networks that must support management applications with high frequencies of use.

That orientation encourages the use of portable computers that, by their very nature, cannot be subjected to a requirement of permanent connection. It is compatible with the characteristics of the forthcoming national networks for radio transmission of data. However, our approach can also be applied to static networks. This would result essentially in reduced operating expenses through optimization of exchanges. Small and mid-sized companies, with elements spread out over a vast area, could then benefit from the resources offered by computer networks, without having to devote an excessive budget to it.

2   THE CONCEPT OF PSEUDO-INDEPENDENCE AND ITS IMPACT

The existence of permanent links in static networks induces any processing underway to select the data needed from other sites and, in particular, from host computers. This organization means that diversified applications can be supported without implying significant adaptation. On the other hand, not only are the costs of infrastructure and operation for a general network often disproportional in comparison to the advantages offered, but the interdependence of sites leads to vulnerability.

The advantages and disadvantages mentioned above are reversed in the case of episodic links. The latter are set up at the initiative of the site's management system, according to the processing underway, and are therefore "dynamic". They provide more independence for computers, which can be termed "pseudo-autonomous".

The principle used is close to that of remote controlled clocks. However, the time interval during which an active site (where processing is going on) is autonomous, depends on the impact of the data (location on one or several sites) and their level of coherence. This means that processing will be compatible with the concept of pseudo-autonomy, if its execution is not dependent on immediate exchanges of information with the other sites concerned by the same data. Statistically, this is the case for most processing that intervenes in a management application.

The concept of pseudo-autonomy gives such a network two main properties: distribution of information (data and software) and virtual organization.

2.1 Distribution of information

Each site must have all the elements needed for execution of the processing assigned to it. To that end, a distinction must be made between the notion of distribution, which is similar to duplication (possibly selective), and the notion of dispatching, which can be assimilated with a kind of dispersion of additional information on sites that are often specialized.

Several interesting improvements result from this property to encourage the use of portable computers; they concern :

•The response time, because of local availability of data; alteration due to preparation of exchanges tends to be minimal,

•The availability of sites, because of their independence,

•Protection of data, through duplication that renders pointless the back-ups usually needed.

2.2 Virtual organization

Sites are joined together by a virtual mesh. A subset of these virtual binary relations induces topological relationships characteristic of two sites that share at least one common datum and dependence links on which a hierarchy can be set up between sites. These relationships define a virtual organization. Any inter-site link must comply with a specialized relationship and any exchange must conform to the type of relationship. The virtual organization becomes real according to the nature of the exchanges, conditional on the processing available.

This aspect of our approach favors:

•The evolution of the network architecture: the configuration is easily modified;

•The integrity of sites: as links between two sites are set up at the initiative of either one of them, the computers have more effective protection from interference than in any other organization;

•Decentralized management: the sites reliability is ensured by assigning to each user a field of activity that is expressed in the form of binary relationships, called functional relationships. Topological, dependence and functional relationships can be entrusted to a local manager. The synthesis of these relationships defines the controlled conditions for use of the data in the network.

Unlike information dispatching, which is reflected in the uniqueness of each piece of information, distribution multiplies information. Coherency is achieved when each global datum, expressed in the form of a variable, receives on any site where it is available the value that was given to it at its latest update.

3   COHERENCY OF INFORMATION AND UPDATES

Every piece of data shall be accepted to be associated with the value of a variable stored in a file or in a data base. This means that that variable represents a field in a file or a field indicated by its path in the case of a data base.

3.1   Updates

An update repeats, at the scale of the network, an update to a global data on one of the sites. It corresponds to a set of additional data that follows the establishment of a link at any one site's initiative. Such operations are called exchanges (or transfers of primitives), integration and confirmation. Updating a piece of data can be deferred (and thus group the results of several updates) or instantaneous (and follow any given update).

This approach relies on various notions:

•The stability of data in comparison to a program: this reveals whether or not a piece of data can or cannot be modified within processing;

•the relative impact of data: for any data pair A and B:

•A has direct impact on B if updating or upgrading it implies updating or upgrading B,

•A has indirect impact on B if updating B depends on the value of A.

•The level of coherence of data: weak or strong coherence is a characteristic of the time (deferred or immediate) allocated to data updating so that the processing it participates in remains meaningful. The higher the number of data with weak coherence, the more effective the network. An expert system is presently under study to assess such effectiveness and possibly to improve it by modifying constraints,

•Standardization of the level of coherence: all data must have the same level of coherence, whatever the processing or the site in question,

•Compatibility of levels of coherence: compatibility (C) or incompatibility (I) of the levels of coherence of a data pair is expressed in the form of two tables. If "f" = weak coherence and "F"=strong coherence then:

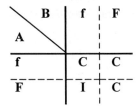

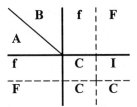

Direct impact   Indirect impact

•Concurrence of access: deferred updating of a piece of data on a site may result from the integration of primitives that certify successive updates of the same piece of data on one or several other sites. This means concurrent access and the need to remedy it by a selection according to time so that when the update is finished, the data has the value assigned to it at its last update. This does not fail to pose tricky problems because of the network's properties.

3.2   Methodological aspects

The problems relative to maintenance of coherency and concurrent access are amplified by the episodic nature of the links and the use of portable computers. To solve those additional constraints, the solutions used are those in the fields of telecommunications and radio time transmission.

3.2.1   Impact of episodic links on coherence

When an event occurs (interruption or deactivation of a program, update of highly coherent data, etc.), the site "links up", in conformity with topological relationships, with each of the sites concerned, which are called participant sites. In the case of repetitive exchanges, it may also either entrust this task to a static site, called the relay site, with which it links up according to a dependence relationship, or let each participant site transmit the exchange to its equivalent.

3.2.2 Impact of the use of portable computers on coherence

Unlike fixed computers, portable computers are often in an inert state (neither active, nor on stand-by). When an event occurs (activation, call-up of a program, etc.), the previously inert computer addresses itself to the "relay" site, to receive pending messages.

3.2.3 Impact of specificity of the network on concurrent access

The integration of primitives on a site must take place in consideration of the time priorities of the updates. Each primitive emitted is stamped with the time it was generated, which means time estimation must be harmonized. As in the case of remote controlled clocks, we consider the drift in time counting on each site during the period it is autonomous to be insignificant, as long as it does not become too great. To remedy this situation for our aims, each exchange carries a time update indication supplied by the emitting site.

3.3   Practical achievements

To make the methods described above reality, there are two types of programs: processes and tools.

Processes are executed in total autonomy when events occur. This is the case for :

•Exchange management processes. These are not concerned by the creation of the link between two sites, nor by the transmission of batches of data. Their role is to manage both the conditions (or events) that induce an instantaneous or deferred update and the stages in it (determination of sites, exchange, integration, decision in the case of an inert participant site, etc.):

•Data access processes: they give access to the representative fields of the selected data, from the primitives sent to them during an exchange or by a user program.

Tools are always implemented by human action and help the manager in his task. On request, they can also assist the process to return to a coherent situation after accidents.

4   DESCRIPTION OF THE NETWORK

The flexibility that is characteristic of the network's evolving nature induces difficulties in description of its architectural and functional properties on the one hand and of the clauses to guarantee the safety of processing on the other.
The guiding idea adopted can be summarized as follows:

•The description of the network can be deduced from that of each of the sites that compose it, because of their pseudo-autonomy;

•The description of each site comes down to two distinct descriptions, respectively known as contextual and functional;

•Execution of any processing must take place in compliance with the respect of the prior descriptions.

4.1   Contextual description

The contextual description (or characterization) is a means to identify the objects that might take part in the execution of any processing and possibly to establish a hierarchical relationship between them. Those objects are divided up between the three components of the characterization:

•The resources, grouping objects ensuring, through their collaboration, all of the processing on the site. This is the case of the executives and the data submitted to them. Executives designate the executable modules relating to "application" software (placed at the user's disposal) and "harmonization" software (taking part in execution of inter-site exchanges).

•The operating context, concerning the objects that dialogue with those that are representative of resources. This category gathers together users and terminals.

•The environment, representing in the form of outside objects the sites with which the active site is likely to set up a link. The static site to which it is connected or the next-highest hierarchical level (relay site) is dealt with in an explicit declaration. Sites sharing at least one piece of data with the active site (participant sites) are dealt with in an implicit declaration, as their role results from the balance sheet of the data distributed, at the scale of the network.

4.2 Functional description

The functional description (or definition of the field of activity) amounts to determining the conditions for participation of each object declared in advance in accomplishment of the processing available on the site.

This means functional relationships that are also known as restrictions; their purpose is to permit or ban any object making up a component to fulfill or from fulfilling the role assigned to it, whether alone or in association with an object from another component.

a. Permission

•Validation permits the object receiving it to fulfill the role for which it is supposed to exist.

•Posing a condition lets each object in a single component fulfill its role if, and only if, they act in conjunction.

•Resource allocation permits an object making up resources to fulfill its role if it is called on from another component.

b. Banning

•Neutralization inhibits validation.

•Dissociation inhibits conditions.

•Exclusion from resources inhibits resource allocation.

These directives are sent through orders that mention the type of restriction and the object(s) it applies to. The process of defining the field of activity they are sent to according to the interactive or "batch-processing" mode ensures their interpretation and execution.

Because they rapidly become complex, bundles of restrictions are subjected to simplification to avoid slowing down the processing. This reduction results from application of a set of rules such as:

•Rules inducing neutralization of any object that cannot be selected because of at least one correlating restriction,

•The rule that any graph representative of a bundle of restrictions will accept a "complementary" graph.

Graphic representations submitted to "zoom" effects are envisaged to enable verification of the validity of the decisions made.

4.3   Controlled use of resources

Any component belonging to an operating or environment context can be the origin of controlled use of data. Data processing by selected executives (application or harmonization) must take place in compliance with established restrictions.

5   THE COMPUTER COORDINATION SYSTEM

The processes and tools mentioned are part of a block of software systematically installed on any site destined to become part of the network, called the "Computer Coordination System".

The term "computer system" is characteristic of any organized group of executives. The term "coordination" reveals its dual vocation:

•Local coordination of the use of the available resources on the site,
•External coordination concerning the exchanges the current site must have with other sites in the network.

The system usually calls on the operating system because of its action on the site's specific functionalities. It is organized around four computer subsystems grouping processes:

•The computer identification system, that can associate with each object a simple identity that is vital for its handling;

•The computer protection system, to express constraints applied to objects, translate them into a manageable form and optimize them;

•The computer harmonization system, that ensures management of automatic information exchanges between sites, in compliance with established restrictions;

•The computer application system, that ensures controlled use of the application executives designed for the site's users and of the tools designed for authorized users.

6   COORDINATION LANGUAGE BASED ON AGENTS

When the basic properties which we attribute to episodic links computer are presented on a global basis, it is evident that various modes of transmission may be required (fixed, telephone, cellular or satellite links).

Exchanges may thus be dependent upon the range of these links and the type of treatment, or a combination of both factors. The sites which use episodic links are organized in sub-units which each use a fixed computer connected to a high speed network. A portable computer used in a fixed configuration may however act as reference site on limited or isolated occasions. This possibility results from the granularity of the process and the detailed parameterisation.

The network coordination system has to manage computers, links, functions, applications and users, making it very heterogeneous in nature.

We feel that the use of the "agent" concept seems very appropriate in the context of this presentation.

What we are working towards at present is the development of an "agent-based language" which will make it easier to obtain an adaptable description of the operating context and its implications.

CONCLUSION

Application of a subset of the methods we are working on has been the opportunity to run a concrete check on their potential and their weaknesses. Episodic links were simulated in the framework of TRANSPAC data transmission and circulation of information flows concerning 20 mini-computers and 190 micro-computers, all static.

We are presently trying to firm up our methodology and make it more rigorous by orienting our work to an "object-oriented" environment. We are focusing our efforts on "man-machine" dialogue in order to make communication of descriptions and restrictions simpler and more reliable. Our results will be tested by means of simulations before being put into application.

KEYWORDS

Cooperative applications , coherence , distributed data , objet environment, traffic computer , episodic links , multi-agent system.

REFERENCES

[1]   Lamport L. (Massachussets Computer Associates) Time, Clocks and the Ordering of Events in a Distributed System, Communication of the ACM , Vol 21,7, July (1978).

[2]   Faul S. R., Parnas D. L., On Synchronisation in Hard-real-time Systems, Communication of the ACM, vol 31,3, March (1988).

[3]   Kenneth P.B., Maintaining Consistency in Distributed Systems, Cornell University Dept. of Computer Science, Technical Report 91-1240 (1991).

[4]   Tenenbaum J.M., Dore R., Cooperative Information Gathering: A distributed Problem Solving Approach, U Mass Computer Science, Technical Report (1994).

[5]   Satyanorayanan M., Kistler J. J., Disconnected Operation in the CODA File System, Proc. ACM SIGOPS'91, Pacific Grove, CA Oct.(1991).

[6]   Cardelli L., OBLIB: A language with distributed Scope, Research report 122, Digital Equipment Corporation Systems Research Center, Palo Alto, CA June (1994).

[7]   Forman G. H., Zahorjan J., The Challenge of Mobile Computing, Computer Sciences and Engineering, University of Washington, Dec.(1993).

[8]   Teraoka F., Tokoro M., Host Migration Transparency in IP Networks: The VIP Approach, Sony Computer Science Laboratory Inc., SCSL-TR-93-001, Jan.(1993).

[9]   Perkins C., I.P. Mobility Support, Internet Engineering Task Force Draft, Oct.(1994).

[10]   Imielinski T., Badrinath B. R., Wirless Computing, Communication of the ACM, vol 37,10, Oct.(1994).

Dynamic Management of Cooperative Applications for Mobile Systems

Pierre-Guillaume RAVERDY, Phillipe DARCHE[1] and Bertil FOLLIOT[2]

Laboratoire MASI, Institut Blaise Pascal, Université Pierre et Marie Curie,
4 Place Jussieu, 75252 Paris Cedex 05, France, E-mail: {raverdy,darche,folliot}@masi.ibp.fr

ABSTRACT

Management of nomadic computers (either portable laptops or mobile robots) in actual networks brings new challenges for efficient resources access and cooperative work. New systems have to cope with communication breaking off. Systems should also manage resources mobility (due to hardware location change or cell change for wireless communication), that may lead to prohibitive resources use due to communication delay/cost. We propose a new resources management scheme that takes these new challenges into account and we apply it in a robotic environment.

RESUME

La gestion d'ordinateurs nomades (robots mobiles ou ordinateurs portables) dans le cadre de réseaux classiques de communication amène de nouveaux problèmes pour la mise à disponibilité des ressources réparties sur le réseau et le travail coopératif de plusieurs entités. Il est d'abord nécessaire de gérer les ruptures de communication, soit volontaires dans le cas d'une déconnection, ou impromptues dans le cas d'un passage dans une zone d'ombre pour les réseaux cellulaires. Il faut de plus tenir compte des déplacements de ressources (déplacement d'un robot mobile, changement de cellule de communication) qui peuvent rendre prohibitif l'accès à une ressource en raison du coût de communication (dans le cas d'applications temps-réel). Nous proposons une gestion de ressources prenant en compte ces différents facteurs et l'appliquons à un environnement robotique.

1 INTRODUCTION

Introducing mobile computers in classical distributed systems brings new challenges for resources and cooperating application management. Due to mobility, the location of hosts, applications and resources can change. A mobile host needs to continue its work while disconnected and to connect transparently to the network from various

---

[1] Affiliation: UFR d'Informatique, Université Paris VII
[2] Affiliation: UFR d'Informatique, Université Paris VII

locations. The obligations to cope with battery limitations and the limited bandwidth of wireless communications are also important for cooperative applications. For these reasons, management of system resources must be dynamic and new management schemes have to be provided for nomadic computing environment. Due to host mobility, location of resources and processes may change.

Thus, the system management must be dynamic. It must support mechanisms to allow disconnection, ensure information consistency during disconnection and allow cooperating programs to resume their communications after host reconnection. Change of location also influences the global system performances by introducing load imbalance due to communication delay. It may be efficient for processes to migrate in order to reduce communication and response time. After a reconnection, processes located on a mobile host need to locate the remote resources they were accessing. Resources managed by this host should also be made visible to other hosts (mobile or not).

We propose a cooperative application management, the territory scheme for a network of mobile robots based on the actor model [hewitt77]. Every network node(host) is a hardware actor that carries out software actors (processes). Each hardware actor is an autonomous communicating entity. The system is composed of a set of system servers and of user processes. An application is composed of cooperating processes using different resources and possibly working on different hosts. Independent applications work on separated territories, composed of one or more hosts.

The first section presents the nomadic computing model with the wireless communications, robotic computers, and resource mobility. Section 2 describes our resource management schemes based on the territory model. Section 3 presents our Actor Network for nomadic robots: ActNet. We conclude this paper in Section 4.

1   COOPERATIVE APPLICATIONS IN MOBILE SYSTEMS

In our model, we consider mobile computers to be computers that are able to move (while communicating with mobile robots) and nomadic computers, those that need to be disconnected from the wired network to change location (notebooks). We first present communication architectures for mobile computers and then the constraints of this new technology.

1.1   Wireless communications

The channel used in mobile communication is the atmosphere. This channel is an extremely noisy one and is subject to various interferences (scrambling, etc..). Information is carried by a wave characterized by its frequency. Three frequency domains are mainly concerned: the visible domain with a coherent laser transmission, the infrared domain and the radio frequency domain. Laser links are rare, and they are mostly used for static point-to-point communications. Due to high attenuations, infra-red communications are reserved for short distance links, a room or an office. Radio-frequency links concern short to long distances. Thus, only these two last communication domains are used in mobile systems.

The topologies used consist mainly of three types: bus, star, and ring. The topology is static. Wireless Local Area Networks (WLAN) use, in most cases, the same channel and the access type is, in general, Pure-Aloha type or Slotted-Aloha type [aloha]. Star topology is mostly reserved for long distance communications (e.g. satellite), and frequency channels are divided among several users. The communication zone is divided into cells, in order to limit transmission power and to avoid interferences. A data concentrator by cell allocates one or several frequencies to one mobile, used for user data and management data. This allocation does not change during the communication if the mobile stays in the same cell. Cells are linked among themselves by specialized wired links (see Figure 1).

1.2   Mobile computing constraints

Mobile communication is characterized by the following criteria:
- energetic autonomy,
- transmission reliability,
- communication speed,
- distances bringing into play,
- cost.

Embedded devices must be equipped with electronic modules using minimum current, because energy is limited (battery). We call that the energetic autonomy criteria. It is fundamental because it has a direct effect on operation duration and transmission power (the maximal distance of communication). The transmission power is generally low (a few watts) and despite using efficient amplification types (C, D in particular), the maximal distance of communication is less than several kilometers, essentially because of channel attenuation. The energetic autonomy which depends on electrical consumption is a few hours.

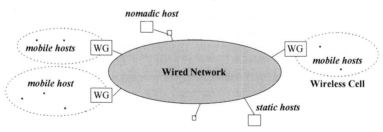

Figure 1. Mobile Networks

Reliability criteria is more difficult to solve because the type of channel used, in our case the atmosphere, is accessible to every one and therefore could be disturbed (intentionally or not). Wired links are more reliable by definition in spite of electromagnetic interference, e.g. crosswalk or attenuation. It can also be subject to intentional access (listening, disruption or intrusion of false data).

The communication speed is higher for a wired link (100 MBits/s) than a wireless one (10 MBits/s), in spite of compression and efficient modulation mechanisms. Moreover, the set of frequency channels is limited in number and in bandwidth.

A system for mobile networks has to take into account the numerous variable perturbations of the communication medium and its limited performances.

1.3   Mobile environment model

Our system is based on the actor model [hewitt77]. An actor can be described as an autonomous active entity which uses messages to communicate. An actor can only be accessed through its message queue. Actors offer a uniform communication scheme among all the entities of our mobile system, hardware or software, static or mobile. This allows implementing transparent services needed by mobile hosts.

Cooperative applications use a set of resources distributed over the global network. These resources can be software (file) or hardware (printer) or more specific ones (motor). After a reconnection, actors located on a nomadic host need to locate the remote resources they were accessing. Resources managed by this host should also be made visible to other hosts.

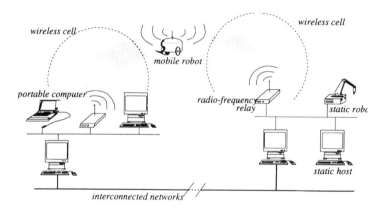

Figure 2. Mobility between two wireless cells

To define the location method of resources after a reconnection, we classified resources in three types:

1. **Static resources** that have a specified location on the network. An actor using these resources still uses the same ones after it migrates or its host moves (i.e printer device).
2. **Duplicated resources** that have fixed locations but are duplicated on the network. After the actor migration (due to mobile hosts or load balancing), the actor will use the closest version of the resource accessible to improve performances (i.e system files).
3. **Mobile resources** that can migrate with an actor to better answer the application need and improve their performances (users' files).

After reconnection, depending on the kind of resource an actor wants to access (static, duplicated or mobile), it calls the resource location, a manager on the network to find a copy, or asks the resource to migrate.

2   TERRITORY SCHEME FOR RESOURCES MANAGEMENT

Cooperative application management in a local network of static hosts already pose many problems like load sharing, fault tolerance and efficient resources access. Numerous studies have been completed on these problems: Utopia [zhou92], and Gatos [folliot92] for load balancing, Coda [coda90] for disconnected file operations, Amoeba [tanenbaum90] for fault tolerance.

This management is even more complex in the case of mobile computers [badrinath93a] due to:

1. frequent disconnection of mobile computers,
2. resources duplication to allow disconnect work,
3. reconnection after a location change.

In our system, an execution territory is associated with each cooperative application.

We introduce the **Execution Territory** (ET) to allow an efficient control of cooperative application processes. An ET, associated with an application, is composed of a set of hosts on which application processes are executed. When an application starts, a territory is assigned to it and evolves according to host load. On this territory migration processes will be carried out to solve load imbalance introduced by process execution.

Each ET is managed by a **Territory Manager** (TM) in charge of data gathering from the hosts belonging to its territory (e.g. inter-process communications, host loads, resource utilization). The TM is also in charge of preserving application information during disconnection.

With this information, the TM maintains an execution graph of the application and is able to detect any load imbalance due to an overloaded host or inefficient resource access. Statistics are only gathered at the territory level by the TM, so that each manager has a local view of the system state.

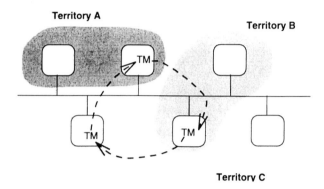

Figure 3. Territory Management

All the TM are linked with a virtual ring, allowing them to exchange management information (see Figure 3). The processes access the resources through resource managers (RM) dispatched over the network.

2.1   Processes and resource migration

An application can be described by a dynamic execution graph that represents resource utilization by the different processes of the application. When a mobile host moves, it can create a load imbalance due to the executing processes or system resources on the mobile host (e.g. a process on the mobile host was formally using a close resource located on a static host. After location change and due to network "latency", the demand on this resource can be drastically costly). Load imbalance can also be the result of application evolution (e.g. start of new processes).

For load balancing, the application territory can proceed to the migration of processes and, in case of resources, can ask for its migration or for the use of another instance (if duplicated) by sending a hint to the resource manager (RM).

If the load imbalance is due to application processes, the execution territory can gain or lose some hosts. In the case of inefficient resource access, and depending on the resource (mobile, duplicated or static), the environment will evolve.

The territory scheme also allows a mobile host to easily reconnect by contacting the last location of its TM. If, during disconnection time, the TM has migrated, the contacted host will ask its own TM to search for the new location of the mobile host TM.

3   ACTNET: A ROBOTIC NETWORK

ActNet, for "Actor Network", is a robotic environment testbed which proposes a development and execution environment for actor based applications. ActNet is adressed to both DAI research and educational environment. [darche93]. Actors communicate through the medium of a local network.

From a hardware point of view, ActNet is a set of heterogeneous actors, which can be split between hardware actors and a software actor embedded by hardware actors. In our model, we have characterized two type of hardware actors:

- Static Robotic Actor (SRA),
- Mobile Robotic Actor (MRA).

Executive sub-networks of moving actors (M.A.S.N.) and sedentary actors (S.A.S.N.) are associated with each type of hardware actor, and Gateways Actors manage communications between sub-networks. Moreover, a users' sub-network (U.S.N.) is dedicated to the development and control of users' applications.

CONCLUSION

The use of nomadic computers implies more secure and flexible operating systems because both applications and resources are mobile. To control the application needs and then decide which process to migrate or which resource to use, we introduce the application territory. This allows to dynamically benefit from all available resources according to application needs. Cooperative application management is carried out on two levels : inside an execution territory for an independent application where a centralized scheme is used, and on the global network with a distributed scheme to equilibrate resource utilization between applications. One major advantage of this model is its scalability (territory size is independent of the global network size).

Having a centralized algorithm allows for better decisions for application management and helps mobile computers to locate formally accessed resources or communicating processes when reconnecting.

We are currently implementing our system for the robotic actors network **ActNet** [darche93]. This network is representative because it includes mobile entities (mobile robotic actors) and static ones (static robotic actors, workstations).

KEYWORDS

Mobile computing, resource management, actor model, load balancing.

REFERENCES

[1]   Hewitt C., Viewing control structures as patterns of passing messages. Artificial Intelligence, 8(3):323-364, June (1977).

[2]   Abramson N., Development of the ALOHANET, IEEE Transactions on Information Theory, 2(32):119-123, March (1985).

[3]   Zhou S., Zheng X.,Wang J., Delisle P., Utopia: A Load Sharing Facility for Large, Heterogeneous Distributed Computer System, Technical Report 257, Computer Systems Research Institute, Université de Toronto, Canada, April (1992).

[4]   Folliot B., Méthodes et outils de partage de charge pour la conception et la mise en oeuvre d'applications dans les systèmes répartis hétérogènes, PhD thesis, Université ParisVI, Dec.(1992).

[5]   Satyanarayanan M., Kistler J.-J., Kumar P., Okasaki M.-E., Siegel E. H. and Steere D.-C., Coda: A Highly Available File System for a Distributed Workstation Environment, IEEE Transactions on Computers, 39(4):447-459, April (1990).

[6]   Tanenbaum A.-S., van Renesse R., van Staveren H., Sharp G.-J., Mullender S.-J., Jansen J., van Rossum G., Experiences with the amoeba distributed operating system, Communication of the ACM, 33:46-63, Dec.(1990).

[7]   Badrinath B.-R., Acharya A., Imielinski T., Impact of Mobility on Distributed Computations, Operating System Review, April.(1993).

[8]   Darche P. and Nowak G., ActNet: A Heterogeneous Network of Actors for Learning of Parallelism, Communication and Synchronization, volume 116 of Control Technology in Elementary Education, NATO ASI Series F, 289-307 Springer Verlag, Berlin (1993).

PART TWO

WORLDWIDE AND REGIONAL INFORMATION SYSTEMS

POLICIES AND PROGRAMS

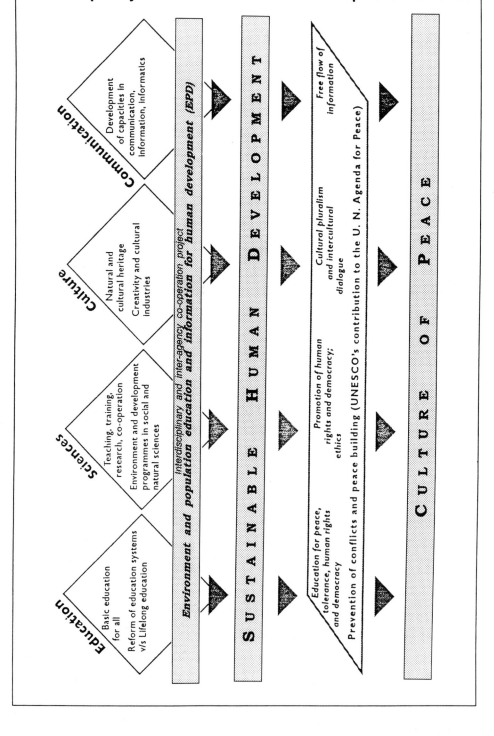

Chapter 4

UNESCO POLICY, WORLDWIDE NETWORKS, REGIONAL EXCHANGE EQUITY

UNESCO POLICY ON DATA EXCHANGE : GRAVE DISPARITIES IN SCIENTIFIC DATA ACCESS

Adnan BADRAN

UNESCO, 7 place de Fontenoy, 75700 Paris

ABSTRACT

Current changes linked to the electronic revolution and to the information revolution presage the arrival of a "knowledge society" in the 21st century. New technologies should rapidly eliminate the usual barriers preventing the passage of information between countries. However, for the time being, some countries are experiencing grave delays and are, in fact, a new class of "information have-nots". UNESCO wants to gradually eliminate regional disparities in information by acting in three directions: developing an international physical transmission network, transmitting data from country to country and, thereby, a policy targeting real support. For these reasons UNESCO is considering the implementation of a "UNESCO Scientific Channel" and encouraging the establishment of a "virtual global library" using electronic publishing. In interdisciplinary sciences and global projects, UNESCO supports many actions. Among others, let us mention the MAB Program (Man and Biosphere) and its GTOS System (Global Terrestrial Observing System), the program currently being developed on Biodiversity and Biosphere Reserves, as well as the International Hydrological Program geared towards the study of climate. Global ecosystems are approached by the IOC

(International Oceanographic Commission) involving 123 Member States. Among other application systems, we can mention the IODE (International Oceanographic Data and Information Exchange System), grouping thirteen Responsible Centers that manage data and assist World Data Centers. UNESCO's objective is to create networks of specialists to improve communications and a fair sharing of knowledge world-wide.

Resume

Les changements actuels associés à la "révolution électronique" et à la "révolution de l'information" laissent prévoir une "société de la connaissance" au 21ème siècle. Les nouvelles technologies devraient éliminer rapidement les barrières usuelles de passage de l'information entre les pays. Cependant les retards de certains pays sont trop importants. L'UNESCO a pour objectif de supprimer peu à peu les disparités régionales dans le domaine de l'information en agissant sur trois voies : celle du développement d'un réseau physique international de transmission, celle de la transmission des données de pays à pays et celle d'une politique de financement de soutiens réels. A ce titre l'UNESCO considère la mise en service d'une "chaîne scientifique UNESCO" et encourage la création d'une "bibliothèque globale virtuelle" faisant appel à l'édition électronique. Dans les sciences à caractère interdisciplinaire et les projets globaux, l'UNESCO soutient de nombreuses actions. Citons entre autres le programme MAB (Homme et Biosphère), et son système GTOS (Global Terrestrial Observing System), le programme en cours de développement sur la Biodiversité et les Réserves de la Biosphère ainsi que le Programme International d'Hydrologie orienté vers l'étude des climats. Les écosystèmes au plan global sont abordés par l'IOC (Commission Océanographique Internationale) concernant 123 Etats membres. Parmi les systèmes d'application citons le réseau IODE, regroupant treize noeuds nationaux qui gèrent les données avec les Centres Mondiaux de Données (NDC). L'UNESCO a pour objectif de créer des réseaux de spécialistes pour améliorer les communications et le partage équitable de la connaissance sur le plan mondial.

1   Introduction

Science has existed since the dawn of human society. As Victor Weisskopf wrote: "Human existence depends upon compassion and curiosity. Curiosity without compassion is inhuman; compassion without curiosity is ineffective". Both curiosity and compassion are essential factors for the development of scientific knowledge. It is widely recognized that modern   society is moving towards a knowledge-based one. Science and its technological applications become crucial elements in the process of economic growth and development.

2   Science and Technology Paradigms

As emphasized in a recent UNESCO publication: "Science and technology exist only through human beings in action in certain contexts and as such cannot be entirely value-free and neutral". We may curse science and technology or bless them (this is what C. Freeman said about technology), but we cannot ignore them. The outstanding progress accomplished by science and, associated with technology, the immense services it renders society depend, not only on the resources allocated for research or on the implementation of deliberate science, technology and innovation policy, but also on the capacity of society to adapt very rapidly to the new needs generated by advances in knowledge and on its ability to process large volumes of information received as a result of scientific activities in order to exploit the results of scientific research in the interests of society.

Scientific research has two products: knowledge and technology. The role of the first was stressed nearly four centuries ago by Francis Bacon: "knowledge is power". However, in the modern world, as R. Clarke rightly indicated, the control of the creation, acquisition and use of knowledge can very often lead to power.

The scientific data in which knowledge is embedded represents the precious heritage of humanity. A variety of experimental methods, advances in modelling and simulation techniques, new mathematical tools for assessing and analyzing vast quantities of scientific data, - all these achievements make it possible to advance scientific research as never before. The free flow of scientific information will further accelerate the progress of science.

3   THE ELECTRONIC REVOLUTION: GLOBALIZATION OF SCIENTIFIC EXCHANGES

This revolution now underway dramatically alters the social order world-wide. The new information technologies are able to eliminate current barriers between countries and individuals imposed by distance and time. The number of computers used in the world seems likely to reach one billion within a few years. Fast improvements in computational power and storage capacity create new possibilities for great expansion, rapidly replacing old intellectual traditions with a new way of teaching and learning science. Such integrated networks have rendered long-distance collaboration, data exchange and even remote control of instruments, routine for scientists.

If an individual scientist operating a personal computer can be considered analogous to a single nerve cell, the emerging global web of information networks operated by billions of educated people working together around the globe becomes analogous to a "global brain" possessing a "global intelligence". Already emerged "electronic communities" of specialists (physicists, chemists, biologists, etc.) pave the way to a new "knowledge society" of the 21st century.

The consequences of such globalization of scientific communication for the further progress of science can scarcely be overestimated.

Several examples can be mentioned.

- Laboratories throughout the world, linked by the network, have begun collaborating to completely sequence the DNA of several organisms, leading ultimately to sequencing the entire human genome. The databases that must be linked include DNA sequences (GenBank), chromosome mapping information (Genome Data Bank) and protein sequences and structure (Protein Information Resource)
- Physicists have enthusiastically developed and used electronic archives in areas such as high-energy physics as an alternative to buying journals costing hundreds to thousands of dollars per year for subscriptions.
- The nature of research itself is changing. Today scientists are seeking answers to more complex problems, while the instruments and facilities needed to conduct research are becoming increasingly expensive and the funding for scientists' projects is becoming scarcer. This strongly encourages increased world-wide collaboration among researchers. There is considerable impetus for such collaboration in oceanographic research, for example, where research projects not only cross the   lines of the traditional scientific disciplines (i.e. , chemistry and geology) but also   require international collaboration among scientists.

4   ECONOMIC INEQUITIES AND INFORMATION SHARING DISPARITIES

All this requires an effective system of global communication.

The globalization of scientific communication is of particular importance to scientists in the developing countries of Africa, the Arab states, Asia and Latin America, as well as to those in Central and Eastern Europe, including Russia, whose participation in information sharing and scientific exchanges has been minimal. Due to existing economic inequities, researchers in these countries have been cut off from the information glut prevailing in the developed world, The new "class" of "information have-nots" has unfortunately emerged.

The consequences of scientific information shortage may be grave for world science. "When the   libraries of Indian Universities can no longer be stocked, the brain cells of an entire subcontinent   are threatened with sclerosis", said an international inter-University network publication.

With international networking, scientists, professors and students from any country in the world   have an almost infinite resource pool from which to seek information and knowledge.

5   INTERNATIONAL CONNECTIVITY IN UNESCO SCIENTIFIC CHANNEL

But of course such international connectivity will not fall from the skies by chance. There are three component parts needed to achieve these data traffic international connections: transmission between countries, data distribution within countries and multilateral (or bilateral) agreements on technical (e.g. standards, addressing, etc.) and policy issues (e.g. financing).

UNESCO has started to work in this direction. Together with adopting our own strategy for improving and modernizing information systems, which should allow us to provide on-line information to Member States, a new project called "UNESCO Scientific Channel" was launched aiming at ensuring international scientific connectivity of Universities and individual scientists in developing countries and in Eastern Europe and Russia and providing a focal point to many intergovernmental, governmental and scientific organisations working in this field. A recent meeting of the think-tank, set up by the Director-General of UNESCO, has produced practical recommendations, in favour of implementing the UNESCO Scientific Channel.

One of the recommendations was to promote the global shift to electronic publishing in science with the purpose of creating a virtual global library. In conjunction with ICSU, UNESCO plans to organize an international Conference on scientific electronic publishing in 1995. It is interesting to note that, contrary to the widespread opinion that public libraries are dying, surveys in the USA, for example, show that in 1992 more than half (53%) of the adult population of that country used public libraries as a key provider of information, as did 74% of the children. According to the survey 99% of all academic libraries in the USA now offer electronic information services.

6   SCIENTIFIC DATA GLOBAL SYSTEMS

Scientific Data in Environmental Sciences: UNESCO ROLE

UNESCO contributes to the environmental sciences and to developing scientifically-based management strategies related to ocean, coastal areas, land, the biosphere and water balance. All these subjects require huge volumes of scientific data. Here are some examples of how UNESCO contributes to receiving and processing these data.

Global terrestrial observing system (GTOS)

Global changes in climate, atmospheric chemistry and land use present a formidable and unique research challenge. The world's terrestrial and associated freshwater and coastal ecosystems are being subjected to changing environmental conditions of an unprecedented scale, both in rate and in geographical range. The ability of human societies to improve, adapt to and benefit from these rapid changes requires fundamental knowledge of the response of terrestrial ecosystems to the forces of global change. The data are required both to detect and monitor changes and to develop and test models for projection of future changes.

To this end, UNESCO, through its <u>Program on Man and the Biosphere (MAB)</u>, has actively contributed to launching and developing <u>the Global Terrestrial Observing</u>

<u>System (GTOS)</u>, an international scientific effort co-sponsored by IGBP, FAO, UNEP, WMO and UNESCO. The basis for GTOS was elaborated at a workshop held in Fontainebleau (France) in July 1992 under the aegis of the Observatoire du Sahara et du Sahel (OSS), the Global Change and Terrestrial Ecosystems core project of International Geosphere-Biosphere Program (IGBP) and MAB. The Workshop succeeded in reaching a number of agreements including:

- a set of basic principles,
- procedures for selecting priority regions for monitoring,
- a sampling strategy combining intensive and extensive measurements integrated with remote sensing,
- criteria for selecting bytes representing the full range of ecosystems, from pristine to intensively managed,
- sets of measurements that characterize the sets, detect the drivers of change and monitor responses,
- data management and quality assurance procedures.

The Scientific Planning Group of this project is currently engaged in studying questions such as: data management, access and harmonization; operation aspects and national needs. This latter point is important since much of the scientific effort is conducted by industrialized countries interested in global change; yet GTOS must also address the specific national requirements of developing countries with less capacity to participate in such efforts.

GTOS plans to be complementary and mutually supportive of the other global observing Systems on the ocean (GOOS) and the climate (GCOS). The terrestrial systems on which GTOS will focus will include:

- the land (topography, terrain form and soils) and its resources, covering the full range from pristine to intensively managed sites for silviculture and agriculture,
- the surface freshwater and hydrology (including the cryosphere) and non-confined sub-surface hydrology,
- their microbes, fauna and flora,
- the human population settlements and the results of their impact on the land.

It is expected that GTOS will cover the broad question of the monitoring of biodiversity, for which there are two UNESCO activities of special relevance: the international network of biosphere reserves of the MAB Program and that part of the

DiverSitas Program focusing on selected groups of organisms (plants, animals or micro-organisms) in a wide variety of sites.

Biosphere Reserves, - Building Up an International Information Network on Biodiversity

One of the major components of the UNESCO MAB Program is the development of Biosphere Reserves and the international network they form. The innovative idea of integrating roles of conservation, research, monitoring and education, and local economic development in one protected area has been widely accepted and put into practice for biodiversity conservation and its sustainable use. As of January 1994, 324 Biosphere Reserves in 82 countries have been designated under the MAB Program.

One of the primary objectives of the Biosphere Reserves project is to develop an international information network in order to generate and distribute knowledge and information on biological resources and biological diversity. This concept of an information network, in particular, distinguishes Biosphere reserves from other protected areas. Indeed Biosphere Reserves have many attractive features for constituting such an information network. The sites already represent some 61% of all 193 biogeographical provinces in the world and cover a total area of more than 200,000,000 ha of terrestrial and coastal ecosystems. Most biosphere Reserves have a long history of scientific research. Many have been conducting long-term biological or ecological inventories and monitoring programs. Important technologies, protocols and innovations in environmental monitoring are also developed in Biosphere Reserves. Examples of the contributions of Biosphere Reserves include the establishment of the Long Term Ecological Research (LTER) sites in Biosphere Reserves in North America, development of a coordinated tropical forest monitoring program in Biosphere Reserves in North and Central America and in Asia, and support for intensive ecological research in developing countries such as the Ecological Research Network in China. Experiments on and management practices of the Biosphere Reserve concept have been undertaken in many individual Sites, especially in those of developing countries, where valuable knowledge on using and managing biodiversity, especially at ecosystem levels, is generated and obtained.

A UNESCO Biosphere Reserve Directory provides an access guide to the basic locations and characteristics of the Reserves, contact personnel and a list of existing environmental databases. A Biosphere Reserve Site Description Database furnishes comprehensive information on the scientific, managerial, social and legal aspects of the protected areas. New databases for major taxa species (MABFauna and MABFlora) and site characteristics of permanent vegetation plots within Biosphere Reserves are being tested in Europe. These new databases may set a prototype for other regions. Other databases are planned, including the on-going research projects in Biosphere Reserves, Biosphere Reserve bibliography and a digital Biosphere Reserve Atlas.

While encouraging progress is being made, a truly functioning Biosphere Reserve information network is deemed a long-term objective. Setting up adequate data standards and data exchange protocols is a time-consuming exercise. There are still Sites where people "re-invent the wheel" in terms of what data are collected, how they are obtained and analyzed. Introduction of new information technologies is also a long-term endeavour, taking into account the large variety of data needs and research interests, different levels of technical capacity in the country and, at the same time, the rapid evolution of the technical tools themselves.

It is in this context that connecting the sites through electronic networks becomes a new element on the agenda of MAB activities. A recent initiative is in the Central European Region, where five countries (Belarus, Czech Republic, Poland, Slovak Republic and the Ukraine) cooperate with the World Bank, UNESCO and other organisations to build up an electronic network.

UNESCO hopes that through this effort a technical package of tools, protocols, training materials and MAB expertise for networking Biosphere Reserves can be developed and, in future, adapted or transferred to other Biosphere Reserves. To this end, UNESCO seeks cooperation with other international agencies and institutes. These questions were also discussed at the international Forum on "Biodiversity, Science & Development: Towards a New Partnership", in September, 1994 at UNESCO.

Within the International Hydrological Program, UNESCO has a project on the "Study of the relationship between climate change (and climate variability) and hydrological regimes affecting water balance components". The impact of various climate scenarios on the hydrological cycle was evaluated.

This project culminated in a workshop with members of the IPCC, held in Delft, The Netherlands in May 1995 to review a State-of-the-Art UNESCO publication.

A separate development is the on-going implementation through ROSTLAC, in co-operation with the World Bank, of LACHYCOS (Latin America and Caribbean hydrological cycle and water resource activities observation and information system) throughout the Latin American region. This initiative will improve the databases for the region as a prerequisite for planning projects in applied research/training.

IOC Data Management Activities

The oceans and coastal terrestrial areas are the most important parts of the global ecosystem. By the year 2000, it is estimated that 75% of the world's population will live within 60 kilometres of the coast. Scientific input towards better understanding of coastal and ocean environments is one of UNESCO's major tasks, in particular of the IOC. The Intergovernmental Oceanographic Commission (IOC) was founded in 1960 as a functionally autonomous body within UNESCO and it now includes 123 Member States. Recognizing the importance of international cooperation in research and monitoring, the IOC promotes scientific marine investigations and related ocean services with a view to learning more about the nature and resources of our oceans and coastal areas.

The Commission focuses on three major objectives.

- to promote and coordinate multinational, cooperative investigations in the broad fields of oceanography and marine Science;
- to provide ocean Services to Member States, including data exchange networks, observing and monitoring Stations, and analysis and forecasting of oceanic conditions that affect coastal areas, such as tsunamis, storm surges and El Nino episodes;
- to foster national capacity building in marine sciences and oceanography through education and training, voluntary cooperation and partnerships.

As the inter-linkages between land and sea become more and more apparent, particularly in light of the predicted effects of climate change on the coastal zone, the IOC'S focus has shifted increasingly towards the development and application of science for the resolution of marine environmental issues. IOC maintains cooperative programs with numerous other international bodies such as UNEP, WMO, FAO and IMO. The IOC also cooperates in joint programs with ICSU and IUCN as well as with regional bodies like ICES. Essentially all of IOC's major programs contain elements that are of direct relevance to integrated coastal management.

Chapter 17 of Agenda 21, adopted by UNCED, calls for new approaches to "integrated management and sustainable development of coastal and marine areas, including exclusive economic zones". It also calls upon countries to "cooperate in the development of necessary coastal systematic observation, research and information management systems". Scientific input is required for essentially all aspects of integrated coastal management: mapping, establishment of baseline conditions, data management, quantification of problems and their causes, predictive modelling, impact assessment, formulation of mitigation measures and systematic long-term monitoring. Unfortunately, our scientific understanding of the majority of coastal processes and systems is far from complete. The established information systems help alleviate these problems.

The International Oceanographic Data and Information Exchange System (IODE)

This was established in 1960 to facilitate the exchange of oceanographic data and information among Member States of the IOC. The International Oceanographic Data and Information Exchange System provides standard forms for coding and reporting data, encourages the preparation of data catalogues and assists in developing national oceanographic data centres. The System is based on the principle that national institutions, international programs and individual scientists contribute data voluntarily to the IODE Data Centers for the benefit of all. System users can then obtain free of charge, or at a very low price, data, data products or data inventory information.

The IODE Network :

National Oceanographic Data Centers (NODCs) and Designated National Agencies (DNAs) which provide contact with the oceanographic programs of Member States. In addition to responsibility for data collection, processing, quality control, archiving and dissemination nationally, NODCs are responsible for international exchange. A total of 44 countries now have such a center.

Responsible National Oceanographic Data Centers (RNODCs) assist World Data Centers with particular requirements for data provision or retrieval and with a particular type of data or specific region. There are 13 RNODCs.

World Data centers for Oceanography (WDCs) receive oceanographic data and inventories from NODCs, RNODCs, marine science organisations and individual scientists, freely exchange data, publications and inventories among one another and provide, upon request, copies of data, inventories and publications. WDCs have held almost three million observations, including 569,000 bathythermographs, 207,000 biological observations and 670,000 current measurements.

Recently, the Intergovernmental Oceanographic Commission of UNESCO evaluated the results of the IODE Data Centres. Over the years, three major areas of change were noted. There is a wider range of marine disciplines; customers are more demanding and ocean science is becoming more global. These changes require NODCs, RNODCs and WDCs to deal with growing diversity of data types and with larger scale programs with a variety of objectives collecting a much larger volume of data from sensors and more sophisticated sensors.

The need for more operational data must be adressed. IODE should move toward IGOSS time-scales and be prepared to deal with a wider range of data types more promptly and evaluate standards, format structures, protocols and ilinkages to operate on a truly global scale.

Customers have become more demanding because they understand the new technologies and expect the data centre to use them and deliver data products through a central inventory of the location of high quality control datasets, e.g. an improved MEDI available on WWW and CD-ROM.

World Biodiversity Database

Support is provided to the UNESCO-initiated Biodiversity Database of the Expert-Center for Taxonomic Identification (ETI), Amsterdam. The Center is rapidly becoming a world leader in the production and publication of taxonomic ultimedia. The overall UNESCO-ETI objective is to set up world-wide networks of specialists in order to increase communication and knowledge-sharing and to develop and produce educational materials and computer-based taxonomic information. ETI compiles information on plant and animal species and feeds it into a unique World Biodiversity Database.At the same time the species descriptions with illustrations, video and sound recordings, as well as identification keys and distribution maps are published on CD-ROM. Located at the University of Amsterdam, as a non-profit foundation, theCenter is funded by the Netherlands Government and the University, with UNESCO providing overall advice as well as catalytic funds for international networking. Individual scientists cooperating with ETI are granted support from national and international (including the European Community) sources.

The UNESCO-published 3-volume "Fishes of the Northeast Atlantic and Mediterranean" (FNAM) became available on CD-ROM following feedback and updated information obtained from a network of 62 ichthyologists. The WINDOWS version is available. Two other CD-ROMs on "North Australian Sea Cucumbers" and "Marine Planarians of the World" were produced as well.

Several CD-ROMs with taxonomic, biogeographic and other biodiversity-related information are being finalized on various groups, including Lobsters (with FAO), Sea Mammals, Pelagic Molluscs and Sponges. The "Five Kingdoms" of Lynn Margulis is being updated for CD-ROM publication and will be of interest to students, teachers and the general public.

With their vast taxonomic expertise, scientists from Russia and neighbouring countries, besides those from Africa, Asia and Latin America, are encouraged to contribute to the biodiversity database. To that end, ETI, with the financial assistance of UNESCO, made an agreement with the Russian Academy of Sciences for the creation of an ETI-Russia branch to deal with marine groups in particular.

Springer Verlag and UNESCO joined efforts with ETI in order to make the CD-ROMs widely available at the lowest possible price.

CONCLUSION

The variety of information systems sponsored by UNESCO in the various aspects of science and technology is oriented by the urgent need to rationalize our vision of the world on the eve of the Electronic and Information Revolution.

UNESCO is fully aware of the difficulties encountered in information sharing and scientific exchange which are often far from being acceptable on certain regional levels. To face the problems created by the emergence of many "Information have-not" countries UNESCO is carrying out intensive action to identify new ways and means to achieve an equitable exchange of information throughout the world and its various specific regional and general contributions and needs in the future.

KEYWORDS

Data Access, UNESCO scientific channel, electronic publishing, network, virtual global library, environmental sciences, biodiversity, GTOS, IOC, IODE.

ACRONYM LIST

UNESCO	:	United Nations Education, Scientific, Cultural Organization
MAB	:	Program on Man And the Biosphere
GTOS	:	Global, Terrestrial Observing System
IOC	:	International Oceanographic Commission
IODE	:	International Oceanographic Data and Information Exchange
IGBP	:	International Geosphere-Biosphere Program
FAO	:	Food and Agriculture Organization
UNEP	:	United Nations Environment Program
WMO	:	World Meteorogical Organization
OSS	:	Observatory of the Sahara and the Sahel
GOOS	:	Global Ocean Observing Systems
GCOS	:	Global Climate Observing Systems
LTER	:	Long Term Ecological Research
IPPC	:	Intergovernmental Panel on Climate Change
ICSU	:	International Council of Scientific Unions
ICES	:	International Council of Environmental Sciences
UNCED	:	United Nations Committee for Environment
NODCs	:	National Oceanographic data Centers
DNAs	:	Designated national Agencies
RNODCs	:	Responsible National Oceanographic Data Centers
WDCOs	:	World Data Centers for Oceanography
ETI	:	Expert-Center for Taxonomic Identification
MOST	:	Management of Social Transformations
WDC	:	World Data Centers

Networking Africa's Scientific and Technical Information Resources

Steve F. ROSSOUW

School of Business Informatics, Cape Technikon, Cape Town, South Africa

Abstract

Access to reliable and dependable information is a prerequisite for a healthier environment. CD-ROM technology and the Internet will be the key to unlocking Africa's scientific and technical information resources. The Index to South African periodicals, available on CD-ROM is suggested as an example for an Africa-wide STI database.

Resume

Un environnememt plus sain nécessite l'accès à des informations fiables et sûres. La technologie des CD-ROM et le réseau Internet apportent des solutions permettant de sortir les resources africaines en information scientifique et techniques de leur isolement. L'index des périodiques de l'Afrique du Sud , disponible sur CD-ROM est présenté ici comme un exemple d'outil de consultation de larges bases africaines de données scientifiques et techniques.

1 Introduction

If data and knowledge are considered essential for a healthier environment in today's world, then few things contribute as much to such an environment, free from sickness and ill-health, as reliable information, appropriate and applicable in a particular region. Following a brief review of the current situation in Africa, a continent wrecked by war, disease, natural disaster and a population explosion, we propose a concept to use information technology, e.g. electronic mail, to collect and make available the wealth of data and information generated by Africa's scientists.

2 The African Situation

Health and disease are topics of great concern in Africa, today more than ever. The world's television and other media show us with monotonous regularity the sad situation of the peoples of Africa: Ethiopia, Somalia, Rwanda, Angola, Mozambique.

These diseases and afflictions are almost unknown in the developed/industrialized countries. Where they do occur, they are treated rapidly, efficiently and speedily. Modern medicine can cure most of mankind's illnesses today, excepting a few such as cancer or Aids. But even then, the treatment of patients occurs under hygienic and manageable conditions. What is the situation in parts of Africa? In Rwanda thousands of men, women and children have died or are dying, not of serious or strange diseases: malnutrition, exhaustion, hunger, terrible wounds, gangrene, dehydration. This is happening in spite of the efforts of relief agencies, that there are doctors there, that food is being distributed by relief agencies, water purification plants are made available. Why then do people still die? People die, even in the absence of war and rebellion, simply because of the magnitude of the problem, the absence of reliable, relevant, implementable information covering health care and medical services under dire circumstances such as no hospitals, or ill-equipped ones, no clean water, not enough nutrition, the press of hundreds, sometimes thousands, of ill and starving people.

3   THE INFORMATION PARADOX

In an era of so-called information explosion, what information might be available to redress the situation? One of the world's major sources of medical information, Index Medicus/Medline, indexes some 3 000 plus medical journals. Most of these titles are published in the industrialized countries, containing largely the result of research carried out in those same countries, some 250 000 to 300 000 citations each year. A veritable deluge of scientific data and information. Information concerning organ transplantation, rare genetic disorders, or the operation of MRI equipment is of academic interest to the medical missionary or "bare foot" doctor in Africa where basic information on pit latrines or inexpensive water purification would prevent more disease than a plane load of antibiotics.

The very basic information, emanating from a make-do approach in one African country that rural doctors, nurses, orderlies even, have to apply is most often what would be most useful under similar circumstances in other African countries. The only problem is that it is not accessible. Not because it is not published, but because in the competition for acceptance by the leading international journals, such basic, almost elementary contributions come a poor second. They do however appear in print, usually in the journal of a local medical society or even in medical publications appearing with the support of one of the pharmaceutical multinationals. Because of the stiff competition for inclusion in the leading indexing and abstracting services (*Index Medicus, Exerpta Medica, International Pharmaceutical Abstracts*), these local journals have almost no chance of acceptance. Their contents are therefore not widely known, sometimes hardly beyond their own country's borders.

To illustrate this state of affairs, *Index Medicus* contains citations from 27 African medical journals, yet SERLINE, the NLM's database of medical journals, lists 42 African journals that are currently appearing. It can safely be assumed that even more medical journals are actually being published in Africa. The 27 indexed titles yielded 1389 citations during 1992. If we take a rough average of 50 articles per annum for each of the 27 journals, and apply that to the 15 journals in SERLINE but not in *Index Medicus*, as many as 750 articles per year from African medical journals never make it to the international databases. Some of those might have been life saving. This problem of the "lost" data has been recognized in South Africa and efforts to collect, index and provide access to a wider regional and international audience is now on a firm basis with the availability of the *Index to South African Periodicals* (ISAP) database, online and on CD-ROM. This state of affairs has been achieved by networking various libraries and information services to cooperatively index particular journals within their fields of interest and then delivering the indexing data to a central organization, i.e. the State Library in Pretoria. The Medical Research Council indexes 20 titles for ISAP, only eight of which are also indexed for *Index Medicus*/Medline. Table 1 lists South African medical journals indexed both for ISAP and MEDLINE.

Table 1 : Journals in ISAP and MEDLINE
Central African Journal of Medicine
Journal of the Dental Association of South Africa
Journal of the South African Veterinary Association
Nursing RSA
Onderstepoort Journal of Veterinary Research
South African Medical Journal
South African Journal of Communication Disorders
South African Journal of Surgery

The Council for Scientific and Industrial Research indexes no fewer than 152 local journals in science and technology, with the Human Sciences Research contributing 81 titles in the social sciences and humanities. All together, some seven contributors between them index a total of almost 500 titles, the majority of which are not indexed for international databases.

The period covered by the database spans 1987 to date, with weekly and monthly updating available from three different online sources. The same period, updated quarterly, is available on CD- ROM. Indexed records are sent in database format to the State Library, where they are transcribed into SAMARC format. As records are received by the State Library's computer services division the ISAP database is updated and made available online and distributed on CD-ROM to subscribers. Extension of the coverage of ISAP to include a greater number of South African periodicals is limited by the cost of full-scale indexing and abstracting. An alternative which offers a solution would be an ISAP supplement solely based on periodical contents page information and omitting thesaurus terms, keywords or abstracts, coverage thereby avoiding additional indexing costs. These journals contain a wealth of information which has been locally generated concerning indigenous discussions or solutions concerning local situations, problems and perspectives.   Quite often neighboring countries in the sub-continent and even further afield confront similar situations and could very well find in these journals solutions more applicable than from sources much further afield. "Libraries in which ISAP has been made available online or on CD-ROM to users have reported a significant increase in the utilization of their South African journal holdings. This suggests that ISAP plays a useful role in optimizing the use of South Africa's indigenous journal literature."   [De Beer et al, 1993].

Table 2 : Journals in ISAP but not in MEDLINE

AIDS Bulletin

Cardiovascular Journal of Southern Africa

Current Allergy and Immunology

Geneeskunde

Journal of Comprehensive Health

SA Family Practice

SA Journal of Continuing Medical Education

South African Journal of Nutrition

South African Journal of Obstetrics and Gynaecology

South African Journal of Occupational Therapy

South African Journal of Physiotherapy

South African Pharmaceutical Journal

---

4   AFRICAN INDEX MEDICUS

So what about developments further afield? "Lack of foreign exchange prevents African libraries themselves from purchasing material published in other African countries. One result is that research carried out in Africa is not disseminated among countries on the continent. Another is that the small market for locally published material means that publishing is uneconomic ..." [Priestly, 1994: 2]. In August 1993 the University of Zimbabwe and the American Association for the Advancement of Science (AAAS) Sub-Saharan African Program co-organized a workshop for university librarians from Eastern and Southern Africa, which had as its theme how to enhance the ability of libraries to provide services. How to make better use of endogenous research was also examined, with a focus on the creation of computerised databases that index African research information (Anon, 1994: 3- 4). One of the ideas discussed at the time, conceived by the countries of the Southern African Development Community (SADC), was an *African Index Medicus*. The indexing requirements envisaged for participants were extremely steep, and required a fully qualified indexer, a copy typist data input clerk, and a qualified technician to run the not inconsiderable technological demands of the ISIS DBMS prescribed for use (Meyers,1994). The *African Index Medicus* (AIM) however is alive and well. Four print editions have been published, and it's been available online on an experimental basis via the WHO/Geneva gopher (Levey, 1995).

The AAAS is providing six academic libraries in African countries with CD-ROM databases in the sciences and the social sciences coupled with document delivery assistance. The goal is to evaluate how well CD-ROM can replace journal literature (i.e., ownership versus access) and to assess all the costs involved. The universities are Addis Ababa, Dar es Salaam, Ghana, Ibadan, Zambia, and Zimbabwe. The University of Malawi is also involved in the project through a grant to the university from the Rockefeller Foundation (Levey, 1995).

Together with the CD-ROM project there are two small collection development studies under way. UWC is carrying out a cost benefit analysis between CD-ROM and online database searching. UDW is examining the special collection development needs of its advice desk/gender centre. Also, Eduardo Mondlane University is going to conduct its own study--this one on Portuguese-language literature needs. Furthermore, an evaluation is under way of CD-ROM databases for their relevance to African teaching and research needs. The evaluation is being carried out by a subset of the CD-ROM pilot project universities.

5   A PAN-AFRICAN STI INDEX?

Possibly the time has come to look at alternatives to achieve the goal of an African-wide index of STI. With vast political changes sweeping the globe, the African continent is also re-examining its possibilities, opportunities and options. The SADC countries, originally banded together to combat what was perceived to be South Africa's destructive, destabilizing influence, are now ready and willing to cooperate with the New South Africa under its first democratically elected president, Nelson

Mandela. "The African continent can undoubtedly benefit by utilizing electronic communication technology to exchange scientific information. Although a number of infrastructural problems still exist, current African networking activities indicate that the advantages of electronic interaction across borders and continents are being realized." (Van Brakel, 1994:1). At the Africa Telecommunication'94 conference in Cairo, Egypt during April this year AT&T proposed the creation of an African information network to connect the continent's nations with one another and with the rest of the world by fibre-optic cables. The AT&T proposal calls for cable-landing points in African coastal nations. Countries in the African interior would be linked to the system via satellite, microwave, radio, cellular and land communications. The network, which AT&T called Africa ONE, would be operated by African authorities, with revenue from the system remaining in Africa (AP, 25/4/1994). Such a scheme, possibly in coordination with developments taking place from the southern tip of the continent, might yet link African nations together to jointly establish a database to unlock Africa's own STI for mutual utilisation by the contributing countries. *"There are several quite successful links that the South African UNINET network are involved with that are rapidly reaching the cost and volume breakover point where it becomes cheaper to put in a TCP/IP link than making do with dialup lines. These are the links to the University Eduard Mondlane in Mozambique, University of Zimbabwe in Harare, and University of Zambia in Lusaka."* (Guillarmod 1994).

Thanks to some local initiatives, several countries already have local nodal points to access information highways. In Zimbabwe; the Mango network groups two hundred NGOs, researchers and universities; in South Africa, Sangonet is aimed mainly at NGOs; in Uganda, the University of Makarere uses its Mukla network to bring in more than 250 users (in 165 sites, mostly in Kampala); in Kenya, Arccnet links 150 university departments, United Nations agencies, government departments and NGOs to the rest of the world; in Ethiopia, Padisnet was set up in 1991 to allow the thirty-six member states of the UN's Economic Commission for Africa to communicate with each other (Muaz, 1994).

As an update to a list originally compiled for a talk to biologists doing research in Africa, Randy Bush has put together an extensive directory of connectivity in Africa, listing countries from Algeria to Zaire reachable by means of Internet (Bush, 1994). If the information is available but not reachable; if the technology is available and coming into place, what needs to be done to make Africa much more self-sufficient concerning relevant and applicable STI? This objective has been eloquently expressed elsewhere: *"The goal that has to be attained is to make learning, teaching and encountering geographically remote fellow-students, teachers and researchers of a discipline a stimulating experience, keeping as much of the expertise where it is most needed for sustainable development: at the disposal of developing countries within their boundaries. In other words: information, ideas and data should move, scientist should not if movement means emigrating for good. Computer-mediated communication could provide a missing link needed to bring together 'virtual' scientific communities, based on field of activity, rather than on the mere coincidence of vicinity."* (Schlegel & Wiedemeyer, 1994).

Communication networks such as the Internet, which links national networks in a seamless manner, are needed to meet the communication needs of researchers, scientists, educators and their institutions. A scientist isolated is a scientist unable to articulate his purpose and needs; such a scientist soon becomes obsolescent (Bellman & Tindimubona, 1994). South Africa has the most developed infrastructure on the African continent, making it a natural hub for the distribution of products and services, including IT, throughout southern Africa. Other countries in southern Africa have already benefited from South African technical assistance (Goodman, 1994). With the normalisation of links with the rest of Africa, indeed, with South Africa having become a fully-fledged member of the Organization of African Unity (OAU), opportunities to formalise links and set up cooperative agreements for the mutual exploitation of indigenous STI by means of the exploding capabilities of the Internet should be grasped.

Optimism about technological progress and opportunities must of course be tempered by the realities of socio-political needs. The new South African government could still choose to shift funding away from sophisticated IT development to equitable distribution of services. Expansion may stop under the new government because many officials and business leaders consider Internet to be a toy of the universities rather than as a critical technology necessary to counteract South Africa's geographic isolation and to ensure information flow to and from Africa. This would also be a setback for the rest of Africa (Wood et al, 1994).

African nations have overcome technical problems (such as poor quality telephone lines) and administrative hurdles (often restrictive legislation) and have recently set up several African links to the world information highways and in particular to Internet. As information technology (IT) becomes more commonplace and essential in modern business, industry and science, the development of links across the African continent will be especially significant for Southern and Eastern Africa (Muaz, 1994).

CONCLUSION

The many network activities in Africa, such as FidoNet, PANGIS, UNINET and others with nodes and links to the Internet all over the continent (Van Brakel, 1994), will have sufficient resilience to enable the continent to at least utilise electronic mail to link to the Internet in such a way that an African STI database becomes a practical, affordable and vital resource in Africa's struggle against hunger, disease and backwardness.

KEYWORDS

SERLINE, ISAP, FidoNET, UNINET.

REFERENCES

[1]   Anon, 1994, Survival strategies in African university libraries: new technologies in the service of information, AAAS Program for African research libraries, Notes, 3(2): 3-4, Winter 1993/Spring 1994 (1994).

[2]   Associated Press, AT&T seeks African network,Press release, April (1994).

[3]   Bellman B. L., Tindimubona A., Global networks and international communications (1991) available through Internet as ftp DHVX20.CSUDH.EDU/ANONYMOUS.VITA/AFRINET.TXT

[4]   Bush R., Connectivity with Africa, version 93.11.18., (1993) URL: gopher://gopher.psg.com:70/0/0/networks/connect/africa.txt

[5]   De Beer M et al., ISAP - Index to South African Periodicals, Pretoria: State Library, Unpublished MS (1993).

[6]   Goodman S. E. , Computing in South Africa: An end to 'apartness'?, Comm Assoc Comput Mach, 37 (2): 21-25, Feb.(1994).

[7]   Guillarmod F F J., Message, Africana-L, Internet (1994)

[8]   Levey L., Email Date: Wed, 3 May 1995 15:57:54 -0500 Subject: African Index Medicus (1995).

[9]   Meyers G., 1994, African Index Medicus: Personal communication, Johannesburg: Wits email id 0371, July (1994).

[10]   Muaz M.A., (1994) Africana-L Date: Sun, 23 Oct 1994 23:06:47 -0400 From: Muaz M. Ata<dscmmax@GSUSGI2.GSU.EDU> Subject: African Nations and the Internet: The Indian Ocean Newsletter, October 15, 1994 SECTION:ECONOMICS; No. 642 HEADLINE: INDIAN OCEAN: Hooking into Internet

[11]   Priestley C., African journals distribution programme, AAAS Program for African Research Libraries, Notes, 3 (2): 1-3, Winter 1993/Spring 1994 (1994).

[12]   Schlegel M., Wiedemeyer L., Fostering brain drain: Data-communications in the developing world with special regard to the situation on the African continent, Communications, 19 (1), 105-126 (1994).

[13]   Van Brakel, Pieter , Internet: Information exchange in the South African region, Paper: Conf. Relevant Info Services Sustainable Development So Africa, Pretoria, May (1994).

[14]   Wood G. A. et al., The information technologies in South Africa: Problems and prospects, Computer, 27, 48-56, Dec.(1994).

New Technologies (Multimedia - Hypertext - Hypermedia) Potential Use in Developing Countries

Lamine ABDAT[1] and Belhadri MESSABIH[2]

[1]*Laboratoire MASI - Université PARIS VI - 4, place Jussieu 75252 Paris Cedex 05, France,*
E-mail : abdat@masi.ibp.fr
[2]*ITODYS - Université PARIS VII - 1, rue Guy de la Brosse, 75005 Paris, France*

ABSTRACT

The fusion of hypertext techniques with multimedia techniques has given birth to hypermedia that makes it possible to explore hyperspaces by means of a non linear strategy . These techniques further offer numerous advantages to users by providing a good support for managing complex information to be used in different fields (education , medicine , industry ...) and for different applications (documentation, knowledge acquisition ...). The problem of mastering these technologies remains unsolved. It would require the capacity to develop new means of hypermedia teaching, of creating libraries on CD-ROM ... In this paper, our intention is to withdraw the veil from some of these new technologies , to present them together with the means and methods for carrying out hypermedia applications. Since the area of application is very broad , we shall voluntarily limit ourselves to that of education where these technologies can reply appropriately to a crucial problem in developing countries .

RESUME

La fusion des techniques de l'hypertexte et du multimédia a donnée naissance à l'hypermédia qui permet d'explorer l'hyperespace selon une stratégie non linéaire. Ces techniques présentent de nombreux avantages pour les utilisateurs en offrant un bon support de gestion d'informations complexes utilisables dans différents domaines (éducation, médical, industriel...) et pour différentes applications (documentation, acquisition de connaissances...). Le problème de la maîtrise de ces technologies reste posé. Il faudrait être capable de développer de nouveaux moyens d'enseignement hypermédia , de créer des bibliothèques sur CD-ROM.. Par cet exposé, nous voulons lever le voile sur une partie de ces nouvelles technologies, et présenter les moyens et les méthodes pour réaliser des applications hypermédias. Le domaine d'application étant très large, on se limitera volontairement à celui de l'éducation où ces technologies peuvent apporter une réponse appropriée à un problème crucial dans les pays en voie de développement .

1   INTRODUCTION

In the early 15th century, Gutenberg revolutionized the world by making possible the propagation of knowledge by printing. Today, with the appearance of individual multimedia computers, books tend to be replaced by optical disks (CD-ROM, CDI) that enable one to stock not only text, but sound, static and animated images as well.

The fusion of hypertext techniques with multimedia techniques has given birth to hypermedia making it possible to explore hyperspaces by means of a non linear strategy. These techniques further offer numerous advantages to users by providing a good support for managing complex information to be used in different fields (education, medicine, industry ...) and for different applications (documentation, knowledge acquisition, etc.).

In developed countries, the computer, already present in schools, will henceforth be "multimedia" and will be linked to the information highway. By an easy and rapid access, the pupil is able to develop interactive educational programs, to contact different libraries in order to consult the document of his choice, to exchange data with others, etc. Knowledge knows no more barriers. In the United States, the intention is to very shortly link up various schools (26,000 primary and secondary schools) to the information highway.

What about other countries in which computers and, to another extent, networks are practically non existent in primary and secondary schools ? In the 1970s UNESCO financed a training program already calling on several media (educational T.V., radio, video films ...) in order to diminish the number of illiterates in several poor countries. Does it today, within the same framework, plan to help countries to attain this technology ?

Even if the answer were "Yes", the problem of mastering these technologies would remain unsolved. It would require the capacity to develop new means of hypermedia teaching, of creating libraries on CD-ROM.

In this paper, our intention is to withdraw the veil from some of these new technologies, to present them together with the means and methods for carrying out hypermedia applications. Since the area of application is very broad, we shall voluntarily limit ourselves to that of education where these technologies can reply appropriately to a crucial problem in developing countries.

2   INTRODUCTION

Equipped with a high-resolution color graphics screen, a high-density hard disk, an optical disk and a sound card, the Personal Computer became **multimedia** in 1991. It became so because it allows associating and managing several media. It groups together text, sound, graphics, fixed images and video.

Often, **hypermedia** is associated with multimedia. One must go back to the **"hypertext"** concept to explain the former. Hypertext defines a particular organization which allows access to data in a non linear form.

The hypertext concept was first introduced in 1945, when Vannevar Bush - President F.D. Roosevelt's adviser - proposed the designing of a system called **MEMEX** to facilitate access to huge quantities of data in an associative way. In his article, he described the building principles of his Memex machine using microfilm, electrical relays, optical sensors, and other tools which are necessary to access a large collection of data through cross-references. This system could not be implemented at that time because the idea was far ahead of the existing technology.

The term "hypertext" belongs to Ted Nelson who used it in 1960 in several papers and conferences. But the first one to apply the hypertext principle was Douglas Engelbert in 1965. He built a textual database **NLS** (oN Line System, known today as **Augment**) that could be used in a multiuser network environment and that allowed linking file segments by cross-references.

Hypermedia is identical to hypertext save that it introduces, in addition to text, multimedia resources (text, sound, graphics...). It is a technique which merges multimedia and hypertext.

3   STRUCTURE OF A HYPERMEDIA

A hypertext (or hypermedia) forms a network of ideas that are different from a database by the existence of active references. These allow the reader to move freely in different directions. Data is stored as separate recordings and is read following different paths [1].

A hypermedia structure is very complex because of the association of several documents of a different nature. The system is composed of nodes and links. The nodes are the information holders and can be of various types (reference, annotation, illustration ...). They are connected together through links which allow the reader to move from one node to another, to have complementary data, etc. The links can be identified on screen either by buttons or icons or by using video attributes (brightening ...). The node and link structure of a hypermedia system is very important because the ease of creation, modification and access depend on it.

4   APPLICATION DOMAINS

Data transfer onto digital optical disks started in 1987. It allows the reduction of storage costs and facilitates line access to data. The first ones to use CD-ROM were aircraft manufacturers. For each aircraft or engine sold, they had to supply tons of maintenance manuals. Computer manufacturers also supply technical documentation on CD-ROM. The use of the CD-ROM has resulted in the decrease of both the too-high printing fees and the important transportation fees. The non-standardized production of disks has reduced their cost by a factor ranging between 10 and 100 as compared to the production on paper.

Nowadays, there is no domain that has not been contaminated by the multimedia "fever". It is encountered everywhere: in the general public domains (encyclopedias, dictionaries, books, interactive games, interactive bounds, computer science bookstands ...) or in the all professional fields (factories, banks, hospitals, law firms, etc.) that use huge amounts of data.

Today the importance of the integration of multimedia and hypermedia no longer needs to be established. The only problem that claims our attention at the present is the development of the application itself. In addition to an important hardware and software environment, it requires a multidisciplinary team grouping scenario writers, programmers, graphics, photographers, directors, sound engineers, etc.

5   HYPERMEDIA IN EDUCATION

The idea of introducing hypermedia into the field of education has evolved since the 1960s. Emphasis was laid on the individualization of education and the autonomous work of the student using different media (education T.V., radio, movie, video ...).

The advantage of the use of hypermedia in C.A.L. is the speed and ease with which a learner can have access to data through a simple path. Hypermedia allow him to have several points of view on a same object (theoretical knowledge, illustration, explanation, case studies, simulation, animated series ...).

It is not easy to design tutorials including various resources by means of hypermedia software because they are not dedicated to C.A.L. Using them as author-systems implies that the author-designer has a thorough knowledge in order to be able to program all the missing interactive functionalities of C.A.L. (analysis of responses, linking, follow up of the learner, etc.) [3] [5].

From these facts which offer enormous organization and navigation potentialities, we have developed a hypermedia environment for the production of computer aided tutorials. The author-designer is thus enabled to produce his hypermedia coursewares with the use of icons alone, without any recourse to programming.

6   HYPERMEDIA ENVIRONMENT TO PRODUCE COURSEWARE

The hypermedia environment to produce courseware is composed of two important sets of tools. The first one ("**author-tools**") allows the author-designer to build up a hypertext database from linear data on the one hand and a set of questions from a mental process on the other. The second set ("**learner tools**") allows a learner to choose guided learning (imposed linking) and/or navigation learning (free navigation).

6.1   The author tools

To produce his courseware, the author-designer uses the following tools:

- **"Doc. Hyp**.", allows the translation of a linear text recorded in a specific format (ASCII, WORD, RTF) into a hypertext data base including all thenecessary links (content, index, chapters).

- **"Questions**", allows generating a set of different types of questions (MCQ, open question, free question...), making up the work-base for the learner.

- **"Résultats**" gives information on both the courseware (consulted questions, cumulated time...) and the learner (session time, number of attempts, trace of actions...).

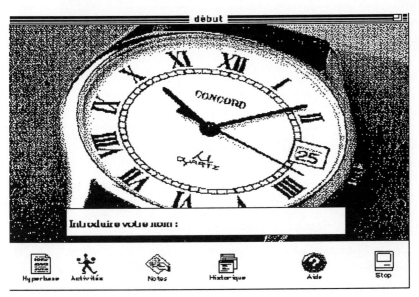

Figure 1. Author tools: Hypertext code to produce hypertext structure.

6.2   The learner tools

These fall into two distinct groups : navigation and questioning processing. The first one means accessing a hypertext data base that can be carried out by clicking either on the icon "cours" or "aide " or "notes" or "historic".

All the other tools, representing the "questioning" group, allow shifting from one question to another, going back to the content, validating the answer, and leaving the tutorial mode with or without resumption.

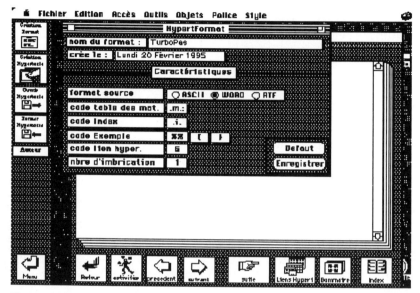

Figure 2.. Learner tools, navigation tools.

7   THE PROBLEMS POSED

The concept of hypertext is recent and the problems posed are numerous. Critics are generally concerned with :

- the **architecture** (inner organization) of hypermedia and the cognitive aspects (navigation, user interface);

- the enormous **required effort** to implement a new hypermedia document;

- the **accommodation** of hypermedia systems designed for accurate applications and that cannot be subsequently altered or used differently;

- the **portability** of the associated database where there is no standard yet.

As it is not possible to develop them all, we will only present the problems pertaining to C.A.L. or, in other words, the conversion of the linear structure into hypertext structure and navigation.

7.1   Linear conversion : hypertext

There exists no universally acknowledged formal model that allows the conversion of a flat linear structure into a hypertext one. Rearick describes in [4] the different existing tools and the different methods used to achieve this conversion. Most hypertext system author-tools are used manually to define the nodes and establish the corresponding links. This operation remains in fact possible for small texts, but it becomes rapidly sophisticated as their number increases. To make this conversion easier, several techniques have been developed. They generally rely on either the use of markus (**SGML** - Standard Generalized Markup Language) or on a lexicological processing (lexical, semantic, syntactical and statistical analysis).

In our case, we have adopted the first technique. The production is achieved automatically thanks to the different markers (beginning/end of node, reference/information link) contained in the linear text. Since this conversion can never be completely automated, we have evolved other tools usable by the author to manually process the produced hypertext text. He can thus add, modify and delete nodes as well as links.

7.2   Navigation in hypermedia system

Hypermedia is a potentially dangerous information system due to a phenomenon known as "disappearance in the hyperspace". While exploring the data network, the learner would wish to answer questions such as : where am I ?, where is he ? what can I do there ? [2].

Two phenomena have been identified :

1)   **"confusion"** : the learner does not know where he is in the navigation of the linear text and no longer knows how to direct himself according to his project.

2)   **"cognitive overhead"**: the effort of concentration necessary for the management of several research directions reduces the attention capacity available for the main task.

The actual state of research on the mechanism that can be used in a hypermedia system (aid to navigation), is oriented towards three main directions :

- **spatial representation** : proposes views of local or global graphics synthesis of data structure.

- **chronological representation** : represents the relationships between data while locating them in relation to reader's approach (trace).

- **filtered representation** : offers the researcher the means to reduce his scope of vision by having him concentrate on his centres of interests.

In the environment allowing for learning through discovery, one should be able to combine exploration and a system of active aid. This imposes the use of several techniques. In the learner-tools developed by our environment, we find three icons (aid, historic, course) that allow navigation. The **"aid"** icon, whose technique relies on a filtered representation, allows access to one part of the hypertext database: the one defined by the author. The **"historic"** icon gives the chronological representation. Finally, the **"course"** icon offers total freedom of navigation.

CONCLUSION

This study has allowed us to present hypermedia under all its facets. Its importance as a tool in education does not need to be established, but its use as an author-system poses several problems. The first one concerns the conversion of the existing educative documentation (books, booklets, textbooks, course medium, etc.) into hypertext. At the present time, it remains manual and uses the author-tools of hypermedia systems, which require a considerable effort in addition to time. The second problem relates to the programming of the different missing interactive functions of C.A.L. such as response analysis, notation, learner follow-up. Our environment for the help of computer-assisted design of hypermedia tutorials takes over one part of the problem. It allows more particularly the rapid production of hypertext data bases as well as sets of questions.

KEYWORDS

Hypermedia, Hypertext, Multimedia, C.A.L.

REFERENCES

[1]   Conklin, Survey of hypertext, Microelectronics and computer technology corporation, STP 356-86, Rev A (1987).
[2]   Edward D.M., Hardman L., Lost in hyperspace, cognitive mapping and navigation in a hypertext environment, Blackwell, Oxford (1989).
[3]   de La Passardiere B., Validation of CAL environment for HyperCard, Symposium on computer assisted learning, University of Surrey, April (1989).
[4]   Rearick T. C., Automating the conversion of text into hypertext in Hypertext/Hypermedia handbook , Berk E., Devlin J. (eds) (1991).
[5]   Younggren G., Using an object-oriented programming language to create audience-driven hypermedia environments in Text, Context, and Hypertext, 75-92, Barrett E. (ed) (1988).

BARRIERS TO INTERNATIONAL TECHNOLOGY TRANSFER

Abdoulaye GAYE

République du Senegal, Secrétariat Commission Nationale pour L'Unesco
67, rue Cornot Boyeux, Dakar, Senegal

ABSTRACT

The commercial importance of products is often ignored when studying technology transfers. Several types of such transfers are examined here. They include the financial barriers linked to equipment investment , the inadequation of local markets to proposed products or ideas, the adaptation of products locally and, especially, their industrial limitations and, lastly, the capability of local satellite factories and the levels of technical cooperation with the outside world. In many countries , the framework of transfers will probably become governmental in the future.

RESUME

L'importance commerciale des produits est souvent ignorée dans les études de tranfert technologique dont plusieurs classes sont examinées ici: les barrières financières liées aux investissements d'équipement, l'inadéquation du marché local aux produits ou aux idées proposées, l'adaptation locale des produits, leurs contraintes industrielles et les capacités des manufactures satellites locales et des niveaux de coopération technique avec l'extérieur. Les transferts de technologie pour de nombreux pays deviendra probablement gouvernemental dans le futur .

1 INTRODUCTION

Frequently in research and development we tend to ignore the sale of products as an important way of achieving technology transfer. Yet economically and politically, this is probably the most important mode of technology transfer. Such transfer could be visualized by the user rather than the supplier. The user's circumstances determine transfer barriers as much as does the supplier's situation. From that point of view we can identify four classes of technology transfer :

1• where the investment barrier in a foreign country is the major problem in introducing new technology, i.e the capital resources to create know-how or manufacturing capability are critical to overcome technology transfer.

2• the local application barrier for the use of the product in the local market where adapting it to the local market is the critical problem.

3• the adaptation barrier where the problem is, to rescale or modify the manufacturing process, either to meet local market needs or the local scale of production.

4• the technical capability barrier typically associated with satellite manufacturing. With local technical capability often at a rudimentary level, the initial problem is to determine what level of technology can be pursued on a cost effective basis in manufacturing of products or components to be imported into developed countries.

2   INVESTMENT BARRIER

We examine these in turn, starting with the investment barrier. Here, typically, the technology is very developed and sophisticated involving expensive tooling and highly specialized equipment. Thus, the smaller size of foreign markets - even in developed countries - makes the returns or the investment unattractive. One approach developed countries prefer is the manufacturing associates program. They try to divide the product's technical requirements so that those portions of the product requiring less sophisticated technology can be made in the local economy, transferred to foreign subsidiaries or associates and there assembled into the final product.

Another way of dealing with this same investment barrier is to establish relationships with some foreign companies in which we sell them the first two prototypes, then we sell them a set of drawings, and they can manufacture all they want based on those drawings. Here, in most cases, we are dealing with very competent and sophisticated associates who clearly have the technical capability to create new generations of equipment if it were economically feasible. The critical problems in achieving technology transfer in such conditions are usually in manufacturing quality control, not in product design or even in modifications to fit local circumstances.

The most difficult task is to identify deficiencies in the specifications, because such specifications are never complete. In many cases, we don't even know what is missing because much of the necessary information exists in the mind of people on the manufacturing floor. Our primary response to this problem is to arrange a very intensive interchange of people. For the most part, our associated companies send their experts to our manufacturing facility in the U.S.A so that they can observe, work carefully with their counterparts here, and learn how the product is manufactured. As required, we also send people to the foreign plants to help troubleshoot.

3   APPLICATION BARRIER

The application barrier is typically associated with the sale of materials and components where, export sales are often difficult if not impossible. One cannot transfer applications directly from local to foreign markets, a process that involves the sale of materials and components. Three kinds of constraints impede export sale :

1• The scale of operations different in developing countries, so that a use which may make economic sense in these does not necessarily make sense elsewhere.
2• The vendor infrastructure that supports an industry is different in various countries with respect to availability of components, price, quality, assurance of delivery, etc...
3• In some cases the customer requires different features, quality or performance.

For all these reasons the economic advantage of the transferred technology must be demonstrated in the specific context of the local economy. In developed countries particularly, this barrier is clearly not due to local technical inadequacy. Often local manufacturing is indeed economically valid.

One technology transfer route that Americans have found effective is to set up joint ventures with companies in Japan or Europe. We then have a competent technical organization, and the transfer of manufacturing technology is not difficult. One must first find a way to combine local talent and our own to learn how to modify a product's properties or components to suit it to the local market, local needs, then to identify those applications that make sense in those local markets. The most expeditious way to surmount the application barrier is to lean very heavily on local nationals. With passage of time, the involvement of foreigners tends to diminish.

4   TECHNOLOGY ADAPTATION

This is most frequently involved in technology transfer to foreign manufacturing affiliates for servicing local or regional markets. The problem is to optimize designs and specifications for greater efficiency. Domestically, we purchase or develop special purpose equipment to yield high volume at minimum cost and we tailor product design for manufacture on such equipment. We assume an available sophisticated vendor infrastructure to assure not only high quality components but also supply reliability and certain quality. All foreign manufacturing subsidiaries present the reverse situation. Most often volume will be quite low, certainly much lower than we intended when first designing the product; manufacture will have to use general purpose equipment which is more labor-intensive. Often the vendor industry will be smaller, less sophisticated, and less adapted to serve local needs. Consequently, the decision to make vs. buy will be based on quite different trade-offs.

The manufacturing system optimum for this situation is almost certainly ill-suited for our design. Thus, local technical talent is needed to make necessary changes. These people must be thoroughly familiar with the manufacturing capabilities of the local plant, able to redesign the product both to be optimal for that manufacturing setup and frequently for the local market as well and modify specifications, materials, and processes to be economically attractive in their particular circumstances. It is difficult to understand which aspects of a specification are critical to performance. Because specifications are always a mixture of economic and performance trade-offs, these need to be dealt with separately to successfully modify designs and specifications.

5   LOCAL CAPABILITY

The final barrier, local technical capability, is associated with off-shore satellite manufacturing, chosen when seeking very low costs, e.g. by taking advantage of low labor rates. Such opportunities are found in developing countries. They most often start by a process, usually an assembly operation where investment is very low. Experience shows that in initiating off-shore satellite assembly we start a process that leads to ill-foreseen manufacturing arrangements. One may start with a simple electronic assembly involving wafers for integrated circuits that are scored, broken up, encapsulated, have leads attached and are incorporated into products. With progress along the learning curve, the complexity and size of the assembly operation grows as one discovers additional cost benefits that can be taken advantage of locally. One will likely go back from assembly to fabrication as local capabilities grow both in the plant and the supporting industrial infrastructure. Also, as local aspirations grow and change we learn more about local availability and how to benefit by it.

6   CONCLUSION: THE FUTURE

Traditionally, BIG BUSINESS tends to deal principally with private companies elsewhere. There is an implicit assumption, and sometimes even a contractual obligation that a commercial relationship will last for a very long time. In the future, we will clearly deal primarily with governments rather than private companies in technology transfer negotiations. We will sell technology per se, not just through products nor with know-how and exchange agreements. An on-site technical capability will be created including facilities and trained manpower which will then be operated by the local government and that will put us in a different world.

"I'd like to emphasize that we must begin to change our point of view in technology transfer. We must learn to price value and avoid handing other countries a competitive advantage by selling them technology for much less than it would cost them to develop it themselves... In many cases...[there will be] ...a one-shot sale... no continuing stream of income... from royalties or from future sale of products and the pricing of that large one-shot arrangement determines whether or not the transaction was profitable. This situation calls for a different way of thinking and one which I think is going to be very challenging. "Lowell W. Steele, January 1974, General Electric Co. ".

KEYWORDS

Barriers, transfer, limitations, business.

The Development of a Scientific Research Data Network System in China

Zhihong XU

Laboratory of Computer Chemistry, Chinese CODATA Committee,
Chinese Academy of Sciences, Beijing, China

Abstract

A first computerized network was set up between three local networks (LAN) in the Universities of Qinhua, Beijing and the Academy of Sciences. This network became the National Computer Facility of China (NCFC). A multilingual query system provides access to sectorial information. The Chinese CODATA Committee is working to coordinate a large number of originally independent databases. The problems of liaising through INTERNET are discussed here as are those that can arise when creating limited local LAN which maintain an active cooperation with CODATA's international groups, dealing with problems concerning production and communication of data.

Resume

Un premier réseau informatisé a été mis en place entre trois réseaux locaux (LAN) dans les Universités de Qinhua, de Beijing et l'Académie des Sciences. Ce réseau est devenu le National Computer Facility (NCFC). Un système d'interrogation multilangue donne accès aux informations sectorielles. Le Comité CODATA de Chine travaille à la coordination d'un grand nombre de bases de données indépendants à l'origine. Les problèmes de liaison via INTERNET sont discutés ainsi que ceux liés à la création de LAN locaux qui maintiennent une coopération active avec les groupes internationaux de CODATA dans les domaines de production et de communication des données.

1 The Development of a Computer Environment

In the past two years, the computer hardware and software environment for Chinese data systems have taken a big step forward. A computer network system, including three large Local Area Networks (LAN) in Qinhua University (Qinhua-net), Beijing University (Beijing-net) and Chinese Academy of Sciences (CASnet), have been set up. It is called the National Computer Facility Center (NCFC). Hundreds of PC computers, dozens of VAXes and other computers, and also dozens of work stations, such as SGI, SUN and others are the constituent parts of this system. Optical fibers covered the three LAN areas. This project was supported by the National Planning Committee with the aid of world bank credit.

In addition, the negotiations for connecting to the INTERNET made some progress. Now it is in the phase of adjusting the system in consistency with the international system. The Chinese Academy of Sciences (CAS) undertakes the task of organizing work on the Chinese continent.

In order to help the micro PC users far from the NCFC, several small network systems with telephone connections have been set up, e.g. the Chemistry and Chemical Engineering network, the Material network, the feed stock prescription network are set up or going to be set up for common services. The National Science and Technology Committee and Chinese CODATA Committee Secretary guide and help in this work. In addition to the above, the library of CAS cooperated with Qinhua, and Beijing University set up a retrieval service system for readers, and it includes international retrieval, Western Language Journals Storage retrieval, Chinese Chemical Literature retrieval, Chinese Physics Literature retrieval, Astronomy retrieval, etc.

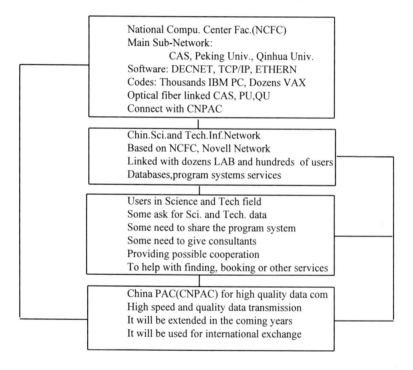

Figure 1. The NCFC and Service Group Relations

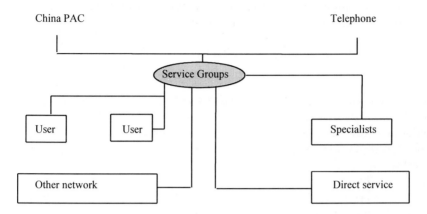

Figure 2. The General Concept of Setting up Service Centers

2 DATA, DATABASES AND NETWORK SYSTEMS

In the past decade, many databases have been set up. In accordance with the Chinese CODATA Secretariat, up to now, 110 databases in the field of science and technology have been set up in China, among which there are three databases in agricultural science, seven in the life sciences and medicine, 26 in nature resources and the environment, 37 in physics and chemistry, 35 in engineering and technology.

Below, we will introduce briefly: 1) Materials Databases, e.g. the Aeronautical Materials database has been set up and is used for design; meanwhile expert systems are being developed in some specific fields to help this work; 2) Atomic and Molecular Data Works, e.g. two issues of a bulletin on atomic and molecular data were compiled and disseminated to related centers; 3) Nuclear Data, in which some experimental data and compiled data were collected and provided to scientists for their use; 4) Environment Data, two handbooks on "Application Codes for Rivers, Lakes and Reservoirs of the Nation" and "Application Codes for Coastal Waters of the Nation" have been completed, and 6,000 records of toxic chemicals data have been collected; 5) Geoscience Data, in this field the first national symposium on thermodynamics of natural processes was held last year, and a series of data activities was negotiated, 6) Mechanical Structure and Design Databases, which was set up in the past years and a Handbook on Fatigue Design has been issued for use; 7) Data on Crop Gemplasm and on Feed, this is used to serve agriculture and feed stock, and is welcomed by many users.

In addition to the above, there are some databases developed in CAS, and the databases in the field of chemistry and chemical engineering will be introduced below briefly. The main databases will be listed in Figure 2. Most of these databases at first were built from different disciplines, and then found a series of users in wider fields. For literature retrieval several libraries have connected with international retrieving centers, and also several ministries and CAS have begun to use some domestic systems, e.g. the Chinese Chemical Abstract, Chinese Physical Abstract, The Spectroscopy Instrumentation Abstract, Astronomy Abstract, etc.

3   THE INITIATION AND DEVELOPMENT OF NETWORK SYSTEMS

About 70 are built in a PC/DOS environment. Few network systems in the fields of sciences and technology were in use one year ago. Early last year, with the improvement of computer network systems and telecommunication conditions in our country, in addition to the direct retrieval with the international system, such as DIALOG, STN and others, several network systems began construction. For the library, the CAS's Information Center has set up a system, part of it is already in use to serve readers. Also with the support of the National Sciences and Technology Committee several service systems in the fields of chemistry and chemical engineering, material sciences, and feed stock system are going to be set up. At the present moment, some small Novell Networks have been used, mainly through the telephone. Such systems initially can only be used in small circles for specific purposes. Then they will be expanded and coagulated into a big system with more high speed telecommunication measures. This kind of work is under consideration and organized by the CAS in the NCFC environment. As the first step of data service work some service groups are going to be set up to serve the users for different aspects. In Figure 3 some groups have begun work and some are in the preparatory period.

- **numerical chemistry databases**
- **numerical databases in other fields**
- **retrieval database systems and help to international STN**
- **full text database of Chemical Engineering Encyclopedia**
- **special monograph series for Chinese CODATA**
- **connection to other related service system**
- **patents and know-how retrieval**
- **technical information service for production work**
- **science and technical services for daily life**
- **E-mail or other service measures.**

Figure 3. The Main Content of the Service Groups

In the middle of this year China was linked to INTERNET, and the CAS with Beijing Univ. and Qinhua Univ. entrusted NCFC to organize the Chinese network connected with INTERNET.

Real use of the network system to serve comprehensive users has been delayed mainly due to insufficient software work, because there are different kinds of mainframe computers and also a great number of IBM PC personal computers. In

China we have to face the problem of setting up hybridized computer network systems, but it will take quite a long time to solve the software problems. So progress in really using the network system may be delayed for some time.

4   DATA PRODUCTION AND DATA USERS

Scientific and technological data usually are generated in research and then used for both scientific research, industrial and social services. To my understanding, the history of data generation can be expressed as in Figure 4. In the first period of development, it is easy to pay attention to research and innovation itself, and less attention to data, data collection, data processing, data rules study. With mass scale production of industry and social progress, this is the bottleneck.

Most of scientific and technological data has a publicity angle for people, and different countries and disciplines are more and more eager to share data. Nevertheless, supporting data generation, collection, processing and dissemination becomes more and more difficult. In developing countries, people like to invest in business to make money quickly. This is a serious problem we have to face.

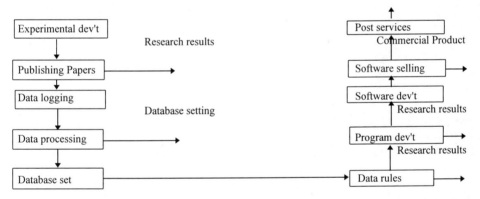

Figure 4. The Flow Diagram of Data Processing

How can we overcome this bottleneck for the Scientific and technological data and database business? I am sure this is a most important problem for our international CODATA society.

One suggestion is that CODATA, through its different task groups, initiate some data projects for international cooperation and ask the National Science Foundations (NSF) of all countries who like to share the results of data and databases to provide some support, and other countries who like it should pay for it.

Another suggestion is that the task group should use as much as possible the low cost staff in some developing countries like China, India and East European countries.

5   INITIATION OF SETTING UP SOME SMALL LAN

With the highly sophisticated development of computer network systems and the conditions of telecommunications, each small academic circle in this area may organize some LAN (Local Network System), at first by telephone, and with the progress and improvement of telecommunications, linking to some large network systems, e.g. INTERNET, BITNET, EURONET, STN, etc. At last year's Fifth Asian and Pacific Chemistry Conference, and the 3rd ChIN(Chemical Information Network) seminar, there was some discussion about setting up LAN, at first, with a directory of addresses, telephone numbers, FAX, and E-mail of the participants to bring chemists closer. During the conference period itself, the optical fiber telecommunication between East Asian Countries began to function.

Of course, commercial use of the optical network system will forge ahead of other things, because of stronger economic bases. But with more popular E-mail, most governments will set up some policy to support its academic use, at least during the initial period. This will then become available for more and more universities and institutions. In China we also intend to organize network systems for some large research groups. Several LAN in academic circles exist. Further, retrieval of literature systems has begun. To initiate such LAN, CODATA task groups can link scientific workers throughout the world by using the highly developed E-mail systems. For developed countries it will be easy technically, but for developing countries versatile methods may also be adopted, e.g. the telephone line to connect to a computer station and then link up with the world system.

Today, telecommunications and computer network systems draw the world closer and closer, especially for participants distributed throughout the world. For essentials like basic data, every group and country needs data but cannot always invest a lot of money in this basic study. Hence it is vital to link data workers. I hope that developed countries can give more help and contribute more during the initial period.

KEYWORDS

China, ST data Network, NCFC, CODATA coordination, LAN, Internet.

Chapter 5

NUMERICAL AND FACTUAL DATABASES

INTEGRATED INFORMATION MANAGEMENT FOR PHYSICS

Eberhard R. HILF, Bernd DIEKMANN, Heinrich STAMERJOHANNS and Jacob CURDES

Department of Physics, Carl von Ossietzky University; 26111 Oldenburg, Germany
E-mail : hilf@merlin.physik.uni-oldenburg.de

ABSTRACT

The change of document handling from printed-on-paper to full electronic handling is described in terms of a phase transition. The present actions and plans of the German Physical Society are given. The embedding into international and interdisciplinary actions is emphasized. Some examples of present experiments and projects are given, in particular a distributed data base for large molecular mass spectra, a distributed abstract retrieval engine, a LANL-server connected local preprint service, and an oral presentation.

RESUME

L'évolution du traitement de documents sous forme de papier-imprimé à une technique totalement électronique est décrite dans les termes d'une phase de transition. On présente les actions et les plans actuels de la Société de Physique

Allemande. On insiste sur les opérations conduites pour s'inscrire dans des actions internationales. Quelques exemples d'expériences en cours de réalisation sont présentés. Il s'agit en l'espèce d'une base de données distribuée relative aux spectres de masses de poids moléculaire élevés , d'un moteur d'extraction de résumés dans un système distribué , d'un serveur LANL connecté à un service de prétirage et enfin d'un système de présentation orale.

1 PHASE TRANSITION IN INFORMATION HANDLING

The phase transition form printed-on-paper handling of information (publishing, sending, storing) to fully electronic processing throughout requires a total recast of information and document handling. The past system has led over the centuries to a sophisticated professional and differentiated scheme tuned almost perfectly to the needs of the scientific community with the instruments available at that time. Although all of us are so well acquainted with it in our daily professional life we recapitulate it briefly here to pave the way for the projects to come. We have to point to those advantages we may not be aware of but want to keep, and to the disadvantages we have automatically adjusted to but which could now be cured. We will briefly summarize and focus here on examples such as the printed scientific journal scene, the oral presentation, and the large scientific data bases, but we will not dwell on books, movies, sound pieces, etc. Industrial revolutions, induced by the upcoming of a new technique, from written to printed words, from horse to car, from ground transport to airplanes, etc. seem to have some properties in common with phase transitions as studied in physics such as liquid to vapor, ice to liquid, smooth to turbulent flow. We are thus tempted to briefly take this apparent analogy and draw some perspectives from it as a stimulus for discussion.

Phase transitions lead in a short period from an established ubiquitous stage with not the slightest idea that any different stage could even possibly exist, to a totally new scenario of a new stable, quickly established ubiquitous stage. The phase transition comes about by spontaneous small scale fluctuations which however can then grow rapidly with no resistance (such as the E-print server [1] started by P. Ginsparg just three years ago in his spare time, now comprising more than 27.000 papers per year). None of the established structures survive despite (or because of) their great inertia. The later the fluctuations start, the less bright is their future. Thus we think it is high time to set the scene to allow for new 'experiments ' in our field.

1.1 The scientific journals

The scientific journals served well the needs of the scientific community.   The established scheme comprises perfect readability, world wide distribution, long term security and integrity by distribution and storage in thousands of world   wide distributed libraries, peer reviewing, combining individual articles of related topics to volumes. The journals are well known to the customers, who thus know where to look for desired information.   The system of peer   reviewed scientific journals is truly international and interdisciplinary. Journals in neighbouring fields or in other countries can be trusted to be organized pretty much like each other. Thus the reader, working in a field between traditional ones, like chemical physics, biophysics, etc. or the mobile, internationally cooperating scientist can find the information in his field organized in the same way to which he is accustomed. There are disadvantages, which one got used to, and which can be cured now : the information became accessible to the user only after up to a year, whereas by the introduction of the global E-print-servers the information of a paper gets worldwide access immediately, giving more time to the peer reviewing process offline.The production process can certainly be drastically reduced if one skips the printing, and offers the documents online only, leaving the printing job to the reader locally with his different demands for quality. It will also attract the development of new commercial services such as printing and sending of documents on demand in the required quality. Other services such as the present commercial journal distributors, the libraries, the commercial abstract services reduced and reshaped to serve new needs such as information brokering

In the past the refereeing process for large journals, such as Physical Review was already automatized, e.g. a numerical programme selected the referees from the stack of active authors by sophisticated and trained criteria. Curiosities found in prestigious journals, such as Phys. Rev. exploiting the L^{A}T$_E$X files received from authors to prepare the printout but then destroying the original files are now certainly terminated. Refereeing up to now was not able to check whether the received text of a scientific paper is new in the copyright sense. The supposedly expert-referee may remember the scientific content of many of the papers in his field and thus judge the originality of the contribution. But up to now he is unable to fight eventual misuse by authors using either their own earlier L^{A}T$_E$X files as a source of their paper or even copying part of the L^{A}T$_E$X files from papers accessible on the INTERNET online preprint archive services, often named E-print archives. We found an example [2] where several printed pages of a paper stemmed from the same several years old L^{A}T$_E$X file and were already used in five other papers sent in by different authors and successfully accepted by two different and most prestigious scientific journals, namely Phys. Rev. and Phys. Lett. Clearly, only an eventual linking of the data bases of the E-print servers and the publishers with a pattern recognition programme will solve this misuse. Of course, other techniques are also being used to circumvent the copyright such as scanning-in articles, passing the file through an OCR letter-identifier program and inserting it into one's own text. Clearly the countermeasures of the publication services have to be upgraded, and are more important than the intellectual discussion on copyright.

1.2 Oral presentation and conference proceedings

Proceedings of conferences (such as this one) have been a tremendous task: Organizing the abstracts, preparing transparencies for the actual oral presentation and writing the full text of the contribution by the authors, sending a diskette, resetting the lay-out, printing, distribution, etc. The larger the size of the conference, the later the proceedings reach the readers (typically over one year for a large international conference). Thus the abstract, the actual talk and the written contribution in fact serve different needs of information and communication. Exploiting the new tools allows one to support the personal communication at the conference instantaneously, to have almost immediate 'proceedings', and establish a permanent net of information for all those interested in that field.

Electronic services and programming provides a big step towards automation and instantaneous available information. To give an example: this talk had been arranged as a set of .html files to be presented at the session of the meeting by a LCD-display, using a 486-SX25 notebook with the Unix-operation system Linux. The necessary information by other providers to the World Wide Web of the INTERNET had been linked to. By calling these before the session at home, they were automatically loaded into the PC, linked to the university network by means of a proxy-server with a cache function. This programme is also used, by the way, at many INTERNET nodes at present, to store non-permanently all files called for from the WWW. It has greatly reduced the WWW-traffic on the INTERNET at our place by at least 30 %, since many files are called for locally by several users, having naturally similar interests, being in the same institution. Thus online access at the oral session is mostly needed only for real time-wise online applications.

The book of abstracts and the proceedings volume can be replaced by a Conference home page with online applications filling out an INTERNET form, posted by the organizer. Here the applicant deposits the link (URL) to the title page of his contribution, stored of course locally at his WWW server. The referees of the conference then have time to decide whether to include the contribution in the official net of URLs of the conference or not. The main part of the conference organization that remains is thus the organizing of the net-access pages, the refereeing, some services such as allowing search and retrieval through index files created by searching the contributions. The server would offer, as we do for example for this talk, (as we do on our server) the abstract [3] available since the deadline, the actual talk [4], available before the conference, and this contribution [5] available since February 1995, as a set of .html or alternatively as a .ps file. Thus the needs of a variable oral presentation, of a permanent access to the information by the author, the immediate availability of the file, and its refereeing can be individually served

1.3 DDD distributed document database

A consistent scheme for distributed integrated information handling has been designed and set up to be used by the Physics Departments. The national institutions (DPG, APS, ..) are closely cooperating. It comprises local internal and external WWW servers for any kind of locally produced scientific material with a link to central institutions such as libraries, publishing companies with their services (refereeing, distributing,..). Different retrieval software on such a net are tested at the moment. A European cooperation   DDD-phys [6] is planned to design and experiment with large physics data sets including the integration into the cooperative writing and the electronic publishing process. Technical tools have to be developed, such as compression of data before electronic transfer, applying a proxy- server with a cache function to reduce the network load for more-than-once-called-for data.

1.4   Global E-print servers

With the installation of the LANL E-print-archive server by P. Ginsparg in 1991 for Physics preprints a new way of providing information was born. Authors send in their documents as L^AT_EX (or **.ps**) files, by e-mail : they are immediately (without peer reviewing) world wide accessible by anyone via the INTERNET without any charge. The misuse has turned out to be negligible, due to the extremely tough competition in the fields first using this service.

At present, a net of interrelated servers is forming at the Los Alamos National Laboratory , the Italian scientific information center SISSA, Brown University, the Stanford Linear Accelerator Laboratory SLAC,... In 1994 about 27.000 papers had already been reviewed, thus superseding any traditional journal. In the same period, University libraries continued to cancel the ordering of journals, while the publishers increased prices to keep the profit margin constant. For example, our University can afford only 72 out of 1.200 journals of a major publisher. The papers of the other journals, if one happens to know of them, have to be ordered by FAX from the provider Technical Information.

Almost all preprints sent to the online E-print servers are later published in peer reviewed journals. About 50 % of the articles at present published in prestigious journals in High Energy Physics were first sent to an E-print archive. Interestingly, at present these services get an exponentially increasing response from other fields, such as chemical physics, solid state physics, experimental physics.

There is intensive discussion on how to add new services to it, such as sophisticated search engines printing on demand taking care of complex figures,..

1.5   PRL, PL and others

By July 1995 several publishers have announced that their prestigious journals would be available online, such as Physical Review Letters of APS, and Physics Letters B of ELSEVIER Science. The prices of these new services will be found via tests and pilot experiments. Certainly, these services will be complemented by others such as sophisticated search engines, user surfaces, cross links to the referenced paper's full text, if available in the same publisher's data base and citation statistics. Although at first glance competing with the E-print archives, they are complementing their free-to-anyone (including underdeveloped countries) services for those laboratories which can afford the highest quality professional service.

1.6   Search and retrieval from abstract services

With the necessary linking of the data bases of publishers and E-print services the search for documents will retrieve either the abstract and bibliographic information or the full document. The present abstract service data base hosts will thus evolve into more general information brokerage services skipping their original tasks.

1.7   UNIrech, a universal abstract retrieval software

UNIrech [7] is a software package designed by us with the aim to facilitate the access to databases in the University and to record and protect database access. UNIrech allows a simple and controlled access to external databases. It is accomplished by sub-passwords issued by the administrators in the departments. Inquiries are on-line and possible by command files. The connection to the database suppliers is established automatically. The programme unit is presently used by about 75 departments (35 physics departments, 35 mathematics departments and 5 informatics departments. The local administrators in the departments have been supported by training courses. This programme can be used wherever database inquiries with costs are part of the scientific work and where this service should be available directly from the normal place of work.

1.8   Distributed data base EMS-NET

In the special field of molecular mass spectrometry with its especially large spectra and its numerous number of spectra on the one hand and its mostly non- permanent but immediate use on the other hand, a scheme for a distributed but linked data base has been designed and successfully tested [8].

1.9   Our own experience

At our laboratory we put up one of the earliest WWW-servers in Germany [9]. By now, this server is called about 2000 times per day. Services designed to be of use to any physics department are especially well recognized, such as the searchable list of WWW-servers of Physics Institutions throughout the world, Europe [10] and Germany [11]; the forms-based ARCHIE retrieval service, the overnight preprint service, which picks the most recent abstract of the LANL server for those fields of interest locally and prepares them for easy reading (.ps) and storing. A good set of link pages leading to a wide range of services useful for physicists are offered on the Web.

2   INTERNATIONAL AND INTERDISCIPLINARY ACTIONS

2.1   Actions by the DPG

The German Physical Society is planning an integrated information management of document servers for their physics departments at Universities [12]. The authors there are practically all equipped with a UNIX-workstation connected to the INTERNET. Physicists mostly can adapt more easily to new techniques due to their computer literacy. By now, almost all Physics Departments have their own WWW server. A subset of their task are the documents, locally produced by the authors. For them, with the presently discussed and at our site tested scheme, a local document database will be set up, which comprises coherently all locally produced documents, independently of their content, status and aim. The differentiation depends on whether it is stored locally, permanently or for a limited period of time, or whether it has been sent to an E-print service such as the LANL- server, in which case the local database, instead of serving the document itself, just provides the link. The same holds for papers sent to publishers, where the link is set as soon as the publisher makes the full body of the file publicly available. The key feature of the distributed linked document data base is the search engine. At first, in a fruitful collaboration with the Computer Science department group we tested the bibliographic store-search-and-retrieval engine for distributed databases, OMNIS-MYRIAD, resulting in an extensive test report [13] by G. Möller and H. Stamerjohanns. With its ineffective use of the slow networks in Germany, and its emphasis on scanning, and a small development basis, it was seen as more effective for a local library system than for the distributed physics servers discussed here, but useful for all paper documents. At present several search engines such as WAIS, HARVEST [14] are tested at our laboratory and will be adapted to this service. The search engine will not dig through all distributed documents but just through the distributed server's index files generated by local HARVEST gatherers. The DPG thinks that the learned societies responsibility is to develop, run and offer such a service together with further services such as E-mail addresses, Institute information, teaching material, and administration information to serve the needs in information and communication of its 26.000 members.

2.2   International cooperation

The DPG has set up a close cooperation with the APS (American Physical Society), the IoP (Institute of Physics, UK), as well as with CERN and several publishers. A joint project is planned together with the APS. Within the European Union, at least for physics, a similar scheme of integrated distributed servers for the Physics Departments is at present in a planning stage. Partners will be the Elsevier Science Springer, VCH, RANK XEROX and the database host Fachinformationszentrum FIZ Karlsruhe. It comprises a printing on demand service.

2.3   International and Interdisciplinary Coherence of Efforts

For the DPG efforts in information and communication services development have to be embedded and coherently organized together with the other scientific fields and projects of other countries. In the winter 1994/1995 the four learned societies in Germany, DMV (German Mathematical Society), GDCh (German Chemical Society), GI (German Computer Science Society) and the DPG have worked out and agreed on a detailed cooperation treaty signed by their presidents. They put into operation a joint technical committee IuK (Information and Communication) in early spring 1995 to work out the necessary joint projects, standards, etc. They have formed jointly a control committee, of which major publishers, the German Central Library TIB (Technische Informations-Bibliothek), the data base host FIZ Karlsruhe, are members. Their recommendations will be subsequently forwarded to the respective societies to be put into action. All four societies are in different but similar stages of applying for funding by the German Education and Science, Research and Technology Ministry (BMBF). The BMBF had independent and timewise disjoined plans of funding experiments of the four societies. In the subsequent discussions between the Societies and the partners in industry it has become clear, that it is of utmost importance to keep the coherence of the services across the scientific fields during the transition period. Thus a new scheme of joint efforts will be necessary to work out the planning and finally, the operation stage. The BMBF is committed to publish its new scheme on information and communication by the summer of 1995.

CONCLUSION

We live in a favourable time of an industrial revolution, from printed to electronic information, a transition phase to a new way of communicating with and informing each other. In science we have to see that the benefits are exploited, but that the advantages of coherence, both international and interdisciplinary, are kept.

KEYWORDS

Physical society, publishing, archiving, integration, communication, web, WWW, ARCHIE, HARVEST, information broker.

REFERENCES

[1]   http://xxx.lanl.gov/
[2]   A confidential reference will be given on request to publishers
[3]   http://www.physik.uni-oldenburg.de abstract
[4]   http://www.physik.uni-oldenburg.de/documents/UOL-THEO3-95-2/eg_foilsebs/eg_foilsebs.html
[5]   http://www.physik.uni-oldenburg.de/ documents/UOL-THEO3-95-2/codata7/codata7.html
[6]   http://www.physik.uni-oldenburg.de/ddd-phys/
[7]   http://www.physik.uni-oldenburg.de/Docs/ivs/UNIRechWeiter.html
[8]   http://www.physik.uni-oldenburg.de/~severien/edms/edms.html
[9]   http://www.physik.uni-oldenburg.de
[10]   http://www.physik.uni-oldenburg.de/Docs/phys-links/europe-phys-links.html
[11]   http://www.physik.uni-oldenburg.de/Docs/phys-links/de-phys-links.html
[12]   http://alice.physik.uni-oldenburg.de/bmbf95
[13]   http://www.physik.uni-oldenburg.de/stamer/pub/offis/B1-Erfahrungsbericht.ps.gz
[14]   http://harvest.cs.colorado.edu/

NUMERICAL DATABASES-CAN WE AFFORD THEM?

Ekkehard FLUCK [1] *and Henry V. KEHIAIAN* [2]

[1] *Gmelin Institute for Inorganic Chemistry of the Max-Planck-Society, Varrentrappstraße 40/42, D-60486 Frankfurt, Germany*
[2] *ITODYS, Université Paris 7, 1 rue Guy de la Brosse, 75005 Paris, France*

ABSTRACT

After some historical remarks the necessity for numeric databases is shown. It is demonstrated in which way the production costs for numeric databases can be reduced. A specific project (ELDATA) is described in detail.

RESUME

Après une brève introduction historique, la nécessité de l'existence de bases de données numériques est démontrée. On expose comment les frais de production de ces bases peuvent être réduits. Un projet spécifique (ELDATA) est décrit en détail.

1   INTRODUCTION

In 1778 the first chemical journal appeared in Germany. Its title was "Chemical Journal for the Friends of Physics and Chemistry, Pharmacology, Household Skills, and Manufacturing". The editor was Lorenz von Crell. Shortly after von Crell's journal, the oldest chemical journal that is still published, "Annales de Chimie", appeared in France during the Revolution in 1789. Many others followed quickly. Very soon it was recognized that the published knowledge therein had to be critically assessed, condensed and organized according to the kind of substances.

The solution at that time were handbooks. Handbooks opened the possibility for systematic presentations which allowed the scientist or researcher to obtain information on a certain topic.

The first Handbook of this type appeared in 1817. It was the first edition of "Gmelins Handbook of Theoretical Chemistry" which appeared in three volumes and later turned into today's "Gmelin Handbook of Inorganic and Organometallic Chemistry". In 1985 the Gmelin Institute started to build up a numeric database, the Gmelin database, which is available online through STN International since December 1991. The Gmelin database is designed to be complementary to the Handbook.

2   WHY DO WE NEED NUMERIC DATABASES IN CHEMISTRY?

A simple example can make clear that even a combination of a few questions can create a problem when we are looking for chemical and physical facts: We want to search for magnetic phenomena of superconducting ceramics which contain barium, copper, and oxygen but not yttrium as elements and which have a critical temperature above 1960°C. Furthermore, we want to know the synthesis and crystal properties of the materials.

In order to find the answer in the primary literature, thousands of articles would have to be found and read. In printed handbooks, such as the Gmelin Handbook, a search through many volumes and chapters would be necessary. Obtaining the answer from a bibliographic database would require a far more extensive indexing than is available today.

Similarly, an industrial chemist may want to analyze a competitive product. He determines some characteristic data of the substance, such as its melting point or some spectroscopic properties. Neither abstracts nor journals on the shelf nor Handbooks will help to find the substances to which these data belong. The numeric database, however, will immediately give the answer.

3 _ HOW CAN THE COSTS FOR PRODUCING DATABASES BE REDUCED?

Using numeric databases, however, is expensive. Can this be changed? Our experience in building up the Gmelin database has shown that the largest cost factor is caused by excerpting the data from the published scientific literature. It is necessary to use experts in the field in order to build up a high-quality database. The high costs of producing databases are reflected in high costs for using them, very often too high for the academic user. The costs of producing the numeric database and for the users can only be reduced when the producers of data contribute to the input by submitting the data in a structured format to database producers. This can go parallel to the writing of the manuscript for the paper.

The excerption programs should be provided to the authors in form of formatted data sheets or electronic data media. These could then be submitted to the editor together with the manuscript for publication and transferred to the database for processing. Even if the producers of databases were to pay a fee to the publisher for handling the data forms or diskettes, the overall cost would be lower than excerpting the data later. Moreover, the information would be available earlier, and, what is even more important, they would be of higher quality, because it is the producer of the data who decides which data are made available to the database.

The suggested procedure[1] is partly working already in the field of crystallography. Zeitschrift für Kristallographie[2] makes use of modern electronic technology for publishing results in databases.

The journal offers to submit new crystal structure data in the form of the structure solution package via electronic mail. Data will be checked, printed partly in Zeitschrift für Kristallographie, and transferred within three months to databases, such as the Cambridge Crystallographic Database for organic compounds or the Inorganic Crystal Structure Database for inorganic compounds.

The communication in the journal includes a structure diagram. This procedure allows quick access to new results in databases. In addition, the authors receive credit via a short paper which can be listed in their lists of publications.

In a similar way, other numerical experimental data can be stored in databases without being printed in full detail in scientific journals as suggested before. This way, one can cut down the amount of the primary literature to an acceptable level without losing the essential information. It would allow the researcher to survey the frontiers of his or her specialty and to stay in touch with other areas of his or her specialty or perhaps with other scientific disciplines. It is understood that the publishers of the various journals still have the option to choose which and how many data they want to accept for printing or which data they want to reserve exclusively for the data banks.

At a certain point legal questions will come up. In a round-table discussion during the General Assembly of IUPAC in 1993[3] questions were asked such as:

Why do the producers of the data have to pay for access to their own products or who owns the data in the database?

These questions are not new. One must realize that they have been asked ever since scientific results have been made available through journals. It is the compilation of knowledge which must be paid for, whether it is published in journals, handbooks, or databases.

Since scientific journals exist, considerable contributions by the authors have always been made to the publishers by free delivery of manuscripts including art work, sometimes in camera-ready form, free proofreading, free peer-reviewing, and sometimes even by paying page charges. Without these contributions, most of the journals would not be able to exist.

A project of the type which is in line with this suggestion is already under way. A new journal entitled ELDATA The International Electronic Journal of Physico-Chemical Data[4], has been designed and initiated at the Institute of Topology and Dynamics of Systems (ITODYS), part of the University of Paris VII.

4   ELDATA. THE INTERNATIONAL ELECTRONIC JOURNAL OF PHYSICO-CHEMICAL DATA

The journal looks essentially like any other journal publishing physico-chemical data with the difference that each printed issue is accompanied by a diskette containing all the primary numerical data in a well defined property-specific format. The data from the diskette can be viewed on the computer screen, printed, graphed and/or transferred as ASCII files to the application programs of the readers or to data banks.

The diskette of each new issue of the journal is a cumulative one, i.e., contains all the previously published data, along with the updated indexes, computer searchable according to properties, authors, and chemical systems.

The first objective of the ELDATA Journal is to establish codes and storage formats for well-defined physico-chemical properties[5].

The policy of the ELDATA Journal is to present in the printed version the essential numerical data, with a graph whenever useful, in a standardized format. The experimental details are given in the text along with introduction, source of materials, comparison with other data, theoretical interpretation or discussion, if any, and references.

The second objective of the ELDATA Journal is to work out and test a mechanism for transferring the data from the authors to the editor and referees and, if accepted, to the publisher, and then from the publisher to the subscribers.

Obviously, the proposed procedure of data publication will be successful if, and only if, other journals, ultimately all the primary data sources (journals, proceedings, reports, etc.) publishing numerical data, adopt this procedure. It will be necessary that CODATA, (for the general concept and design) and other international organizations, (such as IUPAC through its Committee on Chemical Databases and specialized Commissions for specific property types) examine, amend, and finally recommend it.

There should be no restriction in using the procedure by any publisher.

We believe that the present proposal presents considerable advantages for all the actors involved in the process, from the data producers to the end users, including the intermediate ones, i.e., editors, referees, and publishers of primary data sources, as well as of derived data sources (data compilations, handbooks, etc.) It is hard to imagine the disappearance in the near future, if at any time, of printed journals and books. These satisfy the specific needs of categories of readers, are often sponsored by various national or international institutions or organizations with particular interests, hence also styles of editing their publications. However, the technical data themselves contained in these publications are of general use and their accessibility in a standardized and computerized format must be granted.

The suggested procedure requires the cooperation of authors, editors, referees, publishers and data base producers.

Admittedly, authors will have an additional burden in submitting their data to the editor on diskette, following an imposed pattern; in exchange they will receive the data of other authors in a clear and fully documented form, on diskette, and this will be of considerable help in their scientific work (finding data, comparing one's own data with literature data, using data, etc.). Receiving data from authors in the standardized format on diskette and the existence of property-specific computerized indexes will help in comparing the new data with previously published data, will permit the verification of the primary data as well as of the derived data, will ensure that all the uncertainties and other auxiliary information are stated, will ensure a uniform and clear definition of the chemical systems and reported properties.

The Editor will be able to select those parts to appear in print and those to be put on diskette only. This may improve the quality of the papers by highlighting the essential results and removing cumbersome tables from the printed text without losing the primary information. The uncomfortable solution of placing data in Data Depositories or Microfiches can be completely abandoned.

The procedure will permit the direct transfer of all new data to data banks. A royalty or other type of agreement with the Publishers may be envisaged.

The end users, who are to a great extent identical with the authors, will greatly appreciate the proposed procedure. The printed journal will permit them to glance through and read comfortably the published articles and eventually find interesting new facts, the existence of which could not be anticipated if they were merely stored in data banks. On the other hand, the diskette containing indexes and data will permit, at any time, to localize easily the desired reference-system-property, and extract and use whenever necessary the data.

In view of all the above-listed arguments, we strongly believe that the proposed procedure is a realistic approach appearing at the appropriate time. The continuous increase of data needs, of the number of data produced by improved experimental techniques, and of new journals and other data sources, will make this approach, or a similar one, indispensable. The rapid development of the computer technology can only facilitate the implementation of the procedure in the future. The ELDATA concept[6] offers ideal possibilities to transfer information between authors, editors, publishers, and end users, using modern networking.

KEYWORDS

Journals - handbooks - numerical databases - ELDATA

REFERENCES

[1]   E. Fluck, Memorandum on EXPERIDAT, Gmelin-Institut, Frankfurt am Main,   Germany
        Aug.(1991).
[2]   Schulz H., von Schnering H.G, Zeitschrift fur Kristallographie, R. Oldenburg Verlag (ed)
        Munich, Germany.
[3]   E. Fluck, Round-Table Discussion, IUPAC General Assembly, Lisbon, Portugal, Aug.(1993).
[4]   Kehiaian H.V (Editor-in-Chief) ELDATA:The International Electronic Journal of Physico-
        Chemical Data, ELDATA SARL, Montreuil, France. Printed Volume 1, Issues n° 1 and 2, 180
        pp, (1995).
[5]   Kehiaian H.V, General Guide for Users of ELDATA Publications, ISBN2-9507664-5-5, 51 pp
        (1995) [ELDATA SARL, Montreuil, France, Free copies of this guide may be obtained from the
        Editor].
[6]   Kehiaian H.V, Report, IUPAC General Assembly, Guildford, U.K, Aug.(1995).

Teaching Biology by Video Images Assisted by Computer : Embryological Laboratories

Valdiodio NDIAYE

Département de Sciences Naturelles, École Normale Supérieure, B.P. 5036, Université Cheikh Anta Diop , Dakar-Fann, Senegal

ABSTRACT

Observing microscopic embryonic slides in university laboratories is improved thanks to video recorders which allow us to project slide-images on TV screens. The video recorder helps teachers to contact students about observed microscopic slides. It helps to overcome some difficulties linked to the microscopic observing slides, favoring discussion between teachers and students about the same observed microscopic slide. However, some difficulties continue to exist for a not insignificant number of students: changing plans of slides, going from 2 dimensional sight (2D) to 3 dimensional sight (3D) and vice versa, as well as identification of various embryonic areas. Using computers allows putting digital images in place of analogical ones on the same slides. This allows a significantly more important number of students to overcome all the difficulties previously enumerated.

RESUME

L'observation de coupes d'embryons au microscope en T.P. à l'Université est améliorée grâce à l'utilisation de la vidéo qui permet d'envoyer des images de ces coupes sur des écrans. La vidéo aide à établir la communication entre enseignants et étudiants à propos des coupes observées. Elle aide à surmonter certains obstacles liés à l'observation de coupes microscopiques en favorisant la discussion entre enseignants et étudiants à propos de la même préparation observée. Cependant des difficultés subsistent pour un nombre non négligeable d'étudiants: le changement de plans de coupes, le passage de la vision en 2 dimensions (2 D) à la vision en 3 dimensions (3 D) et vice versa, ainsi que l'identification des différentes zone embryonnaires. L'utilisation de l'ordinateur permet de remplacer les images analogues par des images numérisées des mêmes coupes. L'aide didactique apportée par l'ordinateur permet à un nombre d'étudiants significativement plus important de surmonter tous les obstacles précédemment énumérés.

1   INTRODUCTION

In teaching biology, observation takes up a great deal of time. Some biologists consider this activity so important (BRICAGE and NABVERA, 1987) that they do not hesitate to insist that, more than teaching and use of some techniques, objective and intellectual observation is the beginning of all scientific training. Although this thinking is exaggerated and positivist, the problem of observation in Biology is indeed essential. To improve the students' faculty of observation, biologists use various didactic aids (GIORDAN, 1988; ASTOLFI, 1988). Thus, many biologists use machines to improve observation : telescopes, magnifying glasses, microscopes and various media, as the diapo projector, the film, and, more often nowadays, the analogical video image or the digital image.

As part of this programme, we were led to carry out research on using video images in laboratory teaching at university level (CLEMENT et LE GUELTE, 1986; CLEMENT et NDIAYE, 19g7; CLEMENT et NDIAYE, 1989; NDIAYE et CLEMENT, 1988 a et b, NDIAYE et CLEMENT, 1989, NDIAYE, 1990).

2   MATERIAL AND METHOD

In embryology laboratories, for instance, the students' classic work consists in observing, analyzing and interpreting microscopic embryonic slides (Figures 1, 2, 3a, 3b, 4a, 4b). The difficulties they meet in leading students to aim at objectives of laboratories forced teachers (in Lyon, in Dakar) to introduce video in the teaching of embryology, through a system of microscopes with a tritube connected to a videocamera which can project the slide image to be observed onto TV screens appropriately arranged in the laboratory. In Embryology, the great difficulty many students meet concerns changing slide plans and consequently, the problems of directing, of going from 2D images (2 dimensional vision) to 3D images (3 dimensional vision), of going past the vision from the plan to the space and vice versa. This must be done to understand and correctly interpret the microscope slides or their video images.

One of the various aids offered to students for this purpose is to use the possibilities of the video images and those of computer digital images. In that way, the images to be observed, transferred in a computer connected to a video recorder are shown to students in the plan and in the space. It might be even better if the images came with their interpreted diagrams and with the insertion of a cursor to plot the transition from 2D vision to 3D vision and to their interpreted diagrams.

Teachers responsible for these laboratories, in second year university science, and students of these courses were questioned.

3   RESULTS

3.1   Observing slides only with microscopes

Some students succeeded in aiming objectives and observing slides of embryos with microscopes alone, accompanied by some explanations. However, our experience

(NDIAYE, 1990) showed there are significant numbers of students who do not see at all, whatever the explanations may be. These are among the difficulties to which teachers drew attention and which they pointed out during the interviews (NDIAYE, 1990):

" If you have such a situation with embryo slides and with this kind of equipment, even when you really describe something to the students, you notice that a few of them immediately "see"; there is no problem. But some of them do not see anything and have no representation. As a matter of fact, they have in front of them many structures they are not able to order in space. Therefore, our goal is to "create limits" in the structures they see, so that they can be correctly coordinated; that is more or less, our work. Describing things verbally may be good but is not sufficient. Even if you tell the student " look above, on your right in the scope of your microscope, round about "3, 5, 11 o'clock", OK, he sees or doesn't see. If there is a cell, he will see a cell; but if there is a structure to be eventually identified, - and it should be taken into account the fact that sometimes, these structures are broken - so if there is such a structure to be identified, the student doesn't necessarily see it. "

The students also express their difficulties.

A.N " Yes, I agree that it is not easy to observe everything in one's first year. It's true that it is not obvious without saying that the teacher's explanations are not so clear.

It's hard because it's our first year...If we had been taught from the beginning to...yes, it is not obvious, we don't have enough time. But we are directly in year 2, overcharged, and four hours in front of a microscope; it is not obvious."

A.R " Furthermore, it is something totally new since we have never done laboratory work before. So it is not so easy to be in front of a microscope and to do what is to be done and to see what we are asked to see"

3.2   With the help of a video

With the help of a video, contact with the students is significantly improved, the quality of work is really better when the video images of the same embryo's slides are projected. The teachers give further testimony:

" So, the fact that we can present it (the microscopic structure to be observed) in advance on standard slides which are not selected, present it on a screen, comment and describe its structures, direct them, subdivide them..., all this gives the students an opportunity to have a better understanding of what they have before their eyes.

The second fact is that it contributes to partially solve the problem of the lack of teachers; four T.V sets take the place of three or four teachers. It 's not ideal... but it can help.

Therefore, there are two advantages in proceeding thus:

- One gives the students a "structure" and helps him to "structure" by himself what he sees;

- One partially solves the problem of lack of teachers.

... "When the student - individually, doesn't really understand. In Embryology, for instance, things are happening in space, and if the student doesn't really understand what is going on before his eyes, he can take his slide, his own slide which is in his microscope and bring it to the video, and there, we can comment on it together (teacher and student). It is his equipment, not only an equipment with which he can compare his slide which is, however, like the one he has to compare to his own. It is his own slide".

3.3 But difficulties remain. And it is to solve them that we must resort to the resources of the computer.

This experiment which just started seems to be of great help to teachers and students in achieving the objectives set in these laboratories, such as observing embryo slides at different ages, knowing how to identify the embryonic organs and tissues, orienting the slides in space, proposing an interpretation of the microscope preparations or video images viewed in correct diagrams. Since the setting up of such a system, more and more students successfully observe slides. This is the official statement of teachers:

" Therefore there are no more problems; understanding is generally very, very swift..

Then, in the descriptive part, the coupling of video and computer together is absolutely necessary. And, if the first stage, that is to say, the understanding of plans of slides given, is not good, we obtain nothing at all by training exercises, i.e., we cannot hope to obtain an understanding of other plans of slides. Therefore, this system of images may be considered as the means to good understanding. That is my opinion.

OK., there, we compensate for an absolutely scandalous inefficiency. I think that we succeeded in almost correct teaching in spite of this reduced number of teachers, thanks to this system. Because without that, teaching is, let us call a spade a spade, foolish, and I think it should be suppressed; if not, it would be swindling students.

Let us say that it should be a help, to both student and teacher, but it is not a means to get rid of teachers".

How to assess this help ?

"It is difficult to give a very unbiased assessment, but we can make a comparison, i.e., the few situations in which we did not have this system, (neither computer, nor video) and there we realize that it is very difficult: the students have great difficulty in understanding and this is well shown by their diagrams; they are bad. It's very difficult, but it can be tested through the students' understanding when we meet them again in training exercises. If we don't have this kind of equipment (the system) or when for any material excuse, i.e. lack of classroom when, as usual, we were told to get out, it is enough to drive you absolutely mad, because you have students who always hang on to your jacket, or to your overalls, who question you "what is this, what is this...". And, practically, you can show we are significantly below the number of teachers required, as the standard number is one (teacher) for nine (students) as planned in agreement with the State, and in fact, we are two (teachers) for 52 (students), as on the last day, when you came with me. It is enough to drive you mad. Result, teaching is impossible or of bad quality".

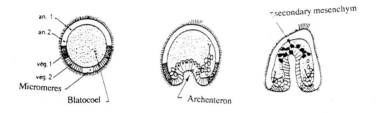

Figure 1 : Sea-urchin's embryogenesis
Diagrams of blastula, young grastula, old grastula (LE MOIGNE, 1979, modified).

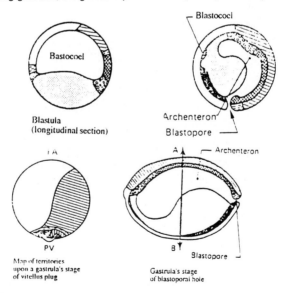

Figure 2.: An amphibian's development
Diagrams of a slide of blastula and various slides of grastula (LE MOIGNE, 1979, modified)

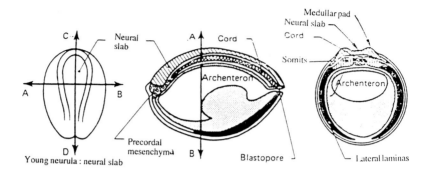

Figure 3a : An amphibian's development

Diagrams of a young neurula's neural slab, and showing two perpendicular plans of slides of neural slab (LE MOIGNE, 1979, modified)

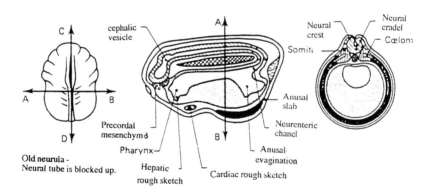

Figure 3b : An amphibian's development

Diagrams of a old neurola (the neural tube is blocked up), and showing two perpendicular plans of slides (LE MOIGNE, 1979, modified)

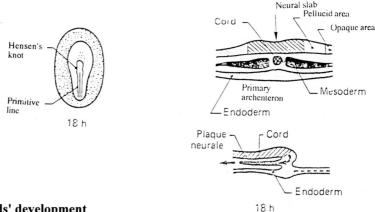

Figure 4a : Birds' development

Diagrams of an external view of longitudinal and cross sections of 18 hours old blastodisc through Hensen's knot of chiken's embryo (HOUILLON, 1967, modified)

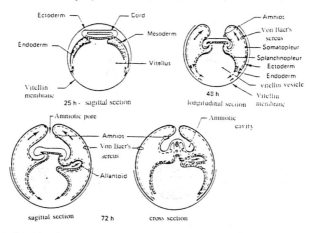

Figure 4b : Birds' development

Growth of birds' embryonic annexes of 25 hours, 48 hours, 72 hours old. Embryo's dimension and the annexes' one was systematically exaggerated in comparison with the vitellus one. The arrows point out the direction of growing of annexes (LE MOINGNE, 1979, modified).

4   DISCUSSION AND CONCLUSIONS

Before the advent of new technologies, the teachers and their students went on doing Embryology in their laboratories. And in spite of difficulties, they succeeded in realizing the observations of the embryo slides. Yes indeed ! the efforts of teachers and students were considerable, and for all that, results were poor. Many students did not succeed. But the knowledge was present, given by the microscope. It is not created by introducing new technologies (video and computer). They help (ASTOLFI, 1988) students to appropriate it more easily and teachers to improve significantly their contact with their students. At the very most, presentation of knowledge was considerably improved by digital images. This technology of digital images, in introducing motion thanks to the computer, brings a new dimension to slide observation. It brings dynamics to observation which makes it easier to understand changing plans, dimensions and consequently directing slides.

Thus, video coupled to computer system is a didactic aid (GIORDAN 1988; ASTOLFI, 1988; NDIAYE, 1990) for teachers to improve contact with students, and for students themselves to improve the quality of observing. Introducing motion makes it easier to understand changing plans.

KEYWORDS

Didactic, embryological laboratories, laboratory observation, video-images, computer, computer-images.

REFERENCES

[1]   Bricage P., Nabwera A., Techniques et méthodes didactiques, In Guide de l'Unesco pour les professeurs de biologie en Afrique, Unesco BREDA (ed) , Dakar (1987).

[2]   Astolfi J. P., Quel(s) sens pour aides didactiques ?, In Les Aides Didactiques pour la Culture et la Formation scientifiques et techniques, Giordan A., Martinand J.L., Souchon C., Actes JIES XI, 347-356 (1989).

[3]   Clement P., Le Guelte L., Quelles utilisations de la vidéo pour des Travaux Pratiques d'Ethologie? Evaluation des avantages et limites de plusieurs formules., Projet de recherche, Laboratoire d'Ethologie et Equipe de Neuroéthologie, Rénovation Pédagogigue de l'Enseignement Supérieur, Université Lyon 1 (1986).

[4]   Clement P., Ndiaye V., Observer des animaux vivants et/ou des documents vidéo en TP d'Ethologie? I - Protocole expérimental, in Modèles et simulation, Giordan A., Martinand J.L., Actes JIES IX, 223-230 (1987).

[5]   Clement P., Ndiaye V., Répulsions et attirances: l'animal vivant ou son image vidéo ? Une recherche sur des TP d'Ethologie: aspects affectifs, In Les Aides Didactiques pour la Culture et la Formation scientifiques et techniques, Giordan A., Martinand J.L., Souchon C., Actes JIES XI, 499-511 (1989) .

[6]   Ndiaye V., Clement P., Observer des comportements d'araignées sur des animaux vivants et/ou sur des documents vidéo en Travaux Pratiques?, In Communication, Education, Culture scientifiques et industrielles, Giordan A., Martinand J.L., Actes JIES X, 335-348 (1988).

[7]   Ndiaye V., Clement P., Observer des animaux vivants et/ou des documents vidéo en Travaux Pratiques ?, Pédagogiques (AIPU) 8 (2) 443-460 (1988).

[8]   Ndiaye V., Clement P., L'Irremplaçable enseignant de TP (avec ou sans vidéo), Une recherche sur des TP d'Ethologie: aspects cognitifs, In Les Aides Didactiques pour la Culture et la Formation scientifiques et techniques, Giordan A., Martinand J.L., Souchon C., Actes JIES XI, 347-356 (1989).

[9]   Ndiaye V., Evaluation de l'utilisation de la vidéo dans des Travaux Pratiques universitaires de Biologie, Thèse de Doctorat présentée devant l'Université Cl. Bernard (1990).

THE STATE OF CHINESE MATERIALS DATABASES

Zhihong XU

Laboratory of Computer Chemistry, Chinese CODATA Committee, Chinese Academy of Sciences Beijing, 100080, China

ABSTRACT

I The general Situation of Material DataBases in China (MDC);
II The Main Features of MDC;
III The Related Basic Work for Data and Database;
IV International Cooperation .

RESUME

I Situation Générale des bases de données matériaux en Chine (BDM).
II Caractéristiques essentielles des BDM .
III Travaux de base associées aux données et bases de données .
IV Coopération Internationale .

1   THE GENERAL SITUATION OF MATERIALS DATABASES IN CHINA(MDC)

It is clear that materials databases were initiated from detailed practical requirements. Until now in China they are still on a very small scale and sometimes even with some non-compatible or redundant data. But in accordance with the requirements, dozens of databases, including related databases, have been set up, and some of these are in use.

According to the Chinese CODATA Secretary's incomplete documentation there are the following series of Materials Databases. [2]:

Table 1. Incomplete List of Materials Databases in China :

Aviation Materials Databases, including a Series of Databases
Databases of Metallic Materials Heat treatment
Database of Sea-water Corrosion
Databases of Atmospheric Corrosion for Iron and Steel
Databases of Atmospheric Corrosion for High-polymers
Databases of Soil-Corrosion
Database for Alloy Steel Systems
Databases of Atmospheric Corrosion and Aging of Synthetic Materials

Atmospheric Databases
Reliability Database and Software for Materials
Advanced Ceramic Materials Database
Materials Strength Database
Materials Property Database for Mechanical Engineering
Corrosion Literature Database(Chinese Characters)

In addition to the above, there are still some small scale databases, for example, Moulding and Die-casting Steel Heat Treatment Database, Steel Selection for Carburation Database, etc.

2   MAIN FEATURES OF MDC

Material Databases are initiated from many specialized institutions or large plants, and they need to accumulate the data for their own use. For example the Materials Strength Database, Materials Property database for Mechanical Engineering, were worked out by the plant itself for their own use. So the first Aviation Materials Databases include several small databases.

If there were some financial support, national or international, then the results could be used in wider circles.

Further more, big problems like Sanjia Reservoir (biggest in the world), need quite a lot of basic data, especially about the anti-corrosion problem for different materials, like seamless steel pipes, welding steel pipes, surface layer spraying steel pipes, cement pipes, cement blocks, poly-vinyl chloride pipes, on the one hand to collect all samples buried 30 years ago, on the other, to bury a lot of samples for getting more data.

From the above statement, it is clear that we need to set up the Materials Databases in Different Natural Circumstances (atmosphere, sea-water, soil). This work is now under consideration and design.

Materials database work needs international cooperation, especially for standards of materials. We could not set up the whole system for China, and there is lack of money to support this kind of work independently.

However, from the large scale of national construction, it is clear that database work is becoming more and more important and is realized as such by the leaders of engineering projects.

3   THE RELATED BASIC WORK FOR DATA AND DATABASES

In contrast with the above work begun for practical specific requirements, there is some basic work to support materials study. The main basic work is from Chemistry and Chemical Engineering Database aspects, as listed below.

Table 2. Databases in Chemistry and Chemical Engineering

Inorganic Thermo-property Database (ITDB)
Knowledge Based Organic Property Database (KB-OPDS)
Inorganic Property Estimation System (IPES)
Mass Spectrum Database (MSD)
Infrared Spectrum Database
NMR Spectrum Database
Photo Electro Spectrum Database (ESCA)
Toxicity Database System
X-ray Crystal Database

Inorganic Property Estimation System (IPES)
Crystal Structure Database
Photo-electronic Spectrum Database
Related Chemical Engineering Databases

Some of the above listed databases are international cooperative works, e.g. the ITDB, ESCA are cooperative with the NIST of USA, and some were bought from foreign countries; the rest are carried out domestically.

In addition to basic database work, there are some program systems and expert systems derived for specific points of view. For example, for the advanced Ceramic Materials Database, there are some functions to help you select the materials if you can specify your requirements [2]. Another example is to search for new alloys or intermetallic compounds with the help of large amounts of data on known compounds and mathematical tools with computer use. Then the new compound with some specific property is obtained. It is verified by using the experiment to get several new intermetallic compound materials. In this work the pattern recognition technique was used [3].

Further efforts are deployed to set up a platform for materials Database work. This is one way to help materials database development generically. The schematic drawing is shown in the figure 1.

With this idea, the author is trying to formulate a detailed database in the field of materials design.

For example [3] we are trying to set up an expert system to help people select composite materials for high quality. This work is still going on.

In the field of activity coefficient for metallic alloy system, a lot of experimental work has been carried out and many data files accumulated.

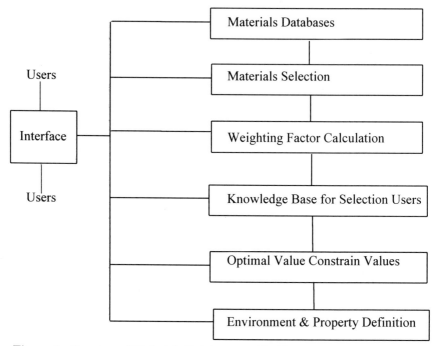

Figure 1. Structure of Materials Database and its Usage

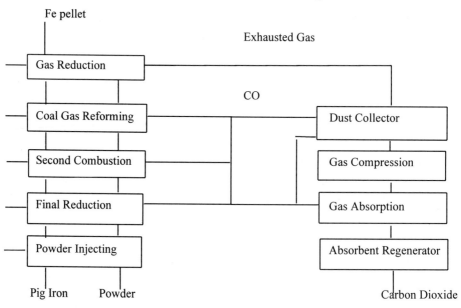

Figure 2. Using Databases to Support Simulation

Interesting work has been done by [4], in which the activity coefficients are correlated with periodic tables and molecular weight.

These results have been programmed and will be linked with the ITDB database system. In order to help the new metallurgical process development, the ITDB and IPES databases will also be used.

In the figure 2 we see that the simulation process has been carried out with the aid of ITDB and IPES.

4   CONCLUSION

The general tendency of new materials development and especially the supporting system for new materials development need a lot of investment, and at first it is mainly in a dispersed form. With progress, the generic subsidiary systems, more basic work and different layers of the platform become more important day by day. Meanwhile, with the high speed with which new materials emerge, materials databases will need more and more work to make them complete.

INTERNATIONAL COOPERATION

To progress further and improve our communication potential we expect through an increase of our association with CODATA to promote international cooperation, and welcome members of CODATA who want to join us in any form of cooperation..

For the task group, it is desirable to ask members to join and to provide them with some rights or advantages in data use. If helpful, the task group could send some formal letter of invitation to the member's government, or national science foundation to help them to apply for support from their country. I am sure the sharing of resources will stimulate interest in supporting data and database work.

The work on computer aided material and molecular design is the newest area originated from the requirements of practice. Last year after we hosted a ChIN (Chemical Information Network). Seminar we published a special bulletin named "Computer Aided Materials and Molecular Design" [l], and this can be exchanged with our counterparts. Such efforts will help us to push for international cooperation.

I hope that the CODATA task groups can help in obtaining some local or global cooperation. It is inevitable that such cooperation will be mutually advantageous. The developed countries can lower the cost of working staff, and the developing countries will have the chance of making some contribution to international development of science. All these efforts will also have to be considered in conjunction with the new programs of ICSU/CODATA where interdisciplinary exchanges become essential in such fields as for instance, environmental planning and regional development.

KEYWORDS

China, materials database, database list composites, international cooperation.

REFERENCES

[1]   Xu Z., Wen H., Computer Aided Materials and Molecular Design, Sciences Press, Beijing (1993).
[2]   Data File from Chinese CODATA Committee Secretary (1994).
[3]   Internal materials of LCC (1994).
[4]   Ding X., Doctorate Thesis (1992).

Chapter 6

BIOINFORMATICS WORLDWIDE : DATABASES AND NETWORKS

BIOINFORMATICS - PULLING THE EUROPEAN STRINGS TOGETHER

M.L.Harrie LALIEU

Library KNAW, P.O. Box 41950, Amsterdam, The Netherlands

ABSTRACT

This paper deals with the problems and challenges regarding a future European information infrastructure for biotechnology. Strategic issues relating to database hosts, networks, and databases are successively treated. The conclusion is that European telecommunication infrastructure requires urgent improvement and specialist interest databases are increasingly necessary .

RESUME

Cet article concerne les problèmes et défis propres à la future infrastructure européenne pour la biotechnologie. Les problèmes relatifs aux serveurs porteurs de bases de données , aux réseaux et aux bases de données sont traités l'un après l'autre. En conclusion il apparaît que l'infrastructure européenne des télécommunications doit être améliorée de toute urgence et que le développement de bases de données spécialisées devienne de plus en plus nécessaire.

1   INTRODUCTION

Biotechnology is increasingly dependent upon information and bioinformatics. This was begun by the molecular biologists with their nucleotide and protein sequence databases and the specialist services needed to transform such data into useful R&D material. These developments are evolving rapidly in size and sophistication, so that we now also see the emergence of specific information infrastructures. To date these are being built primarily around, academic/publicly funded centres, such as the European Bioinformatics Institute (EBI) and the rapidly growing European Molecular Biology Network (EMBnet) series of bioinformatics nodes (currently 26 spread throughout Europe). Many of these centres concentrate on factual data (such as sequence databases). Such material is really only of use to the R&D scientists themselves: the information intermediary has little influence or role in such areas. These changes in where information is targeted mean that scientific information professionals must review their needs, training and future policies, and that the library-based infrastructure must also change to accommodate many more "end-users".

Nevertheless, the traditional literature-based services are still very important. Therefore there should be a seamless join between biological literature and data services, as has been realized in America, mainly due to secure public funding. The databases and banks were originally seen as international, and a number remain so. But there are strains on the international scene because of the rather heavy funding of the American services and their availability on the Internet. Europe does not control the destiny or content of many essential databases, nor can it be guaranteed future unfettered access. Such potential problems are not just of concern to the information producers, but also to the users. Surprisingly few (European) users know exactly who owns or funds the information sources they use. Large companies may be expected to find ways to circumvent any future barriers, but the smaller and middle-sized enterprises active in European biotechnology all require a stable European information infrastructure.

Thus there are enough problems and opportunities to be examined. As Europe lacks a central facility, any response will have to come from an alliance: from the database producers, the EMBL/EBI and the many individual centres of expertise such as national bioinformatics nodes. This collective intelligence could be of great use in strengthening the European future.

2   STRATEGIC ISSUES

Further to the 1990 report on Bioinformatics in Europe, and taking the latest developments into account, the strategic questions are presently being addressed by the Biotechnology Strategic Forum (BTSF). The BTSF membership consists of 11 European database producers and publishers active in biotechnology. This paper deals with a series of strategic issues facing the biotechnology information community, which have recently been discussed by representatives from biotechnology information producers and users, plus some representatives from funding and intergovernmental bodies interested in the discipline; specifically problems surrounding database hosts, networks, and databases are treated.

2.1 Database hosts

Efficient, stable database hosts are essential for the further development of the market. There is some concern that the present economic situation surrounding the European commercial database hosts is unhealthy. A scenario where all of the relevant R&D related data is eventually to be stored on American or international database hosts located in America is now possible. This would be highly undesirable, especially for Europe's small and medium sized companies who are unable to use American "daughter" companies to access data in the USA.

It is generally agreed that biotechnology information is international so that safeguards against any political and geographical restrictions to access should be developed. The best guarantee seems to be to locate essential databases, or copies of databases, on European computers under European management and law. While commercial database hosts normally offer many files, the variety and range of databases used in biotechnology mean that a market scenario where larger and smaller database hosts, each with a defined and well researched mission statement and market niche, interact through integrated networks and interfaces, would be welcome. These hosts might work far closer with the producers and so we would see an environment of dispersed or federated databases. This would also allow the producers of specialist databases to find both better host conditions and more users. Navigation between the various data resources will then become a greater problem; there will be a greater need, not a lesser one, for more efficient locating of databases, and Europe will have to pay attention to producing the required software for this to take place.

A key need for industry is quality control, but the explosion in the number of services and files is making quality control and the location of the correct information source for a specific need more difficult. Cross database searching is already a help to the user who is able to look across a number of files for relevant material - for instance DIMDI has already harmonized similar databases into a SUPERBASE structure - but this cuts the usage time in the individual databases and therefore royalties, thereby threatening some of the specialist database producers. Europe should make an effort to use modern information tools, such as the World Wide Web, to make new files available and to advertise and market biotechnology products, services and resources available in Europe and thus ensure that users can be served from local markets.

Overall, the biotechnology R&D community, industrial and other, would benefit from better coordination between the hosts, the producers and the users.

2.2   Networks

The huge increase in size and use of the Internet has opened new opportunities for the users and producers of biotechnology information. Nevertheless, there are too few quality control tools for the commercial user. In fact all databases should have a seal of approval. Another problem facing the industrial users is security. Overall, better and securer access to the Internet-based databases needed for biotechnology R&D is essential, as industrial companies, but also many advanced academic research teams, cannot afford the risk of anyone breaking into their systems.

Both academic and commercial users will need help to navigate through cyberspace. Sign-posting and quality control refereeing is required and these needs should be concentrated on in a scientific way so as to combine the best of all environments. The present European telecommunication infrastructure requires urgent improvement. European networks are too slow, too narrow and too expensive. While satisfactory for ftp transfer due to improved data compression techniques, they are not adequate for guaranteed on-line interrogation. Many European producers, including the newly formed European Bioinformatics Institute, have to use the American networks to distribute their products. Many future uses of networks will require sending images. Data compression has, until now, compensated for the growth in traffic, but continued growth will overload the existing networks to such an extent that extra bandwidth will be essential. Networking is of such fundamental importance that the Commission of the European Communities must be stimulated to do all it can to improve Europe's position.

The national PTT's are clearly the main stumbling blocks, but also the main innovators, and the weak international and national attempts to break their monopolies have not basically worked as far as cross border interaction is concerned. A period of four years for improvement is too long; Europe has to have superhighways.

In addition to the technological advancement, education and support in this area is essential, because there is in fact a scene of two worlds: the exciting, unregulated, rapidly expanding free world of the Internet, and a more serious, targeted and conservative world of the traditional value-added databases covering scientific information with good access and indexing tools. These are not mutually exclusive and complement each other. While it is now accepted that a better collaboration between the commercial and academic communities is essential, and groups like EMBnet might spearhead the provision of better services and support for industry, the scientific libraries, which are developing rapidly from classical document delivery centres to information centres with all modern tools and services, are very well placed to act as mediator between these two worlds.

2.3   Databases

Databases are developing rapidly in complexity and in number. They are aimed at specific user groups and are often very "state of the art". Despite this, due to their niche position, due to the fact that they are used in a specific part of the R&D circle, many will obtain sufficient commercial use to cover their exploitation costs. A major reason for this is that such databases require specialized staff adding value to basic records and data and are therefore expensive to produce. Seventy-five percent (75%) of these costs are staff-related and, as such products are small in volume, they lack the market size to allow extensive marketing. Specialized databases in particular will have to be user-driven, and so need to reach their maximum market. The producers need easily accessible facilities to mount their databases for interactive searching. These databases would receive more attention if mounted together for better marketing/innovation and so that a user can switch from one data collection to another. This may mean organizing them in clusters but in any case they must be compatible with "like databases". The producers should therefore look for flexibility, with good scientific validation and technological structure. All these developments point to the specialist database benefiting by being placed in a "tank" of data: perhaps in a federated or dispersed database structure. However, even here, producers require strict guidelines and standards. The EBI and EMBnet might help, as could the commercial hosts, by offering guide-lines for data structures and in producing interfaces and gateways to allow the user to reach different data products. Marketing will also have to be improved. The commercial database producers might help by cross referencing their products to special products and the EBI and EMBnet could advertise the availability of the products throughout the community and help with training courses,etc. Even if all these activities succeed, recovering production costs will be difficult. A completely different role for special databases involves the future of the journal, whatever it may be. The industrial user requires well validated material - most accept the journal as being such a product although on many occasions databases are far better : data can be validated, journal articles are not,- refereeing is still a very arbitrary process. There is a general agreement that data will be stored in databases and that scientific insight will be found in journals. But relevant forms of the same kind of subject matter might increasingly be found in specialist databases. There will be a need for alternative sets of validated materials, especially if these involve patent and regulatory material. These products will have to be electronic and will be developed along the same lines as are the specialized databases today.

Thus, the possibility that the user will have to search and use databases as he now uses primary journals must be accepted. There is therefore every need for the present secondary databases to expand their coverage to include specialist databases; these could, on occasion, replace the primary journal as the repository for some forms of information. In that case Europe might design a "root" or "core" database which ties the specialist databases together. A central pointer database, where the records point to other databases identifying where records relevant to the full R&D story are located, would solve many of the problems facing both the specialized data collections and larger databases. Such a database should be built so that a searcher could start a R&D story at any point in the record chain. The Common Core Database in Biotechnology Group (CCDB) is looking at whether such a product can be built. There is still discussion as to whether it should really become a new database or if smart software could provide the solution. The cost of adding value and the issue of copyright and fees are problems for the publishers. Regulations and standards will have to be handled if the correct climate for investment is to be produced. Expert panels should be established to examine the legal and copyright side of databases and electronic publishing.

CONCLUSION

The host world faces many technological challenges. The user is faced with an increasing number of sites where data might be stored. The information producer is faced with the challenges of freely available unrefereed academic material as well as a declining number of hosts. Interaction between all three is essential if Europe is to maintain a competitive and efficient environment which supports the R&D industries relying upon this data and information

The huge increase in size and use of the Internet has opened new opportunities for the users and producers of biotechnology information. Sign-posting and quality control refereeing is required. The present European telecommunication infrastructure requires urgent improvement. Networking is of such fundamental importance that the CEC must be stimulated to do all it can to improve Europe's position

The present secondary databases will have to expand their coverage to include specialist databases. Special interest databases are increasingly necessary. Due to their particular profile many will never obtain sufficient commercial use to cover their production and exploitation costs. A central pointer database would solve many of the problems facing both the specialized data collections and the larger databases

KEYWORDS

Bioinformatics, DB hosts, networks, databases, Internet, Europe.

ACKNOWLEDGMENT

The author wishes to thank Dr. J. Franklin (ASFRA BV, Edam, The Netherlands) for fruitful discussions and for providing basic material.

BIOINFORMATICS IN EAST ASIA

Akira TSUGITA

Research Institute for Biosciences, Science University of Tokyo 2669 Yamazaki, Noda 278, Japan

ABSTRACT

Asia is in various developmental stages in bioscience and bioinformatics. India, Singapore, Korea, China and Taiwan have established an efficient national network and international network system albeit with some limitations. Thailand and Malasia have become aware of the usefulness of the data network these days. Indonesia, the Philippines and Pakistan have initiated database activities in biology, agriculture, biomedicine and biopharmaceutics.

RESUME

Divers stades de développement existent en parallèle dans les biosciences et la bioinformatique en Asie. L' Inde, Singapour, la Corée, la Chine et Taiwan ont créé des réseaux nationaux efficaces et des systèmes internationaux présentant encore certaines limitations. La Thaïlande et la Malaisie sont devenues conscientes de l'utilité d'un réseau de données dans notre époque. L'Indonésie, les Philippines et le Pakistan ont initié des activités de bases de données en biologie, en agriculture et dans les domaines de la biomédecine et de la biopharmacie.

INTRODUCTION

Asian countries are in various development stages for biosciences and bioinformatics. These countries may have several common problems, such as language and computer, although these problems are not necessarily specific to Asian countries but also pertain to developing countries world-wide.

In Asia several countries are more familiar with English historically but countries covering large areas in Asia are unfamiliar with English. The "English familiar" countries are India, Singapore, Malaysia, the Philippines, and Hong Kong. However, many countries use Chinese characters; China, Taiwan, Korea, Japan, Hong Kong, Malaysia, and Indochina.

It is noteworthy that Chinese characters are no longer the same in China, Taiwan and Japan because simplifications were made in different ways in the past 40 years.

Japan, China, Taiwan and Korea operate their computers by their own respective languages and these languages occupy a considerable part of the computers' memories. Sometimes the language memories were used to make up for incompatibility of the computers, i.e. between Japanese IBM-PC and international IBM-PC.

Historically, international policy, national policy and even policies of companies made for incompatibility among computers. In the past, China and India were under international political pressure and IBM-PC or similar computers were the only ones available in these countries as in the past in the Soviet Union and other communist countries. Japan developed its own computers mainly from three major companies which were yet mutually incompatible. National universities were forced to use these computers and this resulted in an incompatible computer gap between these universities. These incompatibilities have given great inconvenience to users and especially to scientific researchers, and limit development in quality and reliability and accessibility of information.

Countries first began to compile statistics of practical information. These activities were conducted or supported by their own governments. The fields were often agriculture, forestry, fishery, health, and economy, where standardization of databases and evaluation of data have become crucial problems (e.g. the Philippines and Indonesia etc.). These data are in many cases country specific and only for inside countries, using their own languages.

The other line of development was due to imported data bases. Such databases are important for human health. For example, medical information and microbial information, which came from NIH-USA, WFCC or CODATA MSDN, have been well accepted by Thailand, Korea, and China.

Molecular biology databases are introduced to Asian countries in different and various ways. Nucleic acid sequence, protein sequence and protein-tertiary structure databases were essentially introduced by the needs of research institutes of molecular biology and biotechnology. The nucleic acid sequence Asian node, DDBJ together with EMBL and GenBank, the protein sequence PIR-international Asian node, JIPID and tertiary structure data base PDB have been extended to theAsian area, and they are now widely used in Taiwan, China, India, Pakistan, Korea and Japan. Japanese databases DDBJ and JIPID input and distribute to the public. China is also preparing to input data with Japanese nodes but no other countries are prepared. One problem is that researchers publish their data in Journals published in the USA or Europe which are retrieved in these areas. Some researchers published data in their own journals as well as in the international journals. These researchers' customs resulted in a limited number of data in the Asian area. The direct submission of data from researchers recently improved the above problem from journal - location wise to research laboratory location wise. When governments support database activity, they demand the compilation of data made with their support, altough this is partly duplicated internationally. This causes unnecessary inconvenience to the users.

Both CODATA hybridoma database (HDB), and microbial strain (MSDN) and World Federation for Culture Collection (WFCC), operated Riken-Japan, have been popular in the Asia region.

Computer networks are also urgent and important in the Asian area as in the other parts of world. Japan, Korea and Taiwan have been connected to the international network, Internet and the network covers 20-40% of the researchers' stations. China is essentially connected to Internet but it does not work all the time and covers very few institutes.

An ideal example was seen in India which was connected to the international database through internal networks. Ten main subnodes and 20 other sub-subnodes are connected and they are respectively specialized and distributed area wise. From these nodes international and national databases are operated.

The other ideal example is Singapore, where a computer-network has been completed and further, a glass-fiber cable net will be completed in the near future. Medical pharmaceutical and biotechnological database activities have been well developed.

Up to now Asian countries generally have been recipients of the well developed databases in biology, but recently we are proud to announce that Asian countries can contribute as donors of useful databases for the world. These data may be Fish-data from Taipei and Animal virus data from Poona, India. Of course, Japan already started such contributions in the past decade as with the nodes of HDB, MSDN and WFCC and molecular biology field JIPIDand DDBJ. Japan also contributes to the human genome, rice genome and other genome projects and part of these are summarized in Table 1. The information written here was supplied by the various reports cited in the references.

KEYWORDS

Network, bioinformatics, Asian data, infrastructure, biology, biotechnology, agriculture.

REFERENCES

[1]   Hu Y., CODATA Proceedings Ser.1 pp 7-14, China (1994).
[2]   Lumbantobing S., ibid pp 23-31, Indonesia (1994).
[3]   Kolaskar A.S. , Samuel S. CODATA Bull. 22, 3, 143-145, India (1990).
        Lal K. CODATA Proceedings Ser.1 pp 35-39, India (1994).
        Arora J.R. et al., ibid pp 58-69, India (1994).
        Kolaskar A.S. , Naik P.S., ibid pp 101-106, India (1994).
[4]   Jhon M.S., CODATA Special Report 12 pp 105-106, Korea (1989).

Park C. , Park K., CODATA Bull. 22, 3, 123-132, Korea (1990).

[5]   Zaidi Z.H., CODATA Proceedings Ser.1 pp 33, Pakistan (1994).

[6]   Sipin G.L., ibid pp 15-22, Philippines (1994).

[7]   Liu M.L., Song C., Huang H.L., NG, S.Y. CODATA Proceedings Ser.1 pp 83-88, Taipei (1994).
        Chen S. , Fan M.J., ibid pp 89-99, Taipei (1994).
        Yuan G.F. et al., ibid pp 114-115, Taipei (1994).

[8]   Atthasampunna P., CODATA Bull. 22, 3, 101-103, Thailand (1990).

ORGANIZATION	NAME	CONTENT	USER	ACCESS STYLE
National Institute of Genetics	DDBJ	Nucleic Acid Sequence	Free Access	On Line (No Charge, Registration)
Tokyo Univ. Inst. Medical Science Human Genome Analysis Center	Genebank, EMBL	Nucleic Acid Sequence	Free Access	On Line, Mail Server, Anonymous FTP, Gopher, WWW (No Charge)
	HyperGenome, Locus-In, ContingMaker, GNOME Genomatica	Tools for Genome Analysis	Free Access Researcher	Anonymous FTP, Client/Server (No Charge, Registration) On Line (No Charge, Registration)
Science Univ. of Tokyo	JIPID Rice 2D DB, T4 Genome DB, E, coli Genome DB	(Amino Acid Sequence) Genetic Map	Free Access	On Line, Mail Server (Charge, Registration)
National Inst. of Cancer Research	JCRB-Celldata JCRB-Gene Genebank GDB TFD	Cell Bank Gene Bank Nucleic Acid Sequence Genome Information Transcriptional Factor	Free Access	Anonymous FTP, Gopher (No Charge)
The Japan Information Center of Science and Technology	GDB DNA database	Genome Information Nucleic Acid Sequence	Free Access	On Line (No Charge, Registration) On Line (Charge, Registration)
National Inst. Agrobiological Resources	DNA databank	Database for Agrobiological Nucleic Acid Sequence	Free Access	On Line (No Charge, Registration)
(Peptide Inst. Protein Research Foundation)		(Amino Acid Sequence)	Researcher	On Line (Charge, Registration)
(The Inst. Physical and Chemical Research - RIKEN)		(Database for Cultured Cell)	Free Access	On Line, Gopher/WAIS/WWW

BIOINFORMATICS IN THE UNITED STATES: RECENT TRENDS FROM A MICROBIOLOGICAL PERSPECTIVE

Lois D. BLAINE

American Type Culture Collection, Rockville, MD, USA

ABSTRACT

The United States bioinformatics community is beginning to focus on database interoperability. The emerging federation concept promotes adherence to prescribed standards in data modelling, syntax, and semantics. The genomic database producers are taking a leadership role in exploring the technical and social aspects of facilitating the retrieval of data from multiple sites in response to complex queries over the Internet. This paper presents an overview of the types of problems that must be solved to achieve full interoperability and identifies major biological database producers in the U.S. that are poised to link with others via the Internet.

RESUME

La communauté bioinformatique des Etats-Unis commence à marquer un intérêt particulier à l'interopérabilité . Le concept émergent de "fédération" incite à adhérer à des standards de modélisation de données en syntaxe et en sémantqiue. Les producteurs de bases de données sur le génome ont un rôle meneur dans l'exploration des aspects techniques et sociaux utiles pour faciliter la collecte de données à partir de nombreux sites afin de répondre à des questions complexes émises sur Internet. Cet article présente un survol des types de problèmes à résoudre pour réaliser une interopérabilité complète et pour identifier les principaux producteurs de bases de données biologiques aux U.S.A. susceptibles de se lier à d'autres par le biais d'Internet.

1   INTRODUCTION

The increasing utility of computer systems for solving biological problems commands much attention in the United States as evidenced by new academic programs that combine the disciplines of computer and biological sciences, long term commitments for infrastructural funding in specific areas of bioinformatics, and, most recently, the emerging concept of the federation of biological data that insures interoperability across disparate systems and disciplines -- the matrix of biological knowledge.

Since the 1960s the U.S. has played a leadership role in supporting the development of online resources for biomedical and biotechnology information. Among the pioneers and the forerunners of what we know as bioinformatics today were the U.S. National Library of Medicine's MEDLINE system, BIOSIS, and Chemical Abstracts Service - all bibliographic information services that took advantage of technology to store and disseminate biological information. These literature storage and retrieval systems were followed by increasing numbers of "factual" databases, e.g. those for storing and retrieving nucleic acid sequence and protein structure data.

Today, access to computer technology is so widespread that few biologists in the U.S. do not make use of automated systems for managing laboratory data. Furthermore, the growth of the Internet and the development of software tools that facilitate storage and dissemination of data in a networked environment, has resulted in the proliferation of biological data resources that are now available to researchers throughout the world.

The challenge is now to enhance the tools and the database structures to insure true database interoperability. Interoperability means that data stored in disparate sources and systems can be browsed and retrieved by issuing complex queries from any node on the Internet. In the U.S., this concept is being termed "the federation" of biological databases.

2   GENOMIC DATA RESOURCES IN THE UNITED STATES

To date, the U.S. genome data community has been primarily responsible for providing the impetus for the "federation" concept. An Informatics Summit, sponsored by the Office of Health and Environmental Research of the U.S. Department of Energy in April 1993 (Department of Energy, 1993) effectively articulated the rationale for establishing a community of genomic database producers who pledge to develop and subscribe to standards regarding syntax, semantics, and management/curation issues.

The genome project is indeed the focal point of Bioinformatics activities in the U.S. Sequence data, because of its ubiquitous application and the high demand for access to it, has been referred to as the "backbone" of the biological knowledge base. Although some might disagree with this concept, the genomic databases have become linkage points for virtually all other types of biological data. It is becoming more apparent that sequences alone are not terribly useful without a rich set of annotations and links to additional data resources that more fully describe gene expression.

Participants at the DOE Informatics Summit (Department of Energy, 1993) made the following clear distinctions among local, collaborative, and community databases that comprise the genome informatics efforts.

"Local Databases are usually developed at one site and designed to handle specific, local needs. They are usually a closed resource, available only to local researchers, and containing both raw data and refined information....Tightly integrated into local bench research, they must be flexible and capable of rapidly tracking changes in local experimental protocols. The requirement for flexibility and responsiveness often exceeds a need for robustness and general applicability.

Collaborative databases are conceptually in the middle ground between local and community systems. Information is collected from a larger set of collaborating researchers, perhaps those working on a particular chromosome. Again, both raw data and refined information are included, with an increasing emphasis on integrating findings from several laboratories.

Community databases are shared resources, open to the entire research community....Because these systems must meet the consensus needs of the entire community, care must be taken in their design to ensure that the databases are sufficiently flexible and robust to address the needs of different user communities. Since users need to integrate findings from several different community databases, each community database should be designed as a component of a larger information infrastructure for computational biology. Specifically, community databases should recognize the biological interdependence of information in multiple databases and should provide support for integrated queries involving multiple databases. To this end, they should be built from standard components and must be well documented.

Obviously, the development of community databases requires much cooperation from a social and technical standpoint. Technical and semantic standards must be documented and adhered to by all database producers participating in the federation.

Lack of semantic standards has been a major roadblock in linking data stored in the major U.S. genomic data resources, such as GenBank, the Protein Identification Resource (PIR), the Genome DataBase (GDB), and the Ribosomal Data Project (RDP), although software is now available to facilitate these links. Representatives of these U.S. databases are active international collaborators and some are members of the CODATA Task Group on Biological Macromolecules. Most have also participated in workshops in the U.S. to study and solve interoperability problems (NCHGR GESTEC Report, 1994) (Bult CJ et al, 1994).

The CODATA Task Group works on an international level to stimulate development of semantic standards across macromolecular data resources as does the CODATA Commission on Biological Terminology. While there is still much to be done to achieve true interoperability among these genomic resources, a well documented recognition of the steps necessary to achieve the desired federation is an important first step toward the goal.

Genome database (GDB) is now in the process of constructing a "mini-federation" as a test of the concept. Common server interfaces, a common communication language, and a common schema description language are being designed to be portable across platforms and domains, in the hope that other biological databases can adopt GDB's code for membership in the larger federation. (Li and Fasman, 1995).

Table I. Genome related data resources in the U.S. working to achieve interoperability

Name of Genomic Resource	URL address
NRL 3D -sequence-structure database	http://www.gdb.org/Dan/proteins/nrl3d.html
PIR(1-3): The Protein Identification Resource sequence database	http://www.gdb.org/Dan/proteins
The Genome DataBase	http://gdbwww.gdb.org/
The Mouse Genome Database	http://www.informatics.jax.org/mgd.html
National Center for Biotechnology Information (GenBank)	http://www.ncbi.nlm.nih.gov
Lawrence Berkeley Laboratory Human Genome Center	http://www.lbl.gov/LBL.html
Plant Genome Center	http://probe.nalusda.gov:8000/index.html
Caenorhabditis elegans database	http://eatworms.swmed.edu/VI_home.html
Drosophila database	http://wwwleland.stanford.edu/~ger/drosophila.html
Yeast database	http://genome-www.stanford.edu/VI-yeast.html
Human Genome Project	http://www.ornl.gov/TechResources/Human_Genome/genetics.html#hgp
Baylor College of Medicine Human Genome Center	http://gc.bcm.tmc.edu:8088/home.html
Cooperative Human Linkage Center	http://www.chlc.org
Los Alamos National Laboratory Biosciences (LANL)	http://www-ls.lanl.gov
Resource for Molecular Cytogenetics	http://rmc-www.lbl.gov/

Stanford Human Genome Center	http://shgc.stanford.edu/
TIGR - The Institute for Genome Research	http://www.tigr.org/
University of Michigan Human Genome Center	http://www.hgp.med.umich.edu/Home.html
University of Pennsylvania	http://www.cis.upenn.edu/~cbil/chr22db/chr22dbhome.html
University of Texas Health Science Center at San Antonio Genome Center	http://mars.uthscsa.edu
Whitehead Institute Center for Genome Research (MIT)	http://www-genome.wi.mit.edu/
Washington University Genome Sequencing Center	http://genome.wustl.edu/gsc/gschmpg.html
Washington University Center for Genetics in Medicine	http://genome.wustl.edu/cgm/cgm.html
Yale/Albert Einstein	http://paella.med.yale.edu/chr12/Home.html

Genome related data is but a microcosm of the entire biological knowledge base. Although some progress is being made towards interoperability of genomic data resources, the magnitude of the problem is much greater if we consider the plethora of biological data that will eventually form the matrix of biological knowledge.

To illustrate the diversity of resources within even a subdiscipline of biology, the status of networked microbiological data in the U.S. has been explored and examples of work towards linking and standardizing the data models is described.

3   MICROBIOLOGICAL DATA RESOURCES IN THE UNITED STATES

The goal of obtaining complete sequences for organisms is more easily achievable in the microbial world because of the relative small sizes of the genomes. Data resulting from complete sequence projects is now becoming available and numerous experiments are underway in the U.S. to link these datasets with others for interpretative purposes.   From molecular evolution to metabolic pathways, the combination of genetic and phenotypic data is a powerful tool to elucidate biological processes.

The Argonne National Laboratory in the U.S. is experimenting with the integration of biological data to support interpretation of microbial genomes, including those of

Methanococcus jannaschii, Mycoplasma capricolum, Escherichia coli, Salmonella typhimurium, Bacillus subtilis, Pseudomonas aeruginosa, and Saccharomyces cerevisiae.

Sharing of data resources

The PUMA project (Gaasterland, 1995) is a system that attempts to integrate structure and function data utilizing metabolic pathways, sequence alignments, and phylogenetic trees. It is a collaborative project, combining the attributes of the EMP, Selkov enzyme database, a comprehensive collection of published metabolic pathways, with sequence data from several labs throughout the U.S. Phylogenetic trees are being derived from ribosomal RNA sequences maintained by the Ribosomal Database Project (RDP) at the University of Illinois. "Organizing a database on an established phylogenetic framework allows the user to restrict a search to any chosen set of organisms (thus making the search more sensitive). Furthermore, a graphical tree representation allows convenient picturing of the phylogenetic distribution of any attribute, annotation, etc.; this is also scientifically interesting, as the taxonomic validity of certain properties is debatable." (Gaasterland, 1995).

The Bergey's Manual Trust and Bionomics, International, a private, non-profit organization in the U.S. are in the process of standardizing the terminology in the Bergey's Manuals of Determinative and Systematic Bacteriology. Simultaneously, they are proceeding with the design and development of a comprehensive database describing the phenotypic characteristics of most known bacteria. When complete, this database will be an invaluable tool for integrating with other resources, such as PUMA. A similar effort by the International Committee on the Taxonomy of Viruses (ICTV) to standardize the terminology for description of virus characteristics is being primarily supported by the U.S. National Science Foundation. It is anticipated that this standardized list of descriptors will form the basis for a World Virus Database to be developed by ICTV.

Linking data resources with the WWW

A less ambitious, but effective method of linking data resources is the use of html and the World Wide Web (www). The American Type Culture Collection, the largest and most diverse service culture collection in the world, provides access to its microbiological and cell line data via the www. While not fully linked to other microbiological data resources at present, the figure below illustrates the utility of providing instant links to related resources. Work to complete these links is underway.

Interoperability, the capacity to search and analyze data from disparate databases simultaneously across the Internet, is seen in the U.S. as an essential element in the advancement of bioinformatics. Three major issues being addressed are:

1) syntax, e.g. schema design, data types, and formats;

2) semantics, e.g. entity descriptors, atomization of concepts, controlled vocabularies; and

3) database management, e.g. curation of the data, scope, data retrieval, and external communications (Bult, 1994).

FIGURE 1. Potential Microbiological Data Links to ATCC Catalog Data

Cryphonectyria parasitica
ATCC 38985
S.L. Anagnostakis EP 394 (Endothia parasitica).
Genotype: cre-1 met-1 ts+
Compatibility group v-c 39.
USDA Permit PPQ-526
Growth Conditions: Medium 1085 24C
Shipped: Test tube
Price Code: W
to order; *media composition*; *other collections holding strain*; *additional strain data*; *host information*; *sequence data*; micrographs: *spore*, *EM*, *SEM*; *taxonomic data*; *species data*; *metabolic pathways*; *literature references*

A quotation from Toni Kazic's abstract, presented at the 13th International CODATA Conference in Beijing (Kazic, 1992) aptly summarizes the challenges facing the bioinformatics community as we move toward realization of practical access to the matrix of biological knowledge.

"Large volumes of diverse information require conceptual models for their organization and intelligent use by humans. Representing data and ideas in a flexible, consistent way is particularly acute in biology. Here, data are only partially complete, come from many disciplines, and describe the same object from different points of view and to various degrees of detail. Biologists study extremely complex systems whose regularities are marked by numerous exceptions and about which it is difficult to formulate strongly predictive theories. The fundamental challenge is not just to enumerate information for retrieval and "manual" thinking, but to represent data and the underlying biological concepts with which we synthesize them so that automated reasoning is more fully supported. No longer a repository of objects and their attributes, the new database would become a dynamic, bill-of-materials, whose part-subpart relations express functional and structural relationships, and would serve as a multi-dimensional spreadsheet for formulating and testing hypotheses."

Fortunately, this viewpoint is now gaining momentum in the U.S., and resources are being applied to attain the required level of sophistication in data management to achieve the objectives of full interoperability among biological data resources. Interfacing different databases will imply the development of specialized gateways and the use of "intelligent" agents able to navigate in different files.

Table II. Networked Microbiological Databases in the United States

Microbial Data Resource	URL Address
AIDS Patent Databases	http://patents.cnidr.org
American Type Culture Collection	http://www.atcc.org
University of Arizona: The Tree of Life Phylogenetic Navigator for the Internet	http://phylogeny.arizona.edu/tree/phylogeny.html
Arizona State University: Rethinking AIDS	http://enuxsa.eas.asu.edu
Bowling Green University, Algal Microscopy & Image Digitization	http://www.bgsu.edu/Departments/biology/Algae_Images.html
Brown University: TB/HIV Research	http://www.brown.edu/Research/TB-HIV_Lab/
California Polytechnic University: Reviving Ancient Bacteria	http://baretta.calpoly.edu/cano/bact-article.html
California State University: Microbiology	http://arnica.csustan.edu/MI.html
University of California: Dep't of Microbiology & Molecular Genetics	http://hornet.mmg.uci.edu/~hjm/projects/micro/micro_faculty.html
The Computerized AIDS Ministry	http://hwbbs.gbgm-umc.org/
Centers for Disease Control and Prevention(CDC)	http://158.111.115.15/mosaic/home/home.html
Cold Spring Harbor Laboratory: Quest 2D Protein Database	http://www.cshl.org
Duke University: Chlamydomonas Genetics Center	gopher://atlas.acpub.duke.edu:70/11/"
Ebola Virus Information	http://www.best.com/~pierre/ebola.html
EcoCyc: Encyclopedia of E. coli Genes and Metabolism	http://www.ai.sri.com/ecocyc/ecocyc.html

Emory University: Dept. of Medicine, Division of Infectious Diseases	http://www.emory.edu/MED_INF/IDWEB.html
University of Florida: Dept of Microbiology	http://titan.ifas.ufl.edu/dep/department.html
University of Georgia: Phillip Youngman Lab - Bacillus subtilis	http://py2.genetics.uga.edu/PYhome.html
Harvard University: Daniel Hard and Woody Hastings Lab	http://golgi.harvard.edu/
Gray Herbarium and Farlow Diatom Catalog	gopher://huh.harvard.edu/11/collections_info/huh
Harvard Medical School: G.M. Church Lab	http://twod.med.harvard.edu
Hepatitis C information	http://planetmaggie.pcchcs.saic.com/hepc.html
University of Illinois: Dept. of Microbiology	http://www.life.uiuc.edu/micro/home.html
Indiana University: Paleolimnology/Diatom Home Page	http://nickel.ucs.indiana.edu/~sweets/home.html
The Institute for Advanced Studies in Medicine	http://www.ovinet.com/i001/htm
University of Kansas: Dept. of Microbiology	http://ukanaix.cc.ukans.edu:80/~micro/index.html
University of Kansas: Fungal Genetics Stock Center	http://kufacts.cc.uknas.edu/cwis/units/fgsc/main.html
Los Alamos National Laboratory: HIV Sequence Database	http://hiv-web.lanl.gov
Los Alamos National Laboratory: Human Papillomavirus Database	http://hpv-web.lanl.gov
University of Maine: Dept. of Biochemistry, Microbiology, & Molecular Biology	http://icarus.umesci.maine.edu/micro.html
Massachusetts Institute of Technology: Feline Leukemia Virus FA	http://www.ai.mit.edu/fanciers/other-faqs/feleuk-faq.html
Microbial Germplasm Database	gopher://gopher.bcc.orst.edu:70/
University of Minnesota Medical School: Candida Biology	http://alces.med.umn.edu/Candida.html

University of Minnesota Medical School: Actinomycete-Streptomyces Internet Resource Center (ASIRC)	http://molbio.cbs.umn.edu/asirc/
North American Snakebite Emergency Medicine: Reptile-associated Salmonella	http://www.xmission.com/~gastown/herpmed/salm.htm
Northwest Fisheries Science Center: Molecular Microbiology	http://listeria.nwfsc.noaa.gov/home-page.html
NRSub - non-redundant database of Bacillus subtilis DNA sequences	http://sunflower.bio.indiana.edu:8080/wormweb.html
University of Oklahoma: Microbiology & Immunology Dept.	http://www.microbiology.uokhsc.edu/
Oregon Graduate Institute of Science and Technology: Collection of Methanogens	http://www.ese.ogi.edu/ese_docs/bugs/ocm.html
Oregon Graduate Institute of Science and Technology: Subsurface Microbial Culture Collection	http://www.ese.ogi.edu/ese_docs/bugs/smcc.html
Polio and Post-Polio Resources	http://www.eskimo.com/~dempt/polio.html
University of Rochester: Dept. of Microbiology & Immunology	http://wwwminer.lib.rochester.edu/wwwml/SteveDFolder/mbidepthome.html
The Rockefeller University: Fischetti Lab and Streptococcal Strains Database	http://www.rockefeller.edu/vaf/vaf.home.html
SRI International: EcoCyc E.coli Metabolism Database	http://www.ai.sri.com/ecocyc/ecocyc.html
Selkov Metabolic Pathway Diagrams	http://www.mcs.anl.gov/home/towell/metabhome.html
Stanford University: Center for Tuberculosis Research	http://genome-www.stanford.edu/
Texas A&M University: W.M. Keck Center for Genome Informatics	http://straylight.tamu.edu/straylight.html
Texas A&M University: AAnDB Aspergillus Database	http://keck.tamu.edu/cgi/aandb/anid.html
University of Texas: Stealth Virus Research Program	http://www.usc.edu/hsc/medicine/virus

University of Wisconsin: Institute for Molecular Virology and Ebola Virus Information	http://www.bocklabs.wisc.edu/Welcome.html
University of Wisconsin: E.coli Genome Project	http://www.genetics.wisc.edu/Welcome.html
Yale University E.coli Genetic Stock Center	http://cgsc.biology.yale.edu/top.html
U.S. Environmental Protection Agency(EPA):Genetically Engineered Microorganisms	http://www.epa.gov
U.S. Food and Drug Administration: Foodborne Pathogenic Microorganisms and Natural Toxins	http://vm.cfsan.fda.gov/~mov/toc.html
U.S. National Institutes of Health: Mycoplasma capricolum Genome Project	http://uranus.nchgr.nih.gov/myc.html
U.S. National Institutes of Health: Bioinformatics & Molecular Analysis Section, Division of Computer Research & Technology	http://bimas.dcrt.nih.gov
U.S. National Institutes of Health: AIDS Information	gopher://odie.niaid.nih.gov/11/aids

KEYWORDS

Bioinformatics, United States, interoperability, genome, nucleic acid sequence, protein sequence, microbiology, federation

REFERENCES

[1]   Bult C.J., Interoperability of Biological Databases Meeting Report, The Institute for Genomic Research (TIGR), Gaithersburg, MD, June (1994) available from www.tigr.org

[2]   Gaasterland T., Maltsev N., Overbeek R., Selkov E., PUMA: an Integration of Biological Data to Support the Interpretation of Genomes, in Towards a Federation of Macromolecular Databases, June (1995). Annual Meeting of CODATA Task Group on Biological Macromolecules and FASEB Biomolecular Databases '95, George Mason University, Fairfax, VA available from george@nbrf.georgetown.edu

[3]   Kazic T., Metabolic Pathways Databases: Challenges and Opportunities, CODATA Bulletin.
        Scientific Program and Abstracts, Thirteenth International CODATA Conference, Oct.(1992),
        Beijing, China, 24(2): Apr.-June (1992).
[4]   Li P. , Fasman K., Toolkit Technology for Database Federation, in Towards a Federation of
        Macromolecular Databases, June (1995). Annual Meeting of CODATA Task Group on
        Biological Macromolecules and FASEB Biomolecular Databases '95. George Mason University,
        Fairfax, VA available from george@nbrf.georgetown.edu
[5]   National Center for Human Genome Research , Report: NCHGR GESTEC director's meeting on
        genome   informatics,   Cold   Spring   Harbor,   N.Y.   May   (1994)   available   from
        benton@nchgr.nlm.nih.gov
[6]   U.S. Department of Energy, Meeting Report: DOE Informatics Summit, , Baltimore, MD
        Apr.(1993) available from bioinfo@oerv01.er.doe.gov

MMTDB : THE METAZOA MITOCHONDRIAL DNA VARIANTS SPECIALIZED DATABASE

Marcella ATTIMONELLI, D. CALO, A. DEPASCALI, M. PORZIO, F. TANZARIELLO, M. VITALE and C. SACCONE

Dipartimento di Biochimica e Biologia Molecolare and CSMME CNR, Bari, Italy

ABSTRACT

MmtDB is a specialized database of Metazoa mitochondrial DNA variants. Priority in collecting data is given to Metazoa species whose complete mitochondrial genome has been sequenced. For each species n variants are codified. A variant is any fragment where nucleotide differences (variations) are detected as compared to a reference sequence. Data sources are the Primary Databases (EMBL, GenBank and DDBJ), literature and authors' communications. All the information available from these sources is systematically analyzed in order to extract the minimal set of information required to define a variant. At present MmtDB contains primarily data on Homo Sapiens, related to studies on human diversity and myopathies.

RESUME

MmtDB est une base de données spécialisée de variants de mitochondrial DNA Metazoe. La priorité est donnée à la collecte des données relatives aux spécialités Metazoe dont le génome Mitochondrial est codifié. Pour chaque spécification n variants sont codifiés. Un variant désigne n'importe quel fragment pour lequel des différences de nucléotides sont détectées par rapport à une séquence de référence. Les sources des données sont les bases de données primaires (EMBL, GenBank et DDBJ), la littérature et des communications d'auteurs. Toutes les informations accessibles à partir de ces sources sont systématiquement analysées dans le but d'extraire un jeu minimal d'informations nécessaires à la définition d'un variant. Actuellement MmtDB contient surtout des données de l'Homo Sapiens en relation avec les études sur la diversité humaine et les miopathies.

1 INTRODUCTION

The need to create a Metazoa mitochondrial (mt) DNA specialized database originates from the awareness of a large mass of information on mtDNA sequences, mainly relevant to mtDNA polymorphic features and to mt pathologies, which are not coded in nucleotide sequence databases. This means that the interpretation of polymorphisms relies mainly on human intervention.

The specialized database is thus designed to provide new data structures and to generate new cross referencing relations between sets of data completely unlinked up till now, e.g. significant data for biodiversity studies.

On account of the number of Metazoa and their diversity in terms of structure, organization and gene content, the collection and structuring of data for the MmtDB started from the human mitochondrial genome. This genome is already widely studied, so a large amount of data is available, and their collection is of great importance for the general scientific community.

What do we mean by a variant?

MmtDB is not simply a collection of Metazoa mt DNA sequences but a collection of variants. Indeed due to the highly polymorphic feature of mt DNA, many fragments of the same DNA region and of the same species are sequenced. A variant is therefore, for each species of the Metazoa class, a fragment where nucleotide differences (variations) are detected as compared to a reference sequence (the master sequence).

2   MᴍᴛDB ᴅᴀᴛᴀ sᴏᴜʀᴄᴇ

The Metazoa mitochondrial sequences are retrieved from the EMBL [1], Genbank [2] and DDBJ primary databases. The published sequence data which are not included in the sequence databases are extracted from bibliographic databases (Medline, Current Contents). Unpublished data, kindly provided by the authors, are also included.

3   MᴍᴛDB Dᴀᴛᴀ Sᴛʀᴜᴄᴛᴜʀᴇ

The MmtDB is divided into two large classes: **SPECIES** and **VARIANTS**. Each of these classes is further organized in subclasses. For each *species, n variants* are possible. **Each variant is an entry in the MmtDB database.**

The **SPECIES** class refers to the items in the database which can be associated with a biological species of the METAZOA and of which mt DNA data are available.

The **species** group is defined by :

- a *master sequence*, that is a reference sequence represented by the nucleotide sequence of the complete mt genome, if the genome of that species has been fully sequenced, or of the longest known sequence of that species;

- a *gene map* of the master sequence;

- the *taxonomy* of that species;
- bibliographic references for the master sequence.

The **VARIANTS** class includes information on the diversity of each analyzed DNA sequence with respect to the Master sequence, such as :

- the *analyzed region* of the sequence;
- the *experimental method* used for the detection of the variant;
- the *variation events* (e.g. the differences with respect to the master sequence);
- the *mutated gene* ;
- the *source* from which the DNA was extracted;
- information on the *population*, relevant to the geographic origin of the individual from which the DNA sequence was extracted (see below);
- *cross referencing* to the Nucleic Acids Sequence Database, if the nucleotide sequence of the variant is stored there;
- internal *cross referencing* among different aplotypes of the same individual in different tissues or different aplotypes of individuals from a common pedigree;
- *age, sex and pathological status* of the individual;
- *bibliographic references* for the variant.

When possible, information is included on alterations in the restriction map of the region where the variation occurs.

Variation events

A special feature of the MmtDB is that, unlike primary databases, the entire sequence is not reported; only information on the variated sites, in terms of substitution, deletion and insertion (**variation events**) as compared to the master sequence are recorded.

For each variation event, the following data are stored :

the *position* where the variation occurs referred to the

master sequence;

the *variation code* (according to Table 1);

the mutated gene.;

the *pathogenicity* of the variation event;

→	A	C	G	T	-
M **A**		5	13		
S **T** **C**	6		9	3	14
E **R**					
G	2	10		11	15
S **E**					
Q **T**	8	4	12		16
U **E**					
N **-**	17	18	19	20	
C **E**					

21= string deletion, **22**= string insertion, **23**= A→N, **24**= C→N, **25**= G→N,
26= T→N, **27**= -→N, -= GAP, **N**= ambiguous nucleotides
Table 1. Variation Code

4   MMTDB DATA FORMAT

The information collected is coded and included in a compact format (Figure 1).

A flatfile version of the database can be produced upon request. An example of MmtDB entry in the flatfile format is reported in Figure 2.

5   MMTDB RELEASE 1 DATA CONTENT

The number of variants already stored in MmtDB is reported in Table 2.

Moreover, the metazoa mtDNA data available through the primary nucleic acid databases (EMBL Datalibrary, GenBank and DDBJ) and not yet analyzed and structured in MmtDB are stored as **raw-sequence-data** in a special file. These data are related to the SPECIES class of the structured database. The number of raw-sequence data as of September 1994 is 2912 for a total of 875 metazoan species.

```
┌─────────────────────────────────────────────────────────────────────────┐
│ HSP0107                                                                   │
│ RHP0012                                                                   │
│              1                 SfaNI -              11778        ND4  +    │
│              3                                      12385        ND5  -    │
│             10                 HaeIII -             13702        ND5  c    │
│             11                 HincII -             14199        ND6  -    │
│ 1 (AS  SIXX  AL  JAXX  JA      BLOOD      F45YLHON)        AA.II.1         │
│ PCR SEQ                                                                    │
│ 11750-14200              E:MIHSAIA;M75991         F:HSP0090                │
└─────────────────────────────────────────────────────────────────────────┘
```

LEGEND :

HSP0107	= entry number
RHP0012	= reference number code
figures in bold	= nucleotide variation codes
SfaNI - HaeIII - HincII -	= restriction sites lost (-) or gained (+)
figures in italic	= nucleotide varation position
ND4 ND5 ND6	= involved genes
+	= variation associable to pathology by author
-	= variation not associable to pathology by authors
c	= conflicting variation compared to the Master sequence
1	= number of individuals belonging to HSP0107 mitochondrial DNA
AS SIXX	= population code of individuals classified by continental groups AS (Asia), and population groups SIXX (Chinese)
AL JAXX JA	= linguistic code of individual classified by linguistic family AL (Altaic), linguistic group (JAXX), language JA (Japanese)
Blood	= tissue from which the mtDNA was extracted
F	= sex of the individual
45	= age of the individual at sampling
LHON	= individual status
AA.II.1	= family code
PCR SEQ	= method used to detect the variant
11750-14200	= analysed region (positions refer to the Master sequence)
E:MIHSAIA M75991	= cross referencing to the primary databases
F: HSP0090	= internal cross referencing, F is for family relationship

Figure 1. MmtDB compact format

```
ID      MT00932              2451  BP
DE      Pathological Studies on Homo sapiens mtDNA
AC      HSP0107
SM      HSP0000
RN      1
RA      Wallace D.C., Sing G., Lott M.T., Hodge J.A., Schurr T.G.
RA      Lezza A.M., Elsas II L.J., Nikoskelainen E.K.
RL      Science 242 : 1427-1430 (1988)
SO      BLOOD
IN      1; F; 45 years; LHON; AA.II.1
CP      Asia; Japanese
CL      Altaic; Japanese; Japanese
DR      EMBL : MIHSAIA; M75991
DR      MmtDB F : HSP0090
FH      Key                          Location/Qualifiers
FH
FT      ND4                          11778
FT                                   /var= "a->G"
FT                                   /note= "SfaNI lost"
FT                                   /note= "pathology associated"
FT      ND5                          12385
FT                                   /var= "c->T"
FT      ND5                          13702
FT                                   /var= "g>C"
FT                                   /note= "HaeIII lost"
FT                                   /note= "conflict"
FT      ND6                          14199
FT                                   /var= "g->T"
FT                                   /note= "HincII lost"
EE      PCR SEQUENCING
AR      11751-14200
actcaaacta  cgaacgcact  cacagtcGca  tcataatcct  ctctcaagga  cttcaaactc
tactcccact  aatagctttt  tgatgacttc  tagcaagcct cgctaacctc  gccttacccc
ccactattaa  cctactggga  gaactctctg  tgctagtaac.................................
```

Legend:
ID = entry number and sequence length
DE= definition
AC= Mmtdb entry Accession Number
SM= MmtDB MASTER sequence Accession Number
RN= reference number
RA= author reference
RL= journal
SO= analysed tissue
IN= information on the individuals : 1= number of individuals belonging to MT000932 mitochondrial DNA, F= sex of individual, 45years= age of individual at sampling, LHON= pathology; AA.II.1= family code
CP= classification of the population to which the individual belongs
CL= linguistic classification to which the individual belongs
FH= Features Table header
FT= variation description : the involved gene or region, the nucleotide variation region or position, the qualifier **var** specifying the nucleotide variation referring to Master sequence
EE= method used to detect the variant
AR= analysed region (position referring to the MASTER sequence)
DR= reference to the primary database (EMBL/GENBANK/DDBJ); reference to MmtDB

Figure 2. MmtDB FLATFILE format

SPECIES	VARIANTS NUMBER
Homo Sapiens	1144
Rattus norvegicus	38
Mus musculus	12
Bos taurus	27
Gallus gallus	4
Xenopus laevis	4
Cyprinus carpio	3
Strongylocentrotus purpuratus	2
Calidris alpina	35
Dipodomys panamintinus	22
Total	1291

- 2912 Metazoa mtDNA entries are stored as raw data in MmtDB.

Table 2. MmtDB Content

6   HUMAN MITOCHONDRIAL DNA DATA

As already emphasized, the database creation was started with human mitochondrial genome data. These data were coded using as reference the nucleotide sequence published by Anderson et al. in 1981 [3] (**master** sequence), which, despite being a hybrid (was derived from placenta mtDNA and in part from HeLa cell mtDNA), represents an important reference in human variability studies.

The retrieval of human mtDNA data with ACNUC [4] and GCG [5] packages, and an accurate bibliographic search, resulted, for the first release of MmtDB, in 560 human mtDNA D-loop and 584 pathology-associated entries, identified and coded up to present.

The codification of data on the origin of individuals requires a different approach according to the species, in particular when analyzing man. In the following paragraphs the criteria used for the codification of human populations and human pathologies are reported.

7   HUMAN POPULATIONS

The variability of human mtDNA is the result of a series of variation events whose knowledge would significantly contribute to insight in the biological history of our species, clarifying the scope of intra- and inter-population variability, andwould provide an important key to evolutionary dynamics and the consequent expansion in time and space of modern man.

The sample under examination was classified on the basis of ethno-linguistic criteria, assuming a possible correlation between biological, ethnical and linguistic characteristics, despite the evidence that linguistic or cultural evolution has taken place at a faster rate than genetic evolution [6]. In view of this, the possibility to associate a precise codification for the population with the mtDNAs of the subjects under study is of enormous importance.

The classification adopted in the MmtDB, to which Prof. Tommaseo, anthropologist at the University of Bari, has greatly contributed, is largely based on strictly geographical criteria. Human diversity is classified by populations (Bushman, Bantu, etc.) based on their geographical locations (Africa, Europe, Asia, etc.), and different ethnic groups are identified within each population.

In MmtDB the linguistic group of the subject under study was also recorded for the sake of greater accuracy on diversity. Namely, MmtDB linguistic coding is based on Merrith Ruhlen's classification (1991) [7] of the some 5000 world languages into 17 main families (macro-groups or phyla). These linguistic **families** are constructed in a tree accounting for more detailed classification into **linguistic groups** and **languages**.

8   MITOCHONDRIAL PATHOLOGIES

Lately, several molecular studies have described a correlation between the different human pathologies and variations in mt DNA. Such variations include deletions, insertions and point mutations and the studied pathologies, mostly encephalomyopathies, account for a set of disorders of the muscular and nervous systems differing in their clinics, biochemistry and histology.

The classification of mitochondrial encephalomyopathies into the major syndromes - KSS, MERRF, LHON, MELAS, etc. - has given rise to heated debates. Some researchers consider this distinction useful both in clinical practice and as an indication of a different aetiology; whereas others believe the classification is forced and stress the common features of the various syndromes, drawing attention to those cases where features of different defects coexist.

In MmtDB, the information used by the author to define the proband from the pathological point of view is reported in line IN of the flat-file format (see Fig.2).

There are cases where the individual is described as affected by a precise syndrome based on the clinical features; while in others the individual is described only through the clinical, biochemical and histological features if these cannot be ascribed to a single syndrome. This latter case is still under discussion as to its coding in MmtDB.

In MmtDB, whenever suggested by the author, the association of the nucleotide variation with the pathology of the individual under examination is reported (see MmtDB Data Structure and MmtDB Data Format Sections).

The opinions regarding pathogenicity of a nucleotide variation and consequently its association with a set pathology are conflicting; some authors believe a given mutation is the cause of a disease, while others consider the disease more as the expression of the number and type of the mutations. These latter authors suggest, based on the comparison of the mitochondrial DNAs of patients affected by different syndromes, that *"these patients are members of the same gene family, originated from a common ancestor, of molecular genetic entity as "mtDNA disease".* [8].

9 HOW TO RETRIEVE DATA IN MMTDB

A retrieval system based on the compact structure is under development.

The flatfile format will be available in a short time at our ftp site. The MmtDB, in its flatfile format, can be also converted into the GCG format by simply applying the FROMEMBLTOGG program. Such a conversion allows the use of the program STRINGSEARCH, and FETCH available through GCG for the retrieval and extraction of data sets.

As flatfile, MmtDB could be also included in SRS [9] and so ready for retrieval along the network.

ACKNOWLEDGMENTS

This work was partially supported by MPI (Italy), by Progetto Finalizzato Biotecnologie e Biostrumentazione (CNR, Italy) and by Progetto Finalizzato Ingegneria Genetica (CNR, Italy).

KEYWORDS

Bioinformatics, specialized-database, mitochondrial, miopathies, variation.

REFERENCES

[1] Benson D. , Lipman D.J., Ostell J. , GenBank, Nucl. Acids Res., 21, 2963-2965 (1993).
[2] Rice C.M. , Fuchs R. , Higgins D.G. , Stoehr P.J., Cameron G.N. , The EMBL Data Library, Nucl. Acids Res., 21, 2967-2971 (1993).

[3]   Anderson S. , BanKier A.T. , Barrell B.G. , De Bruijn M.H. , Coulson A.R. , Drouin J. , Eperon
        I.C. , Nierlich D. P. , Roe B.A. , Sanger F. , Schreier P.H. , Smith A.J. Staden R., Young I.G.,
        Sequence and organization of the human mitochondrial genome, Nature, 290, 457-465 (1981).
[4]   Gouy M. , Gautier C. , Attimonelli M. , Lanave C., DiPaola G. , ACNUC - a portable retrieval
        system for nucleic acid sequence databases : logical and physical design and usage, CABIOS, 1,
        167-172 (1985).
[5]   Devereux J., Haeberli P., Smithieso. , A comprensive set of sequence analysis programs for the
        Vax. , Nucl. Acids Res. , 12, 387-395 (1984).
[6]   Cavalli Sforza L.L., Piazza A., Menozzi P., Mounation J., Reconstruction of human evolution:
        bringing together genetic, archaeological, and linguistic data, Proc. Natl. Acad.Sci. USA, 85,
        6002-6006 (1988).
[7]   Ruhlen M., A guide to the world's languages, Volume 1: classification Edward Arnold (1991).
[8]   Ozawa T., Tanaka M., Ino H., Ohno K., Sano T., Wada Y., Yoneda M., TannoY., Miyatake T.,
        Tanaka T., Itoyama S., Ikebe S., Hattori N., Mizuno Y., Distinct clustering of point mutations in
        mitochondrial DNA among patients with mitochondrial encephalomyopathies and with
        Parkinson's disease, Bioch. Bioph. Res. Comm. , 176, 938-946 (1991).
[9]   Etzold T., Argos P. , SRS - an indexing and retrieval tool for flat file data libraries, CABIOS, 9,
        49-57 (1993).

Epitope Data Bank

Lunjiang LING[1,3], Junko SHIMURA[2], Hideaki SUGAWARA[2] and Akira TSUGITA[1]

[1] *Science University of Tokyo, Research Institute for Biosciences, 2641 Yamazaki Noda, Chiba 278, Japan*
[2] *The Institute of Physical and Chemical Research (RIKEN), 2-1 Hirosawa, Wako, Saitama 351-01, Japan*
[3] *Present adress : Institute of Biophysic Sinica, Chaoyang, Beijing 100101, China*

ABSTRACT

The fine specificity of monoclonal antibodies is the indispensable information for the elucidation of the protein-ligand interaction. The data on the epitope of antigens have been desperately required in immunology, pharmacology and molecular biology because the epitope is specifically recognized by antibodies. With these ideas in mind, Epitope Data Bank (EPD) was developed as a feasibility study for supporting these fields. The record of EPD is a sequenced epitope locating on antigen molecule with links to PIR-International, GenBank/EMBL/DDBJ and HDB. The software for the retrieval of antigens and epitope sequences was also developed.

RESUME

La spécificité fine des anticorps monoclonaux est une information indispensable dans l'élucidation des interactions protéine-ligand. Les données sur l'épitope des antigènes ont été désespérément sollicitées en immunologie, pharmacologie et biologie moléculaire parce que l'épitope est spécifiquement reconnu par les anticorps. Compte tenu de ces espoirs, la banque Epitope Data Bank (EPD) a été développée au niveau d'une étude de faisabilité pour apporter un soutien à tous ces domaines. L'élément de base de l'EPD consiste en un épitope et sa séquence localisés sur une molécule antigène qui est liée à d'autres sources de données telles que PIR-International, GenBank/EMBL/DDBJ et HDB. Le logiciel pour la recherche de séquences d'antigènes et d'épitope est aussi développé.

1   INTRODUCTION

Monoclonal antibodies have been used as highly specific antigen recognizing protein reagents. Recently monoclonal antibodies had to be characterized on the level of sequences or residues with the progress of molecular biology. To design the potential vaccines, drugs or immunomoduratory factors, epitope information is now becoming more important in the wide area of biology than at the time when the Hybridoma Data

Bank [1] was set up by CODATA and IUIS. Based on the recognition of current biologists' needs that were discussed at the International Workshop of Hybridoma Epitope Data in 1993 (see Table 1), the prototype of Epitope Data Bank (EPD) has been designed and developed.

Kolaskar, Ashok S.	Bioinformatics DIC, Dept. Zoology, Univ. Poona Geneshkind, Pune 411 007, India
Ling, Lun-Jiang	14th Dept. Inst. of Biophys. Acad.Sinica 15 Datun Road, Chaoyang District, Beijing, 100101, China
Lukens, Catherine	American Type Culture Collection 12301 Parklawn Drive, Rockville, MD 20852-1776, USA
Stake, Kazuo	JIPID, Res. Inst. Biosci., Sci. Univ. Tokyo 2669 Yamazaki, Noda, Chiba 278, Japan
Shimura, Junko	Life Science Research Information Section The Inst. Physical and Chemical Research (RIKEN) 2-1 Hirosawa, Wako, Saitama 351-01, Japan
Sugawara, Hideaki	Life Science Research Information Section The Inst. Physical and Chemical Research (RIKEN) 2-1 Hirosawa, Wako, Saitama 351-01, Japan
Tsugita, Akira	Res. Inst. Biosci., Sci. Univ. Tokyo 2669 Yamazaki, Noda, Chiba 278, Japan

Table 1. Members who attended the International Workshop of Hybridoma Epitope Data held at Science University of Tokyo, Noda, Japan 1993.

2   MATERIALS AND METHODS

Sequenced epitope data were screened from published papers. MEDLINE was searched and abstracts were reviewed for the screening. Then the full text was retrieved to extract and arrange the factual data into the data format of EPD. The data format is consistent with the current feature table of PIR-International. For the links to HDB and PIR-International, HDB Gopher server at WDCM [2] and other data servers on INTERNET were searched. For the link to GenBank, PIR-International cross reference field and Mailfasta and blast search [3], were carried out. The corresponding data in the different databases are surveyed among the databases for the concordance of clone name, bibliography and the segment of sequences if available. Data were stored as text files. The data retrieval software was developed.

3   RESULTS AND DISCUSSION

Table 1 shows the members who attended the International Workshop of Hybridoma Epitope Data held at Science University of Tokyo, Noda, Japan 1993. According to the discussion at the workshop, we collected and stored the 200 sequenced epitopes found in scientific articles by the end of the summer, 1994. The definition of the term "epitope" in this project is: *Epitopes or antigenic sites include amino acid sequences or residues of antigens to monoclonal antibodies.* Currently, amino acid sequences or residues were collected in EPD. T-cell epitopes have not been included but are seriously considered as the future scope of EPD or a subset of the database.

Basically EPD is files with a unique identifier for authors, journals and titles, PIR entry codes of antigens, designation of antigens in PIR, alternate designation if one exists, unique accession number of each epitope on antigens, monoclonal antibodies that recognize each epitope, comments, method to determine the epitope, and links to other databases. Generic expression in EPD data table is shown in Table 2.

The sequences are separately stored from the above table to save the disk space and to accelerate retrievals. To retrieve the antigen sequences and epitope sequences on the antigen, the software "EPITOPE" was developed. In EPITOPE, either one of the EPD tables, the whole sequence of antigen with the marks of epitopes at the corresponding positions, or segmental sequences including epitopes can be displayed (see Figures 1-3). Links to such databases as GenBank/EMBL/DDBJ and HDB are included. In addition to PIR entry codes, the link realizes cross references of EPD on Internet.

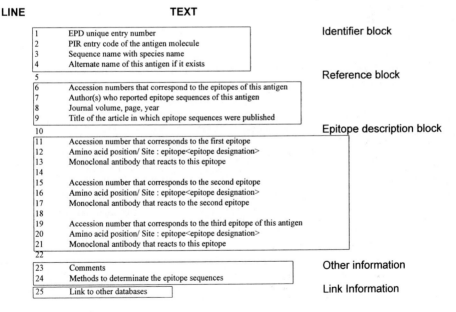

LINE	TEXT	
1	EPD unique entry number	Identifier block
2	PIR entry code of the antigen molecule	
3	Sequence name with species name	
4	Alternate name of this antigen if it exists	
5		Reference block
6	Accession numbers that correspond to the epitopes of this antigen	
7	Author(s) who reported epitope sequences of this antigen	
8	Journal volume, page, year	
9	Title of the article in which epitope sequences were published	
10		Epitope description block
11	Accession number that corresponds to the first epitope	
12	Amino acid position/ Site : epitope<epitope designation>	
13	Monoclonal antibody that reacts to this epitope	
14		
15	Accession number that corresponds to the second epitope	
16	Amino acid position/ Site : epitope<epitope designation>	
17	Monoclonal antibody that reacts to the second epitope	
18		
19	Accession number that corresponds to the third epitope of this antigen	
20	Amino acid position/ Site : epitope<epitope designation>	
21	Monoclonal antibody that reacts to this epitope	
22		
23	Comments	Other information
24	Methods to determinate the epitope sequences	
25	Link to other databases	Link Information

Table 2. Generic expression of EPD data table.

```
>E; LA0075
PIR entry code : RQECA
recA protein - Escherichia coli
N;Alternate names :

C; Accession : LA007501 to LA007502
R; Ikeda, M., Hmano, K., and Shibata, T.
J. Biol.Chem. 267,6291-6296, 1992
A; Title : Epitope mapping of anti-recA protein IgG by region specified polymerase chain
reaction mutagenesis.

A; Accession : LA007501
F; 283-320/Domain : epitope (predicted) <EPA>
A; This epitope is recognized by monoclonal IgG ARM191

A; Accession LA007502
F; 315-33_/Domain : epitope (predicted) <EPB>
A; This epitope is recognized by monoclonal IgG ARM193

C; Comment :
C : Method
Link to : Genbank J01672
Link to : Genbank V00328
Link to : HDB 2000066_ARM191
Link to : HDB 2000065_ARM193
```

Figure 1. Example of the EPD record.

Command "Whole" displays the whole amino acid sequence of antigen. The epitopes
on this antigen will be sublabeled by letters.

```
  1 AIDENKQKALAAALGQIEKQFGKGSIMRLGEDRSMDVETISTGSLSLDIALGAGGLPMGR    60
 61 IVEIYGPESSGKTTLTLQVIAAQREGKTCAFIDAEHALDPIYARKLGVDIDNLLCSQPD   120
121 TGEQALEICDALARGSGAVDVIVVDSVAALTPKAEIEGEIGDSHMGLAARMMSQAMRKLAG 180
181 NLKQSNTLLIFINQIRMKIGVMFGNPETTTGGNALKFYASVRLDIRRIGAVKEGENVVGS 240
241 ETRVKVVKNKIAAPFKQAEFQILYGEGINFYGEKVDLGVKEKLIEKAGAWYSYKGEKIGQ 300
                                    aaaaaaaaaaaaaaaaaaa

301 GKANATAWLKDNPETAKEIEKKVRELLLSNPNSTPDFSVDDSEGVAETENEDF*    352
    aaaaaaaaaaaaaaaaaaaaa
                   bbbbbbbbbbbbbbbbbbbb

COMMENTS for individual epitopes :

Epitope labeled by 'a' : This epitope is recognized by monoclonal IgG ARM191
Epitope labeled by 'b' : This epitope is recognized by monoclonal IgG ARM193
```

Figure 2. A display of EPD:Whole sequences of antigen and epitopes.

RQECA : recA protein - Escherichia coli
contains the following epitopes :

283-320 :
                ... YGELVDLGVKEKLIEKAGAWYSYKGEKIGQGKAMATAKEIEKKVRELLLSNPN...
                    ^^^^^^^^^^^^^^^^^^^^^^^^^^^^^^^^^^^^^
This epitope is recognized by monoclonal IgG ARM191.

315-338 :
... ANATAWLKDNPETAKEIEKKVRELLLSNKPNSTPDFSVDDSEGVAETNE...
                ^^^^^^^^^^^^^^^^^^^^^^^^^^^^
This epitope is recognized by monoclonal IgG ARM193.

Figure 3. A display of EPD : Segment sequences of antigen and epitopes

Recent progress in computer network and related systems materialized simultaneous accesses to independent databases distributed on the network based on TCP/IP, INTERNET. Users can find different facts of either antigens or antibodies at one site even though data resources are distributed in different institutions. Figure 4 (Annex) shows the example of data retrievals by using cross references of EPD on INTERNET.

ACKNOWLEDGMENT

We gratefully thank Mrs. Lois Blaine at American Type Culture Collection for supporting EPD through the information in HDB.

KEYWORDS

Immunoglobulin, monoclonal antibody, hybridoma, epitope, antigenic determinant, segnential epitope, PIR international, protein sequence data bank.

REFERENCES

[1]   Blaine L., Codata/Iuis Hybridoma Data Bank, CODATA Bulletin 23, 92-93 (1991).
[2]   Sugawara H., Ma J., Miyazaki S., Shimura J., An Information Resource for Microbial Diversity, presented at CODATA'94, Chambery, France (1994).
[3]   Stephan A.F., Gish W., Miller W., Myers E.W., Lipman D.J., Basic local alignment search tool, J. Mol. Biol.215, 403-410.

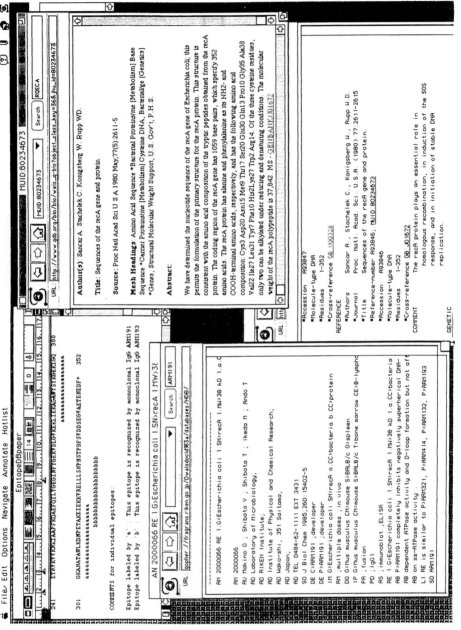

Figure 4

Protein Superfamily Database (Prosup)

Katsuhisa HORIMOTO[1], Kunio OSHIMA[1], Akira TSUGITA[2] and Jinya OTSUKA[3]

[1] Department of Electronics and Computer Science, Science University of Tokyo in Yamaguchi, Onoda 756, Japan
[2] Research Institute for Biosciences, Science University of Tokyo, Noda 278, Japan
[3] Department of Applied Biological Science, Science University of Tokyo, Noda 278, Japan

ABSTRACT

We have constructed a protein superfamily database (PROSUP). Amino acid sequences belonging to the protein superfamilies defined by PIR International are quantified by application of principal component analysis on the basis of the physicochemical properties of amino acid residues. The result of this quantification is that about 70,000 sequences compiled in PIR International Protein sequence database are represented as 940 sets of the numerical values, each of which describes approximately the features of a superfamily. An algorithm is designed for similarity search in PROSUP. In the algorithm, similarity is detected by the tolerance for amino acid residues as well as the resemblance of physicochemical properties, between a query sequence and an aligned sequence. A preliminary demonstration of the program (SUPQ) is presented.

RESUME

Nous avons développé une banque de superfamilles de protéine (PROSUP). Les séquences des amino acides appartenant aux superfamilles de protéines définies par PIR International sont quantifiées par application de l'analyse de composantes principales sur la base des propriétés physicochimiques des résidus d'amino acides. Les résultats de cette quantification qui englobe environ 70.000 séquences compilées dans la base de données PIR International Protein sont représentés par 940 ensembles de valeurs numériques qui décrivent chacun approximativement les traits d'une superfamille. Un algorithme est retenu pour des recherches de similarité. Il détecte la similarité en fonction de la tolérance pour les résidus d'amino acides ainsi que pour les ressemblances des propriétés physicochimiques, ceci par comparaison entre les séquences d'interrogation et les séquences alignées constitutives. Les bases de l'algorithme SUPQ de recherche de similarité et une démonstration préliminaire sont présentées ..

1   INTRODUCTION

With the growth of protein sequence data, the number of the sequences compiled in the protein sequence database amounts to about seventy thousand thus far.

From the viewpoints of both sequence identity and function, these sequences are categorized into groups called the protein superfamilies.   According to the definition of the superfamily by PIR International, about three thousand superfamilies are grouped.   Given that some sequences belonging to one superfamily are described by one representative value, similarity searches will be rapid in contrast to pairwise comparison, and the memory required to store the data will be reduced.   Furthermore, summarization of each family enables us to search similarity of a query sequence in terms of an important feature in each superfamily.

Recently, we developed a method of summarizing a set of sequences by application of the principal component analysis [1, 2].   In the present paper, with the use of our method, we have extensively calculated the sequences of superfamilies, and have constructed a protein superfamily database (PROSUP).   A program (SUPQ) has been designed to inquire into the similarity of a query sequence in PROSUP.

2   CONSTRUCTION OF PROSUP

2.1   Alignments of amino acid sequences

Among some 3000 superfamilies, those containing the sequences that show mutually more than 55% identity are aligned and the alignments are compiled by PIR International. These alignments are distributed as a database 'ALN' by CD ROM. In the first version of PROSUP, we adopted 940 alignments in 'ALN' released on March 31, 1994 with the permission of PIR International, for the present summarization of the superfamilies.

2.2   Quantification of aligned sequences

The application of principal component analysis to amino acid sequences has been described [1, 2]; only a brief description will be given here.

Four properties of amino acid residues, polarity [3], hydrophobicity [4], volume [3], and pKa [5], are adopted as the variables in the analysis, and the samples are 20^3 fragments of three amino acid residues that are generated at random. Each variable is the average value of each property over three residues.

In this analysis, the contribution rates corresponding to the first, second, third, and fourth principal components are 57.5%, 25.3%, 15.8%, and 1.4%, respectively. Thus, the first principal component may be regarded as a numerical value representing approximately the physicochemical properties of residues.

The first principal component is expressed by the following equation:

$$z_i^{(1)} = 0.5510 (x_{i1} - x_1) / \sqrt{\sigma^2_{11}}$$
$$- 0.6123 (x_{i2} - x_2) / \sqrt{\sigma^2_{22}}$$
$$- 0.5510 (x_{i3} - x_3) / \sqrt{\sigma^2_{33}}$$
$$- 0.2086 (x_{i4} - x_4) / \sqrt{\sigma^2_{44}}$$

where x_j and σ^2_{jj} are the mean value and the variance of the j th property in the sample data $\{x_{ij}\}$, respectively: x_1=8.6455, σ^2_{11}=2.4315, x_2=0.7273, σ^2_{22}=0.3416, x_3=82.7045, σ^2_{33}=543.2402, x_4=0.0227 and σ^2_{44}=0.0869.

With the use of equation (1), the first principal components of the fragments vertically aligned in one family are calculated and are represented by one mean value with one standard deviation (SD). In a vacant site of the alignment, the properties are regarded as zero values. Such a calculation is made progressively for three successive residues by overlapping two, from amino to carboxy terminus. Thus, the aligned sequences of one family are quantified as a corresponding set of the mean values with the standard deviations.

2.3 Organization of PROSUP

In the present version of PROSUP, 940 alignments of superfamilies are stored. PROSUP is composed of the following files: FPC.DAT, the first principal component data of superfamilies; SPN.LIS, list of superfamilies; SPM.LIS, list of members in each superfamily; ALN.SEQ, alignment of sequences in each superfamily. These files totally occupy 11Mb.

3 ALGORITHM OF SUPQ

An algorithm is designed to inquire into the similarity of a query sequence in the PROSUP. The program (SUPQ) is written by FORTRAN and runs on a DCL USTATION/750 machine under the VMS operating system. The algorithm is as follows.

3.1 Three numerical measurements for similarity

In a user-defined window size, w, of $z^{(1)}$ values, three values are calculated as measurements for the similarity between a query sequence and the superfamilies : Kendall's rank correlation coefficient (termed τw), a distance (termed Dw), and a degree which shows that a query sequence belongs to the superfamilies (termed Bw). These measurements represent the tolerance for amino acid residues described by the standard deviations as well as the resemblance of physicochemical properties between a query sequence and an aligned sequence. Each definition of three measurements is as follows :

According to Kendall and Gibbons [6], the rank correlation coefficient, τw, is defined by

$$\tau w = Sc \ / \ \sqrt{w(w-1)/2 - \overset{tg}{\sum} u_i(u_i - 1)/2} \ / \ \sqrt{w(w-1)/2 - \overset{ts}{\sum} v_i(v_i - 1)/2} \quad (2)$$

where Sc is the sum of the multiplied scores for all possible pairs of $z^{(1)}$ values of query sequence and the mean values of $z^{(1)}$ distribution of the superfamilies.   The correction terms for any pair scored as 0 in each ranking in equation (2) are $\Sigma u_i(u_i-1)/2$ and $\Sigma v_i(v_i-1)/2$, where u_i and v_i are the number of members which compose the i th tie rank in a query sequence and that in a superfamily, respectively; tq is the total number of the set of tie ranks in a query sequence, and ts is that of tie ranks in a superfamily.

The distance, Dw, is defined by

$$Dw = \Sigma \ |z^{(1)}_{qi} - z^{(1)}_{si}| \ / \ w \quad (3)$$

where $z^{(1)}_{qi}$ and $z^{(1)}_{si}$ are the $z^{(1)}$ values in a query sequence and the mean values of $z^{(1)}$ values in a superfamily, respectively, in the i-th site of a window.

The degree, Bw, is defined by

$$Bw = \Sigma bw_{ii} \ / \ w \quad (4)$$

where

$$bw_{ij} = \begin{cases} 1, & \text{if } (z^{(1)}_{si} + 2SD_{si}) > z^{(1)}_{qi} > (z^{(1)}_{si} - 2SD_{si}) \\ 0, & \text{otherwise} \end{cases}$$

The first measurement expressed by equation (2) detects similarity of rank;   the second by equation (3) measures a resemblance of properties on $z^{(1)}$ value, and the third by equation (4) is a measurement that shows the sequence width which may be a manifestation of the same function.

3.2   Selection of similar region

When w is more than ten, the Sc in equation (2) follows approximately the normal distribution with the mean value of 0, and the variance, $1/18[\{w(w-1)(2w+5)-\Sigma u_i(u_i-1)(2u_i+5)-\Sigma v_i(v_i-1) \ (2v_i+5)\}+\{\Sigma u_i \ (u_i-1) \ (u_i-2)\}\{\Sigma v_i \ (v_i-1) \ (v_i-2)\} \ / \ \{9w \ (w-1) \ (w-2)\}+\{\Sigma u_i(u_i-1)(u_i-2)\}\{\Sigma v_i(v_i-1)(v_i-2)\}/\{2w(w-1)\}]$ [6]. Thus, we can calculate the significance level of τw .

The distributions of Dw and Bw are transformed into the standard normal distributions on the assumption that Dw and Bw follow approximately the normal distributions, respectively.   Then, each significance level is also calculated.

In this way, similar regions can be selected by a user-defined threshold for significance levels of three measurements in terms of the first principal component.

4   DEMONSTRATION OF SUPQ

The procedure for operation of SUPQ is shown in Fig. 1. In this program, a user first inputs a file name of a query sequence, then defines parameter values for judging similarity; a window size and values of three measurements, and finally inputs a file name of the result.   In operating the program, a query sequence is requested to be of PIR International format.

```
A> PROSUP

Logo is displayed.

PROSUP>SUPQ
Query sequence            :test.seq
Window size               :50
Set significance level (%)
Kendall's tau              :5
Distance                   :5
Degree of Belonging        :5
Result file name          :test.res
Now, calculating statics;
        Superfamily No. 1 :
        Superfamily No. 2 :
                 .
                 .
                 .
        Superfamily No. 940 :
Now, searching similarity;
        Superfamily No. 1 :
        Superfamily No. 2 :
                 .
                 .
                 .
        Superfamily No. 940 :
Eureka!

PROSUP>
```

Figure 1.   Example of operation of the program for similarity search (SUPQ).   Bold characters indicate user-defined values or characters.

We evaluated the potential of SUPQ in two cases.   In the first case, a query sequence is the sequence that belongs to one superfamily compiled in PROSUP, and then the program is tested as to whether the sequence is correctly allocated to the superfamily or not.

The second case is that a query sequence is a peptide fragment that was sequenced from two-dimensional gel electrophoresis and could not be identified by a conventional way for similarity search [7].

Figure 2a shows the result of SUPQ in the first case when a leghemoglobin of yellow lupine was adopted as a query sequence. The superfamily to which the leghemoglobin belongs shows the highest score. The other related globin families also show high scores, although other superfamilies are also found.

```
Score [query / Sup.]
270     [ 135 / 135 ] : Leghemoglobin
241     [ 121 / 120 ] : Hemoglobin alpha chain, selected sequences
234     [ 114 / 120 ] : Hemoglobin beta chain, selected sequences
231     [  96 / 135 ] : 3-Methyl-2-oxobutanoate dehydrogenase (lipoamide)
227     [ 102 / 125 ] : Glycoprotein B
224     [ 109 / 115 ] : [Fe] Hydrogenase (EC 1.18.99.1)
222     [ 112 / 110 ] : Myoglobin, selected sequences
219     [ 114 / 105 ] : Vicilin, 14K component
211     [ 106 / 105 ] : Guanylate cyclase (EC 4.6.1.2)
207     [  97 / 110 ] : Kinase-related transforming protein
```

Figure 2a.

Figure 2b shows the result of the second case. In reference to the location of the unidentified fragment and the molecular weight of the protein containing the unidentified fragment [7], ferredoxin is selected as a candidate, among 17 superfamilies that were detected by SUPQ. The alignment of ferredoxin is compared with the query fragment. Although only a few identical residues are found, similar residues in the properties are aligned vertically.

Demonstrations of similarity search in PROSUP by SUPQ (Fig 2).

A query sequence is leghemoglobin of yellow lupine (a) and is an amino terminal fragment of a protein that was sequenced from rice and could not be identified by a conventional method (b). The window size (w) and three significance levels (τw, Dw, and Bw) are as follows: in (a), w=25, τw=5%, Dw=5%, and Bw=5%; in (b), w=16, τw=5%, Dw=1%, and Bw=1%. In (a), 56 superfamilies, which contained the fragment that fulfills the threshold of three measurements, were detected, and ten superfamilies showing high scores were listed. The score was defined in the following way: the number of residues that were detected as similar to each other is counted in the query sequence and in the superfamily alignment, respectively, and then the two numbers are added as the score. In (b), 17 superfamilies were detected. Among them, the most likely superfamily, ferredoxin, was selected, in reference to the location and the molecular weight experimentally identified [7], and the aligned sequences were compared with the unidentified fragment. The most abundant residue at each site in the ferredoxin alignment is denoted in the upper side of the comparison, and identical and similar residues are indicated by ':' and '.', respectively.

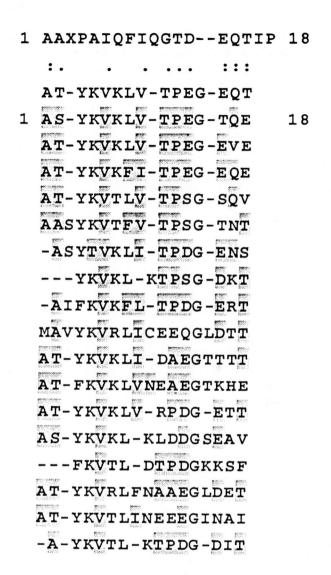

1 AAXPAIQFIQGTD--EQTIP 18

    :.   .   . ...   :::

AT-YKVKLV-TPEG-EQT

1 AS-YKVKLV-TPEG-TQE   18

AT-YKVKLV-TPEG-EVE

AT-YKVKFI-TPEG-EQE

AT-YKVTLV-TPSG-SQV

AASYKVTFV-TPSG-TNT

-ASYTVKLI-TPDG-ENS

---YKVKL-KTPSG-DKT

-AIFKVKFL-TPDG-ERT

MAVYKVRLICEEQGLDTT

AT-YKVKLI-DAEGTTTT

AT-FKVKLVNEAEGTKHE

AT-YKVKLV-RPDG-ETT

AS-YKVKL-KLDDGSEAV

---FKVTL-DTPDGKKSF

AT-YKVRLFNAAEGLDET

AT-YKVTLINEEEGINAI

-A-YKVTL-KTPDG-DIT

Figure 2b : Unidentified fragment, "Ferredoxins, selected sequences".

CONCLUSION

PROSUP stores the sequence data of 940 superfamilies as the numerical values summarized by principal component analysis on the basis of the physicochemical properties, and a program, SUPQ, serves to scan the similarity of a query sequence in PROSUP.   With the growth of sequence data, the potential of PROSUP and SUPQ will increase to investigate its homologous relationship. Thus, the development in this line offers a guideline for detecting the function of protein.

We plan to equip two programs in PROSUP; one is to assign the location of sequence motif [2], and another is to compare simultaneously two sets of sequences. Such equipment will make our database more useful and powerful to search the similarity of protein sequences.

KEYWORDS

Computer algorithm, database, physicochemical properties of amino acids, principal component analysis, protein superfamily, similarity search

REFERENCES

[1]   Horimoto K., Suzuki H., Otsuka J., Data Anal. 4, 33-42 (1991).
[2]   Horimoto K., Yamamoto H.,Yanagi K., Oshima K., Otsuka J., Protein Engineering, 7,1433-1440 (1994).
[3]   Grantham R., Science, 185, 862-864 (1974).
[4]   Nozaki Y., Tanford C., J. Biol. Chem. 246, 2211-2217 (1971).
[5]   Barker R., Organic Chemistry of Biological Compounds, Prentice-Hall, Englewood Cliff (1971).
[6]   Kendall M., Gibbons J. D., Rank Correlation Methods (5th ed.) Oxford University Press, New York (1990).
[7]   Tsugita A, Kawakami T., Uchiyama Y., Kamo M., Miyatake N. and Nozu Y. Electrophoresis, 15, 708-720 (1994).

Concerted Use of Multiple Databases for Taxonomic Insights

Ashok S. KOLASKAR and Prashant.S. NAIK

Bioinformatics Centre, University of Pune, PUNE 411 007, India

Abstract

The Animal Virus Information System (AVIS) with information on more than 1000 viruses is developed to carry out taxonomic research on these organisms. The representation code used for the viruses can cope with 32 properties but, in fact, only 12 characters are necessary to assign a virus to a family. The coding data come from either macrolevels or microlevels of information (i.e. RNA sizes, genome segments) and are provided by numerous world wide biological DB. 3D structural data on proteins can be a necessity for correct identification.

Resume

Le Système d'Information sur les Virus Animaux (AVIS) comprend plus de 1000 virus et sert aux recherches de taxonomie de ces organismes. Le code représentatif des virus utilise 32 propriétés mais en fait 12 caractères seulement sont utiles pour assigner un virus à une famille. Les données utiles proviennent de macrodescriptions mais l'apport de microniveaux est essentiel (ex. taille de RNA, segments du génome). Elles proviennent de nombreuses BD biologiques mondiales. Des données 3D structurales sur les protéines sont parfois indispensables pour aboutir à une identification.

1 Introduction

In biology several new techniques have been developed, due to the advancement of technology, in recent years. In addition to these new techniques, methods used for identification of chemical compounds are also extended to study biological macromolecules and their interactions in a given species. Therefore, one can study large numbers of characters of any organism both at micro- and macro- level.

Such studies can be used to classify organisms. However, macro characters of the organisms alone are not enough to identify a species or sometimes even a class of organisms. Characters most commonly used to classify a mosquito such as *Anopheles stephensi* are not sufficient to identify correctly these species and the introduction of other species of mosquitoes in this class is not uncommon.

The DNA probes developed from mitochondrial mosquito DNA have proved highly useful in identification of true *Anopheles stephensi* (1).

Yet another example where macro- and micro- properties along with its growth studies under different conditions have become essential are in *Entamoeba* strain identification. There are still some doubts regarding *Entamoeba histolytica*. Most scientists believe that there are two strains of protozoan - the disease causing strain *E. histolytica* and a benign strain called *E. dispar*. But the leading Mexican investigator, Esther Orozco believes that *E. histolytica* may be a single species, i.e. able to modulate the virulence (2). In her laboratory it was shown that *E. histolytica* can transform the protozoan from pathogenic to non-pathogenic showing that the organism is very plastic.

There are many other examples in biology where the classification of the species and their interrelationship has not been established unequivocally. Efforts made through Bergey's Manual which provides descriptions of all known bacteria have proven very useful in taxonomy and identification. However, these volumes are outdated and require revision which will include new information at the molecular level including sequence data. The RKC code can be used for transforming Bergey's manual into a database which can then be analyzed with the help of software and also can be updated with little difficulty (3). It has thus become necessary to use the information derived from various biological and physicochemical experiments at macro- and micro-level for taxonomic classification or even to get an insight into taxonomic studies.

There are several data banks in biology which can be used for such taxonomic studies. These include the protein sequence data bank, either from PIR or Swissprot, Nucleic Acid Sequence Data Banks - GenBank, Entrez, EMBL Nucleotide Data Bank and Hybridoma data bank, Cell Culture Information, etc.

Many of these data banks are today available either on the Internet through World Wide Web (WWW) or at a particular Gopher site and thus can be accessed easily. If the software tools could be developed which will allow one to analyze data from these multiple databases one could carry out classification studies with a higher degree of confidence.

Three dimensional structure (3D) data banks such as PDB can also be used in classification. At our Centre we have attempted to develop a software which will allow us to gain insight into taxonomy and identification of animal viruses by using various data banks in biology. Any Virus Information System will also benefit from the sharing of data located in various centers either through convenient gateways or the use of "intelligent agents".

2   METHOD

In the Animal Virus Information System (AVIS), developed at our Centre (4), information on more than one thousand different viruses is collected and coded. This information can be divided into 16 categories as seen in Table 1.

Table 1. Categories used to create the database

1) Virus status and distribution	9) Antigenic relationship
2) The original source of the virus	10) Susceptibility of cell systems
3) Method of isolation and validity	11) Natural host range
4) Physicochemical properties of virus	12) Experimental viremia
5) Stability of infectivity and virulence	13) Histopathology
6) Virion morphology	14) Human disease
7) Morphogenesis	15) Links with other data banks
8) Hemagglutination	16) References

A numerical coding system very similar to the RKC code has been developed to code this information which allows use of software packages like Micro-IS for data query and analysis purpose (5). In addition, all nucleic acid and protein sequence data have been extracted from EMBL and PIR as well as Swissprot data banks for each of these viruses and converted to PRAS format so that a PRAS package developed by us and described earlier can be used to analyze these sequences (6).

From virus properties which are encoded in the AVIS, thirty two commonly studied properties were picked up and organized in hierarchical fashion by taking into consideration their neg-entropy values. These neg-entropy values were calculated using a modified Shannon's entropy function (7).

The modified Shannon's Entropy function is given as follows :

$$H_i = \left[\sum_{k=1}^{m_i} P_{ik} . \log P_{ik} \right] - (1 - r_i) . \log(1 - r_i) \tag{1}$$

where   H = Entropy function (Information content)

i = character number
r = no. of variables in character/total no. of observations
k = varies from 1 to maximum number of states (m) in each test.
P = no. of observations for the variation/total no. of observations

Out of these thirty two values only twelve characters were found necessary and are sufficient for assigning a family to a given animal virus. These twelve characters are those which have the highest neg-entropy values and are given as the first twelve characters among the set of thirty two commonly studied characters (see Table 2).

Table 2. Commonly studied characters of viruses along with modified Shannon's entropy values as calculated using Equation 1 in the text.

Entropy value (-Hi)	Character
0.729	Morphology : icosahedral/spherical/bacilliform pleomorphic/isometric/helical/ovoid
0.447	DNA : circular/linear/super-coiled
0.440	Host specificity : vertebrate/insect/ vertebrate+insect
0. 69	No. of genome segments : 1/2/3/8/>8
0. 10	RNA sense : +ve/-ve
0. 08	RNA size in kb : >15/<15
0. 01	Lipid content : present/absent
0.292	Genome : single/double stranded
0.288	Carbohydrate content : present/absent
0.287	DNA size in kbp : >20/<20
0.284	Envelope : present/absent
0.284	Genome : DNA/RNA
0.269	Replication site : cytoplasm/nucleus
0.26	Buoyant density in CsCl : >1. 0/<=1. 0
0.257	Molecular weight of n.a. : <5/>=5
0.249	Subgenomic RNA formed during multiplication : yes/no
0.2 8	Percentage weight of n.a : <8/>=8
0.225	Size of virion in nm. : <60/>=60
0.21	Molecular weight of virion : <500 M />=500 M
0.205	Replication involves reverse transcriptase : yes/no
0.189	Buoyant density in sucrose : <1.18>1.18
0.181	Sensitivity to ether : resistant/sensitive
0.166	Sensitivity to heat : resistant/sensitive
0.166	Sensitivity to detergent : resistant/sensitive
0.144	Sensitivity to chloroform : resistant/sensitive
0.144	Percentage weight of protein : <65/>=65
0.140	CPE observed : yes/no
0.095	Sensitivity to acidic pH : resistant/sensitive
0.088	Sensitivity to formaldehyde : resistant/sensitive
0.071	Sensitivity to lipid solvent : resistant/sensitive
0.056	Buoyant density in potassium tartarate : <2/>=2
0.0 5	G+C content : <48/>=48

As can be seen these twelve characters include macro- characters such as morphological features, host virus interactions etc. and micro characters at molecular level such as RNA size in kb, No. of genome segments, etc. Some of these characters have been given very great importance by ICTV while formulating their rules for virus classification (8) but other characters were not used as primary characters for assigning the virus family. Thus the set given here is different but common for all families and does not vary as in other approaches such as VIDE from family to family (9). Viruses having an envelope or coat and belonging to a particular family show high sequence similarity among their envelope or coat proteins. Therefore, as a case study we have compared coat protein sequences for viruses belonging to the Nodaviridae family. Multiple alignment of these sequences using

PRAS (6), a multiple alignment programme developed for parallel computer, showed that N-terminal region of these viruses is highly basic and is rich in Arginine amino acid (See Fig. 1).

Figure 1a. Coat protein sequences of the Nodaviridae family members. Note the Arginine rich regions at the N-terminal region.

```
VCBBND      coat protein precursor alpha - nodamura virus
VCBBBL      coat protein precursor alpha - boolarra virus
VCBBFH      coat protein precursor alpha - flock house virus
VCBB2G      coat protein precursor alpha - black beetle virus

VCBBND    1 MVSKAARRRRAAPRQQQRQQSNRASNQP--------RRRRARRTRRQQRMAATNNMLKMS
VCBBBL    1 ------MTPRRQQRPKGQLAKAKQAKQP--------LARSRRPRRRRRAAITQNNLMMLS
VCBBFH    1 MVNNNRPRRQRAQRVVVTTTQTAPVPQQNVPRNGRRRRNRTRRNRRRVRGMNMAALTRLS
VCBB2G    1 MVRNNNRRRQRTQRIVTTTTQTAPVPQQNVPKQPRRRRNRARRNRRQGRAMNMGALTRLS
COMMON      .............R...........Q..........R..RR.............S

VCBBND   61 APGLDFLKCAFASPDFSTDPGKGIPDKFQGLVLPKKHCLTQSITFTPGKQTMLL------
VCBBBL   61 EPGLSFLKCAFASPDSNTDPGKGIPDNFEGKVLSQKNVYTETGVNFSGATTQNVDTYIIV
VCBBFH   61 QPGLAFLKCAFAPPDFNTDPGKGIPDRFEGKVVSRKDVLNQSISFTAGQDTFILI-----
VCBB2G   61 QPGLAFLKCAFAPPDFNTDPGKGIPDRFEGKVVTRKDVLNQSINFTANRDTFILI-----
COMMON      ...PGL.FLKCAFA.PD..TDPGKGIPD.F.G.V...K...............T......

VCBBND  121 -----VAPIPGIACLKAEANVGASFSGVPLASVEFPGFDQLFGTSATDTAANVTAFRYAS
VCBBBL  121 LPTPGVAFWRCIKTATAPAQPAALTTTDVFTAVPFPDFTSLFGTTATNRADQVAAFRYAS
VCBBFH  121 -----APTPGVAYWSASVPAGTFPTSATTFNPVNYPGFTSMFGTTSTSRSDQVSSFRYAS
VCBB2G  121 -----APTPGVAYWVADVPAGTFPISTTTFNAVNFPGFNSMFGNAAASRSDQVSSFRYAS
COMMON      ...........................V..P.F...FG.........V..FRYAS

VCBBND  181 MAAGVYPTSNLMQFAGSIQVYKIPLKQVLNSYSQTVATVPPTNLAQNTIAIDGLEALDAL
VCBBBL  181 MNFGLYPTCNSTQYNGGISVWKGAVQMSTTQYPLDTTPESS----QLVHAITGLESALKV
VCBBFH  181 MNVGIYPTSNLMQFAGSITVWKCPVKLSTVQFPVATDPATS----SLVHTLVGLDGVLAV
VCBB2G  181 MNVGIYPTSNLMQFAGSITVWKCPVKLSNVQFPVATTPATS----ALVHTLVGLDGVLAV
COMMON      ...M..G.YPT.N..Q..G.I.V.K............................

VCBBND  241 PNNNYSGSFIEGCYSQSVCNEPEFEFHPIMEGYASVPPANVTNAQASMFTNLTFSGARY-
VCBBBL  241 GDENYSESFIDGVFTQSINGNAEFPFYPILEGVQTLPGQNVTVAQAGMPFSLDAGAATVA
VCBBFH  241 GPDNFSESFIKGVFSQSACNEPDFEFNDILEGIQTLPPANVSLGSTGQPFTMDSGAEATS
VCBB2G  241 GPDNFSESFIKGVFSQSVCNEPDFEFSDILEGIQTLPPANVTATSGQPFNLAAGAEAVS
COMMON      ......N.S.SFI.G...QS........F..I.EF....P..N..........

VCBBND  301 --TGLGDMDAIAILVTTPTGAVNTAVLKVWACVEYRPNPNSTLYEFARESPANDEYALAA
VCBBBL  301 GFTGIGGMDAIFIKVTAAAGSVNTATIKTWACIEYRPNTNTALYKYAHDSPAEDIIALQQ
VCBBFH  301 GVVGWGNMDTIVIRVSAPEGAVNSAILKAWSCIEYRPNPNAMLYQFGHDSPPLDEVALQE
VCBB2G  301 GIVGWGNMDTIVIRVSAPTGAVNSAILKTWACLEYRPNPNAMLYQFGHDSPPCDEVALQE
COMMON      ...G.G.MD...I.V....G.VN.A..K.W.C.EYRPN....LY.....SP..D..AL..

VCBBND  361 YRKIARDIPIAVACKDNATFWERVRSILKSGLNFASTIPGPVGVAATGIKGIIETIGSLW
VCBBBL  361 YRKVYKSLPVAVRAKLNANMWERVKRLLKAGLVAASYVPGPVGGIATGVQHIGDLIAELS
VCBBFH  361 YRTVARSLPVAVIAAQNASMWERVKSIIKSSLAAASNIPGPIGVAASGISGLSALFEGFG
VCBB2G  361 YRTVARSLPVAVIAAQNASMWERVKSIIKSSLAMASNVPGPIGIAASGLSGLSALFEGFG
COMMON      ...YR......P.AV....NA..WERV....K..L..AS..PGP.G..A.G............

VCBBND  421 V
VCBBBL  421 F
VCBBFH  421 F
VCBB2G  421 F
COMMON      ...  .
```

Figure 1b. Coat protein sequence of the members of the Luteovirus group. Note the Arginine rich regions at the N-terminal region.

```
S11437 Coat protein 1     bean leaf roll virus
VCVQWA coat protein       potato leaf roll virus (strain Wageningen)
VCVQFL coat protein       beet western yellows virus (isolate FL1)
JQ1243 coat protein 1     barley yellow dwarf virus


S11437   1 ---MVARGK--------RVVVRQLQTRARRRLPVVLATAPVRPQRKRRQRGRNNKPRGGN
VCVQWA   1 MSTVVVKGNVNGGVQQPRRRRRQSLRRRANRVQPVVMVTAPGQPRRRRRRRGGNRRSRRT
JQ1243   1 -STVVLRSNGNGSR---RRRQRVARRRPAARTQPVVVVASNGPARRGRRRRPVGPRRGRT
VCVQFL   1 MNTVVGRRIING-----RRRPRRQTRRAQRPQPVVVVQTSRATQRRPRRRRRGNNRTGRT
COMMON   . ....V............R...R....R.......V........R..R.R.........

S11437  61 GFARRSSQVHEFVFSKDNLNGNSKGSITFGPSLSECKPLADGILKAYHEYNITNVELAYI
VCVQWA  61 GVPRGRGSSETFVFTKDNLMGNSQGSFTFGPSLSDCPAFKDGILKAY.HEYKITSILLQFV
JQ1243  61 PRSGGGSRGETFVFSKDSLAGNSSGSITFGPSLSEYPAFQNGVLKA'.HEYKITNCVLQFV
VCVQFL  61 VPTRGAGSSETFVFSKDNLAGSSSGAITFGPSLSDCPAFSNGMLKAYHEYKISMVILEFV
COMMON  .. ...........FVFXKD.L.G.S.G..TFGPSLS.......G.LKAYHEY.I....L...


S11437 121 TEASSTSSGSIAYELDPHLKNTTIQSKINKFSITKSEKKKFSRKAINGQAWHDTSEDQFR
VCVQWA 121 SEASSTSSGSIAYELDPHCKVSSLQSYVNQFQIPQGGAKTYQARMINGVEWHDSSEDQCR
JQ1243 121 SEASSTAAGSISYELDPHCKASSLASTINKFTITKTGARSFPAKMINGLEWHPSDEDQFR
VCVQFL 121 SEASSQNSGSIAYELDPHCKLNSLSSTINKFGITKPGKRAFTASYINGTEWHDVAEDQFR
COMMON ... .EASS...GSI.YELDPH.K.....S..N.F.I............ING..WH...EDQXR

S11437 181 ILYEGNGDAKI-AGSFRVTIKVLTQNPK
VCVQWA 181 ILWKGNGKSSDTAGSFRVTIRVALQNPK
JQ1243 181 ILYKGNGASSV-AGSFKITLRVQLQNPK
VCVQFL 181 ILYKGNGSSSI-AGSFRITIKCQFHNPK
COMMON ... IL.-GNG.....AGSF..T......NPK
```

In fact, repeats of basic aminoacids in N-terminal region seems to be a property of RNA viruses.

We have noticed that plant viruses belonging to Luteovirus group have very similar characteristics to those viruses which belong to Nodaviridae- an animal virus family (see Table 3).

Thus, the main difference between these two classes of virus is the host, where in both cases insects play a very important role. Our analysis suggests that the Luteovirus group may have evolved from viruses belonging to Nodaviridae. Multiple alignment for coat protein sequences of the Luteovirus group showed that there is sequence similarity among these viruses but show little similarity with members of the Nodaviridae family except for the N-terminal region, suggesting that coat proteins of Luteovirus have not changed over the years, probably due to no movement of the virus host and thus, their habitat. On the other hand, viruses belonging to the Nodaviridae family have changed due to movement of its host, whose insects can have very different habitats. It may be pointed out that the vectors for the Luteovirus group of viruses are insects. Some of these insects are host to viruses belonging to the Nodaviridae family. Thus, additional information such as protein sequence data or nucleic acid sequence data is highly necessary to characterize viruses in the future.

In fact, 3D structural data can be used in addition to sequence data to refine classification and identification.

Table 3. The characters used for identification of animal virus family Nodaviridae and the plant virus group Leutoviridae are given. Note the similarities in the character values.

Sl. No.	Ordered features	Families	
		Nodaviridae	Luteovirus
1	DNA/RNA	RNA	RNA
2	Double/single stranded	single-stranded	single-stranded
3	Enveloped/non-enveloped	non-enveloped	non-enveloped
4	DNA size in kbp	-	-
5	RNA +ve sense/-ve sense	+ve sense	+ve sense
6	DNA shape linear/coiled	-	-
7	Viron morphology	icosahedral	icosahedral
8	No. of genome segments	2	1
9	Host type	insect	plant
10	RNA size in kb	< 15 kb	< 15 kb
11	Carbohydrate content	Not determined	None reported
12	Lipid content	None	None

CONCLUSION

The method developed makes use of information at the morphological level and the molecular level for classification. Sequence similarities at protein level have been used to confirm the classification and to postulate relationship among viruses belonging to very different families. In fact molecular phylogeny has been used quite successfully to understand evolution, but to the best of our knowledge, molecular sequence data for classification and identification was not used till now. The software developed is simple and allows classification up to the family level in a deterministic fashion. We are extending this approach to identify and classify viruses up to the species level by using probability matrices which are constructed by studying independent characters with high information content. Precise and accurate values of these characters are used in developing such matrices. In those cases where three dimensional protein structure data is available, we can then use them in our classification studies. However, such three dimensional structural information on protein is available in very few cases. The use of various data banks has become a necessity for correct identification and classification rather than studying only macro-properties.

ACKNOWLEDGEMENTS

We acknowledge the help of the Department of Biotechnology, Government of India, New Delhi for financial support.

KEYWORDS

Animal virus, taxonomy, identification, microstructures, AVIS System, neg-entropy.

REFERENCES

[1]   Cockburn A.F., A Simple and Rapid Technique for Identification of Large Numbers of Individual Mosquitoes Using DNA Hybridization, Archives of Insect Biochemistry and Physiology, 14, 191-199 (1990).

[2]   Cohen J., The Amebiasis Organism: A Jekyll and Hyde Parasite, Science, 267, 82 (1995).

[3]   Krichevsky M.I., Personal communications (1995).

[4]   Kolaskar A.S., Naik P.S., Computerization of virus data and its usefulness in virus classification. Intervirology, 4, 1-141 (1995).

[5]   Rogosa M., Krichevsky M.I., Colwell R.R., Coding Microbiological Data for Computers, New York, Springer (1986).

[6]   Date S., Kulkarni R., Kulkarni B., Kulkarni-Kale U., Kolaskar A.S., Multiple alignment of sequences on parallel computers, CABIOS, 9, 97-402 (1993).

[7]   Shwayder K., Extending the information theory approach to converting limited-entry decision tables to computer programs. Communications of the Association of Computer Machinery, 17, 5 2- 7 (1974).

[8]   Francki R.I.B., Fauquet C.M., Knudson D.L., Brown F. Classification and Nomenclature of Viruses, Fifth Report of the International Committee on Taxonomy of Viruses, Archives of Virology, Suppl. 2, 1-450 (1991).

[9]   Buchen-Osmond C., Crabtree, K., Gibbs, A., McLean, G. Viruses of Plants in Australia : Descriptions and Lists from the VIDE database. Canberra, The Australian National University Research School of Biological Sciences (1988).

INDEX